Advances in
Printing Science and Technology

Volume 2

PROBLEMS IN
HIGH SPEED PRINTING

PROBLEMS IN
HIGH SPEED PRINTING

THE INFLUENCE OF PRINTING SPEED AND PRESSURE
ON PRINT QUALITY

Proceedings of the

Sixth International Conference of Printing Research Institutes

held at Elsinore, Denmark, 1961

EDITED BY

W. H. BANKS

RESEARCH SUPERINTENDENT
PRINTING AND ALLIED TRADES RESEARCH ASSOCIATION
LEATHERHEAD, ENGLAND

SYMPOSIUM PUBLICATIONS DIVISION

PERGAMON PRESS

NEW YORK · OXFORD · LONDON · PARIS

1962

PERGAMON PRESS INC.
122 East 55th Street, New York 22, N.Y.

PERGAMON PRESS LTD.
Headington Hill Hall, Oxford
4 & 5 Fitzroy Square, London W.1

PERGAMON PRESS S.A.R.L.
24 Rue des Ecoles, Paris V^e

PERGAMON PRESS G.m.b.H.
Kaiserstrasse 75, Frankfurt am Main

LIBRARY OF CONGRESS CARD NUMBER 62–15606

Printed in Great Britain by Bell and Bain, Ltd., Glasgow

PREFACE

DEVELOPMENTS in printing will almost certainly be associated with an increase in speed of impression. Many performance tests on paper and ink are made at rates and pressures different from those in the printing operation. The effects on quality of print are far from clear. It was thus timely that the 6th International Conference of Printing Research Institutes adopted as its main theme, " The Influence of printing speed and pressure on print quality."

It becomes immediately clear from the papers and discussions that while the effects of speed and pressure on transfer of ink are established, and are understood, in many cases quantitatively, much research remains to be done in detail before standardized laboratory testing procedure can win universal acceptance. This conference can be said to have defined the problem. In addition to papers describing new work, a useful session was devoted to a discussion of the present and future technical situation in the graphic arts.

The conference met in Elsinore, Denmark, in June 1961 under the chairmanship of Mr. Chr. W. Christensen, Head of the Research Department of the Graphic College of Denmark. This College was the source of the highly efficient organization behind this conference, leavened by the great hospitality of its Director, Mr. Svend Jensen. The most sincere thanks go to Mr. V. Thal-Jantzen in his capacity as a representative of the Association of Graphic Arts in Denmark and chairman of the Council of the College who provided for much of the cost of the conference.

The following Danish institutions also contributed generous financial help for which our thanks are given.

Foreningen for Danmarks Lak- og Farveindustri,
Den Danske Presses Faellesindkøbs Forening,
Knud Højgårds Fond,
Laurits Andersens Fond,
Carlsbergs Mindelegat for Brygger I.C. Jacobsen,
Tuborgfonden,
Direktør, konsul Gustav Smidth og hustru Marie Smidths legat.

W. H. BANKS

CONTENTS

PARTICIPANTS

Country	Name	Institute
Country	*Name*	*Institute*
Austria	W. MUTSCHLECHNER	Graphische Lehr- und Versuchsanstalt, Wien
Denmark	IB HUNDERUP JENSEN JØRGEN REIMANN	Den Danske Presses Faellesindkøbsforening, København
	CHR. W. CHRISTENSEN AAGE FRØSLEV-NIELSEN RENÉ LARAIGNOU ARNE WULFF	Den grafiske Højskole, København
	ULRIK KLÄNING	Laboratoriet for Fotokemi Fotografi og Reproduktionsteknik, Danmarks Tekniske Højskole, København
	H. K. RAASCHOU-NIELSEN	Lak- og Farveindustriens Forskningslaboratorium, København
England	W. H. BANKS V. G. W. HARRISON S. R. C. POULTER R. D. W. MILLER E. J. PRITCHARD	The Printing, Packaging and Allied Trades Research Association, Leatherhead, Surrey
Finland	LARS NORDMAN RALF REHN	Oy Keskuslaboratorio- Centrallaboratorium AB, Helsinki
	OLAVI PERILÄ	Statens Tekniska Forskningsanstalt, Helsinki
France	HÉLENE BENEDITE	Société Professionnelle des Papiers de Presse, Paris
	ETIENNE PASZKIEWICZ	Institut Professionnel de Recherches et d'Etudes des Industries Graphique, Paris
Germany	W. ESCHENBACH KURT WAGENBAUER	Institut für Druckmaschinen und Druckverfahren, Darmstadt
	JOHANNES ALBRECHT HERBERT DÜRNER KARL-HEINS SCHIRMER	Institut der Deutschen Gesellschaft für Forschung in graphischen Gewerbe München
	E. RUPP	Institut für Graphische Technik, Leipzig C1 Gerichtsweg 24

Holland	J. F. MONROY A. J. W. SWEERMAN D. TOLLENAAR	Stichting Instituut voor Grafische Techniek T.N.O. Amsterdam
Hungary	KÁLMÁN LOVÁSZ G. HAIMAN	Nyomdaipari Kisérleti Uzem és laboratorium, Budapest
Italy	GUISEPPE CALABRO INNOCENZO FABBRI	Entre Nazionale per la Cellulosa e Per la Carta Roma
Norway	OTTO JANSEN	Papirindustriens Forskningsinstitutt, Oslo
Sweden	GÖSTA E. CARLSSON ROLF GINMAN HANS SANDER	Grafiska Forskningslaboratoriet, Stockholm
Switzerland	P. FINK	Eidgenössische Materialprüfungs- und Versuchsanstalt, St. Gallen
USA	R. W. PRINCE	American Newspaper Publishers Association Research Institute Inc., Easton, Pennsylvania
	WILLIAM D. SCHAEFFER JACQUELINE M. FETSKO	National Printing Ink Research Institute, Lehigh University, Bethlehem, Pennsylvania
	MARVIN C. ROGERS	Research and Engineering Council of the Graphic Arts Industry Inc., Washington D.C.
	W. L. RHODES	Rochester Institute of Technology, Graphic Arts Department, Rochester N.Y.
	WILLIAM REID	Technical Association of Graphic Arts, Battelle Memorial Institute, Columbus, Ohio
USSR	E. M. MEDVEDIEV	All Union Research Institute of Printing Industry, Moscow

SOME OBSERVATIONS ON THE INK–PAPER RELATIONSHIP DURING PRINTING

by Baysung Hsu

The Printing, Packaging and Allied Trades Research Association,
Leatherhead, Surrey, England

INTRODUCTION

The physical relationship between ink and paper after printing has been the subject of many studies, yet relatively few reports have appeared about the state of ink and paper during printing. There is no doubt that the flow or penetration of ink into paper occurs not only after printing but also during the very moment of printing at a very much faster rate under the printing pressure. This aspect of the physical relationship is worth studying, as many printing faults such as set-off, powdering, strike-through, lack of density, etc. may at one time or another arise from unsatisfactory penetration.

EXPERIMENTAL METHOD

Because of the short interval of printing impression and the small quantity of ink involved, a direct measurement of the flow of ink into paper during printing is difficult and one has to rely upon indirect methods of measurement. One convenient method is to measure falls in the diffuse reflectance of the reverse side of paper as ink flows into the other side under printing pressure. Normally, an incident light beam is scattered back from the large number of fibre–air interfaces in paper. When a coloured liquid advances into paper, it replaces the air in paper and creates fibre–liquid interfaces instead. If the incident light is of a suitable colour, the light flux will be absorbed rather than scattered at these new interfaces. In other words, the effective thickness of paper for the scattering of light is reduced owing to the advance of liquid. The change in reflectance may thus be related to the depth of penetration through the Kubelka–Munk formula.[1] If R is the fractional fall in reflectance and h the depth of penetration, it can be shown[2]

$$R = \frac{R_0 + (1/R_0) - 2a}{R_0 - a + b \coth bSh} \tag{1}$$

in which $a = \frac{1}{2} (R_\infty + 1/R_\infty)$, $b = -\frac{1}{2} (R_\infty - 1/R_\infty)$ and R_0, R_∞ are the reflectances of one sheet of paper and a thick pile of papers respectively. S is defined by

$$S = \frac{1}{bd} \coth^{-1} \left[\frac{(1 - aR_0)}{bR_0} \right] \qquad (2)$$

where d is the thickness of a sheet of paper.

The apparatus for measuring the flow of ink into paper, which has been described elsewhere,[3] is based on the above principle. Because of the object of measuring reflectance during printing the printing action has to be a form of platen printing. Printing takes place from a pre-inked rubber disc placed on an inflatable rubber membrane which forms the top surface of a printing head. Hydraulic pressure originated from a pre-charged gas–liquid pressure accumulator is applied to the underside of the rubber membrane, as soon as a control valve opens. The duration of opening of the valve, and hence the dwell of pressure, is controlled by an electronic timer. These devices enable pressures up to 10^8 dyn/cm^2 and times of dwell of pressure down to about 0·01 sec to be reached.

The diffuse reflectance is measured, as usual, through a photocell and the pressure through a resistance type pressure transducer inserted in the printing head. Both are connected to a double beam oscilloscope so that the reflectance and pressure traces appear simultaneously on the screen, which can be photographed.

All experiments were carried out in an air-conditioned room at 20°C and 65% relative humidity.

RESULTS AND DISCUSSION

Effect of ink film thickness

For a given paper–ink system there are at least three factors which can affect the flow of ink, namely the ink film thickness on plate, printing pressure, and printing speed. The extent of penetration is first of all dependent upon the amount of ink put down on the plate; the heavier the ink film the deeper the penetration. But generally there is a limit to the penetration that can be achieved within the impression phase, no matter how much ink is put down.[3] Figure 1(a) shows that for a carbon black ink (10% by weight pigments in a varnish of 24 poise) and a super-calendered paper, the fall of reflectance increases initially with increasing film thickness on plate, but soon reaches a saturation value. When the printing pressure is raised, the saturation penetration becomes deeper but the film thickness at which the saturation begins does not appear to change very much with pressure. An increase in the time of dwell of pressure, i.e. a decrease in the printing speed, has similar effects as may be seen in Fig. 1(b). The percentage transfer curves are also included in the figures and it is apparent that the maximum of the transfer curve always precedes the saturation penetration. This is not in agreement with the concept that the maximum percentage transfer occurs when a saturated amount of ink is absorbed by the paper.[4] It is suggested that the observed discrepancy between the two arises from the roughness and non-uniformity of the paper surface. Some parts of paper reach saturation earlier

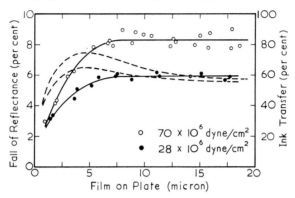

Fig. 1(a). Fall of reflectance (continuous line) of, and ink transfer (broken line) to, super-calendered paper vs. ink film on plate—pressure effect. Time of dwell of pressure: 0·04–0·05 sec. Ink viscosity: 53 Poise.

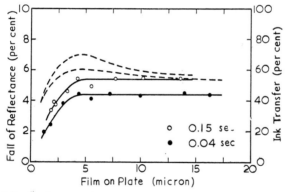

Fig. 1(b). Fall of reflectance (continuous line) of, and ink transfer (broken line) to, super-calendered paper vs. film on plate—time effect. Pressure: 28×10^6 dyn/cm². Ink viscosity: 53 Poise.

than others, so that when an overall saturation is reached over the whole surface there will inevitably be surplus ink over some parts of the surface. The discrepancy is thus expected to be smaller for a more uniform and smoother paper surface.

When either ink or paper is changed, there are markedly different results. For example, if the ink is changed to a more viscous one (10% by weight of carbon black in a varnish of 145 poise) the effect of pressure or speed becomes less pronounced and the film thickness necessary for saturation shifts to a lower value (Fig. 2). When a very porous paper such as antique book paper

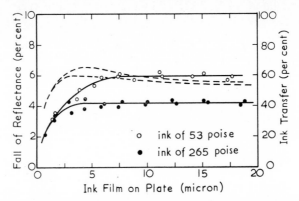

Fig. 2. Fall of reflectance (continuous line) of, and ink transfer (broken line) to, super-calendered paper vs. ink film on plate—ink effect. Pressure: 28×10^6 dyn/cm² for 0·04 sec.

is tested there may be no saturation at all within the practical range of film thickness (Fig. 3).

From the reflectance and transfer curves one can determine the least quantity of ink required to be transferred to paper in order to get the saturation penetration. This quantity is the sum of the ink penetrating into

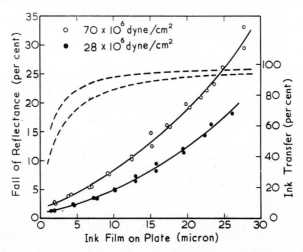

Fig. 3. Fall of reflectance (continuous line) of, and ink transfer (broken line) to, antique book paper vs. ink film on plate. Time of dwell of pressure: 0·04–0·05 sec. Ink viscosity: 53 poise.

paper and that remaining in the surface depressions during printing. As the former may be calculated through the equation of NPIRI[5] the latter can thus be determined. For the super-calendered paper the amount of ink in the surface depressions per cm^2 was calculated to be 0.17×10^{-3} cm^3. The same paper was also examined with the combined roughness–porosity tester[6] and the value* was found to be 0.22×10^{-3} cm^3. In view of the entirely different methods of measurement, the agreement is considered satisfactory.

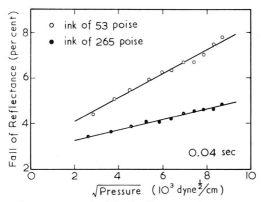

Fig. 4(a). Effect of pressure on the fall of reflectance of super-calendered paper.

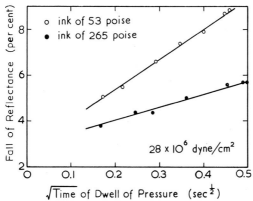

Fig. 4(b). Effect of time of dwell of pressure on the fall of reflectance of super-calendered paper.

Effect of printing pressure and speed

It is already shown above that an increase in pressure or decrease in printing speed results in more flow of ink into paper. But the quantitative relationship remains to be established. This is best done by keeping the film thickness

* Thanks are due to the Stichting Instituut voor Grafische Techniek T.N.O. Amsterdam for making these measurements.

B

constant at some value in the saturation region and varying the printing pressure or speed.[7] Some typical results for the super-calendered paper and carbon black inks are given in Fig. 4 showing the effects of printing pressure and speed, each point being the average of three or four tests. It appears that the reflectance is in approximate linear relations with both the square root of pressure and that of time of dwell of pressure. When extrapolated to zero, all the lines do not pass through the origin but rather intersect the reflectance axis at about the same point. This possible reflectance fall at zero pressure or time is attributed to the immediate wetting of paper surface by ink on being brought into contact. Such fall of reflectance caused by the loss of paper surface for light scattering should be the same at all pressures and speeds, and has to be subtracted from the observed data of fall of reflectance so as to get that caused by the penetration alone.

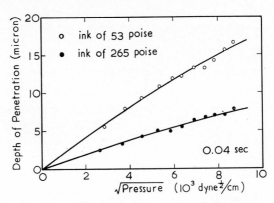

Fig. 5(a). Effect of pressure on the depth of penetration of ink into super-calendered paper.

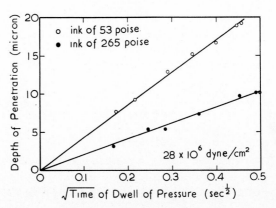

Fig. 5(b). Effect of time of dwell of pressure on the depth of penetration of ink into super-calendered paper.

By means of equation (1) the reflectance data can then be converted into the depth of penetration, as shown in Fig. 5. It is noticed that the depth of penetration is approximately proportional to the square root of pressure and the square root of duration of pressure. From these results it may perhaps be deduced that the porosity of paper is independent of the printing pressure. However, it will be shown that this is not so.

Effect of viscosity

When a series of simple carbon black inks of near Newtonian behaviour and some Newtonian varnishes were studied for their flow into the super-calendered paper, it was found that there is a proportionate relationship between the depth of penetration and the square root of the reciprocal of ink viscosity (Fig. 6). It seems that the viscosity of the ink as a whole rather than

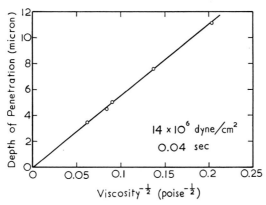

Fig. 6. Effect of ink viscosity on the depth of penetration into super-calendered paper.

the viscosity of varnish or the degree of pigmentation is the determining factor in the penetration during printing. Although the primary particles of carbon black are very small, they are known to be flocculated in ink. It is suggested that the large agglomerates may break up in printing under the high shear stress and a predominant part of the ink would flow into the paper without filtration. This conclusion may not be applicable to other systems of ink and paper, as obviously the problem is determined by the relative sizes of ink pigments and paper pores.

THEORETICAL CONSIDERATIONS

Based on the assumptions that the dimensions of paper fibres do not change significantly with pressure, and that paper behaves linearly under pressure, the author [2] showed that the surface area of contact among fibres is linearly related to the square root of pressure, whence the decrease in pore radius with increasing pressure is inversely proportional to the square root of pressure. If the rise and fall of pressure are very rapid compared with the time of dwell of pressure, integration of the Kozeny's equation in its differential form will result in

$$h = m \sqrt{\frac{(2pt)}{k\eta}} \left(1 - \sqrt{\frac{p}{p'}} \right) \tag{3}$$

in which m is the initial mean hydraulic radius, η the viscosity, p' the pressure under which the pore closes completely, and k a constant which may be taken as 6 for papers.

Equation (3) actually refers to the penetration in the compressed paper. When the pressure is removed the paper will recover from its compressed state, but owing to the viscous drag of ink the part of paper which has been penetrated cannot recover instantly. There is some evidence to show that as soon as this part of paper recovers the space thus created is filled with ink drawn from outside.[2] Therefore, the equivalent depth of penetration in the original uncompressed paper can be shown to be

$$h = m \sqrt{\frac{(2pt)}{k\eta}} \left(\frac{\sqrt{p'} - \sqrt{p}}{\sqrt{p'} - v\sqrt{p}} \right) \tag{4}$$

where v is the fractional reduction in paper thickness under pressure p'.

The curves in Fig. 5 are calculated in accordance with equation (4), in which v is estimated as 0·3 and p' as 10^9 dyn/cm² for the super-calendered paper. These curves are in good agreement with the observed points. From these curves the mean hydraulic radius can be calculated as $0·14\mu$, i.e. $0·56\mu$ in equivalent pore diameter, for the super-calendered paper.

It is clear from Fig. 5 that within the range of pressure covered the effect of pressure on the pore size is not very noticeable. However, according to equation (4) h will first increase to a maximum and then approach zero as p increases to sufficiently high levels. In other words, for a given system of ink and paper at a given speed of printing, there would be a ceiling on the depth of penetration no matter how the printing pressure is varied. At very high pressures the penetration might become less as the pressure is raised, but this will be unlikely to happen in the range of printing pressures normally applied in practice.

REFERENCES

1. P. KUBELKA, *J. Opt. Soc. Amer.* **38**, 448 (1948).
2. BAYSUNG HSU, *Appl. Sci. Res.* A **10**, 277 (1961).
3. R. R. COUPE and BAYSUNG HSU, *J. Oil Colour Chem. Assoc.* **43**, 720 (1960).
4. N. J. BECKMAN and G. R. SEARS, Amer. Newspaper Publ. Assoc. Tech. Report No. 11 (May, 1953).

5. J. M. FETSKO and W. C. WALKER, *Amer. Ink Maker*, 38, (Dec. 1955).
6. A. J. W. SWEERMAN, *Tappi* 44, No. 7, 172 A (1961).
7. R. R. COUPE and BAYSUNG HSU, *Appl. Sci. Res.* A 10, 253 (1961).

DISCUSSION

PRINCE: Was the caliper of two papers investigated the same?

BAYSUNG HSU: No, the super-calendered paper was 80μ thick and the antique book paper 147μ thick.

REID: This should be a powerful tool for examining " strike-through " or " show-through," but what do the measurements mean in regard to the printed surface? Would you care to comment on the relationship between the appearance of the printed surface and the back of the sheet as viewed by the photocell? For example, a dyed vehicle—as might be used in some news inks, for example—might show effects in this test apparatus not related at all to the appearance of the printed image.

BAYSUNG HSU: For a given ink film thickness the deeper the ink penetration, the less becomes the ink left on the paper surface. Thus, a large fall of reflectance from the back side of an uncoated paper usually means a light appearance of the printed surface, but this is only noticeable at rather low film thickness. The penetration of vehicle, dyed or not, which may occur after printing, or during printing on coated papers, can also cause a fall in reflectance from the back side of the sheet. A large fall of reflectance will then be accompanied by a matt appearance, or even powdering, of the printed surface. Colour effects of ink or vehicle can be adjusted by means of suitable colour filters put in the way of the incident light.

CARLSSON: In some previously published work you have shown that the fall in reflectance caused by ink penetration is much lower for newsprint than for offset cartridge paper. How do you explain this?

BAYSUNG HSU: As mentioned in the present paper, the measured fall of reflectance really consists of two components: one caused by ink penetration and the other by the filling-in of recesses in the paper surface. The latter accounts for the initial sudden fall of reflectance reported in the earlier paper. The fact that it was much lower for newsprint than for offset cartridge simply means that the newsprint had a smoother surface than the offset cartridge. This deduction agrees with the Bendtsen and Chapman smoothness data given in that paper (*J. Oil Colour Chem. Assoc.* **39**, 579 (1956)). It also explains why this initial fall of reflectance was almost independent of viscosity.

NORDMAN: Do you find a reversal of the order of a series of paper if you change the time of dwell of pressure?

BAYSUNG HSU: In general, the order would not be expected to be reversed. However, it could happen if the viscoelastic properties of the papers are vastly different. A paper which creeps very easily will have different pore sizes when the time of dwell of pressure is changed; consequently, its order may also change.

SCHAEFFER: Has a stress analysis been carried out on the distribution within the printing head?

BAYSUNG HSU: The printing head is so constructed that the paper is sandwiched between a flat glass block and a thin rubber membrane, on the back side of which a uniform hydraulic pressure is exerted. So long as the membrane remains flat during impression, which is the case in the actual printing region, the pressure must be the same on both sides of the membrane. Hence, the printing pressure exerted on the paper is not only uniform but also equal to the hydraulic pressure applied.

TOLLENAAR: Don't you think that the filtering effect becomes important after the pressure has been released?

BAYSUNG HSU: Yes. It has been pointed out in reference.[7]

TOLLENAAR: Is there any indication of an appreciable capillary pressure in the intercept of the reflectance-pressure curve?

BAYSUNG HSU: I do not think that the intercept could be the result of penetration caused by the capillary pressure which cannot be expected to be greater than a small fraction of the impression pressure applied. Even if the graph is plotted on the basis of impression pressure plus a reasonably large capillary pressure, there is still an appreciable intercept. Furthermore, any penetration caused by the capillary pressure must be dependent upon the viscosity of fluid; yet the intercept is practically the same for many different inks and varnishes investigated. It has also been observed that there is a similar intercept on the graph of reflectance vs. time of dwell of pressure, and this obviously cannot be attributed to the capillary pressure.

SCHAEFFER: The very interesting extrapolation of impression pressures to that required for formation of an impermeable surface depends of course on untenable boundary conditions for capillary flow. Nevertheless, can you estimate the possible error in your estimate?

BAYSUNG HSU: An accurate estimate of error is not possible, but the agreement between observed and calculated curves could mean that the estimated pressure is reasonably correct.

GINMAN: Have you tried to correlate these penetration measurement values with paper properties, especially with the PATRA surface oil resistance value?

BAYSUNG HSU: The two types of papers used in this work are very different. Their penetration results are in the right order as that indicated by the PATRA Surface Oil Absorption Test.

ROGERS: The test area used in this work is nearly infinite when compared with the single printed character such as a halftone dot—what effect might be expected from the influence of ink flow outward at the edges of the smaller characters when compared with those reported here? This is an unconfined system so far as the fluid between printing forme and paper are concerned.

BAYSUNG HSU: I should think that the penetration during impression by halftone dots will be less than that indicated in this work, but the difference may not be large if the ink film applied is thin.

THE INFLUENCE OF PRESSURE, PRESSURE DISTRIBUTION, PACKING AND PRINTING SPEED UPON INK TRANSFER AND COVERAGE IN LETTERPRESS

by Aage Frøslev-Nielsen

Research Department, The Graphic College of Denmark

INTRODUCTION

The prime purpose of this research has been to examine the ink transfer in letterpress at various pressure distributions and speeds. The research involves printing with one ink on two different papers and with five different packings on the impression cylinder.

In the first part of the research the distribution of the pressure in the nip has been considered as the main factor in the ink transfer for a given paper, ink, and speed, and here the printing has been done under two pressure distributions but at the same linear pressure irrespective of the various packing compositions.

The printing was done in a letterpress automat (M.A.N. Polyautomat, 2 revolution press), with an impression cylinder diameter of 260 mm. In order to print under as uniform conditions as possible at the two pressures, the printing was done simultaneously on the two packings by means of a weighable plate.

The first two packings have extremely different properties and were selected only with a view to providing as varying pressure distributions as possible. This is expressed in Table 2 by the various maximum pressures and nip widths for the two packings. Studies were made at seven speeds ranging from 0·63 to 1·19 m/sec. [7]

The subsequent comparisons have been made in a similar way by simultaneous printing on two packings, and have in Table 2 been numbered 1, 2 and 3. In the second comparison the soft packing, II, has been maintained while the hard one has been only slightly altered in its composition (packing

II

III). Thus, approximately the same linear pressure has been maintained for the two packings, and this showed whether this slight alteration has any influence upon the ink transfer. The printing speed was 1 m/sec.

In the third comparison the two packings are conventional ones of different hardnesses. The printing was done partly at a constant printing speed of 1 m/sec and six different linear pressures, partly under constant pressure and at seven different printing speeds. The pressure distributions for the two packings do not vary much, and in order to examine the influence of the pressure distribution upon the ink transfer for identical packings, printing has also been done in the test printing device, the Fogra-tester. Here the plate is cylindrical with a diameter of 65 mm, and the printing is effected against flat mounted packings of a composition identical with those of the letterpress automat.

With a view to the uniformity in the structure of the experiments two very homogeneous, coated printing papers were chosen, the so-called Baryta paper (Baryta I and Baryta II). The two types differ considerably in roughness and absorption. The ink was a conventional black illustration ink of the following composition: 23·4% carbon black, 73·6% linseed oil, 3·0% alkali blue.

During printing the relative humidity was maintained at $55 \pm 2\%$. The thermostat was placed directly above the inking unit and quite close to the first distributor roller, thus ensuring that this area maintained a temperature of $26 \pm 0·5°C$.

PRESSURES AND PACKINGS

The pressure measurements were made before the actual printing by means of a special strain gauge element which replaced the weighable plate in the forme in such a way that the compression conditions were identical with those during printing. A determination of the area under the pressure distribution curves is essential in order to determine the linear pressure, and in the preliminary measurements was estimated by treating the areas as triangular in shape. In subsequent measurements the area was measured using a planimeter. The measurements show that the linear pressure and the maximum pressure do not depend upon the speed, and that the slight differences that might appear in the measurements may be ascribed to the general errors of measurement in the speed range which has been used. Consequently Table 2 gives pressures measured at a speed of 1 m/sec only. By means of aluminium foil placed between the packing and the cylinder, the packings in Table 1 were built up to the thickness necessary to produce the pressure desired. When printing with packings IV and V under various linear pressures, printing was first done under heavy pressure, and the pressure was reduced by removal of metal foil. Thus the composition of the packings was not altered when the pressure was varied.

TABLE 1

Composition of impression cylinder packing	Thickness in mm	Total thickness in mm	Shore-D, hardness exclusive printing sheet
Packing I			
2 acetate sheets	0·53		
1 draw sheet	0·10		
1 printing sheet	0·10	0·73	80
Packing II			
1 polythene foil	0·04		
1 rubber blanket	0·23		
2 polythene foils	0·07		
4 raw rubber blankets	0·99		
1 draw sheet	0·10		
1 printing sheet	0·10	1·53	48
Packing III			
1 polythene foil	0·03		
2 acetate sheets	0·53		
1 draw sheet	0·10		
1 printing sheet	0·10	0·76	80
Packing IV			
1 p.v.c. foil	0·10		
1 cardboard	0·17		
1 cardboard	0·30		
1 p.v.c. foil	0·10		
1 rubber blanket	0·30		
1 draft paper sheet	0·07		
1 draw sheet	0·12		
1 printing sheet	0·10	1·26	65
Packing V			
1 p.v.c. foil	0·10		
1 cardboard	0·17		
1 cardboard	0·30		
1 p.v.c. foil	0·10		
1 cardboard	0·30		
1 draft paper sheet	0·07		
1 draw sheet	0·12		
1 printing sheet	0·10	1·26	70

TABLE 2

Comparisons	Packing	Linear pressure kg/cm	Maximum pressure kg/cm²	Width of pressure nip mm	Type of paper
1	I	565	122·0	8·2	
	II	43·5	50·8	13·2	
2	III	49·7	112·2	7·6	
	II	56·7	68·1	13·5	
3	IV	9·5	22·9	6·1	
		17·5	36·2	7·1	
		31·0	55·2	9·4	Baryta I
		44·0	74·2	10·3	
		56·0	92·0	10·7	
		77·6	117·5	12·5	
	V	10·1	25·5	6·6	
		17·9	37·1	7·8	
		30·9	51·2	9·0	
		35·7	62·2	9·4	
		48·1	80·0	10·4	
		69·7	101·0	11·8	
1	I	50·5	106·0	7·5	
	II	35·9	46·2	12·8	
2	III	38·8	91·4	7·2	
	II	33·7	47·0	12·0	
3	IV	3·1	10·8	4·0	
		8·4	21·6	6·2	
		21·6	38·8	8·7	
		29·1	55·2	9·4	Bartya II
		42·8	75·0	10·0	
	V	63·2	101·0	11·2	
		3·4	11·2	4·9	
		9·4	22·8	6·0	
		22·1	41·4	8·6	
		24·4	48·3	8·4	
		36·9	63·0	9·7	
		50·4	81·2	11·4	

Figure 1 is a diagram of the printing element used and shows the position of the strain-gauges which are connected with a Wheatstone bridge and an oscillograph. The pressure sensitive part, *R*, has been built into a solid steel block, *S*, which during the pressure measurement replaces the printing plate,

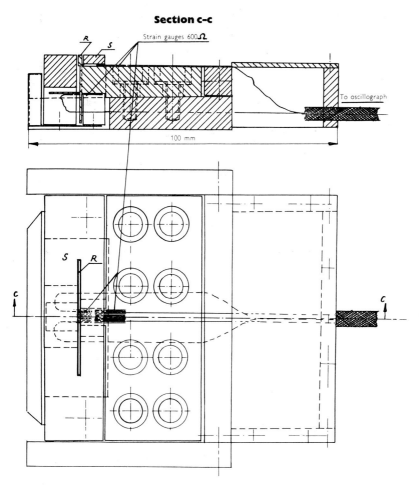

Fig. I. Pressure gauge.

and in Fig. 2 is seen imposed into the forme in the press. Figure 3 shows typical pressure curves measured on packings of types I and II. The pressure gauge is imposed into the forme instead of the plate during the measurement in such a way that the pressures are the same as those during printing from the plate. From 20 height measurements the height of the printing elements were found to be 23·610 ± 0·002 mm and the pressure sensitive part was raised 2/1000 to 3/1000 mm above this; so that its surface was $23 \cdot 612 \pm$ 0·001 mm above the bed. As the plate is level with the non-sensitive part of the pressure gauge, and as the latter has been adjusted with a load such that

Fig. 2. The pressure gauge imposed into the test forme.

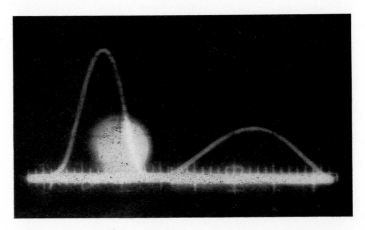

Fig. 3. Pressure curves obtained with hard (left) and soft (right) packing.

the surfaces, R and S, are level, the gauge will record the beginning of the pressure too early. The deformation of the packing is illustrated in Fig. 4. Applying Schleicher's formula[1] for loads at uniform pressure distribution on a rectangular surface with the dimensions a and b, an average deformation w is given by

$$w_{\text{av.}} = \frac{P(1 - v^2)m}{E\sqrt{A}} \tag{1}$$

where P is the load in kg upon A, $m = 0 \cdot 5$ for $b/a = 38$, $E =$ the modulus of elasticity of the packing, v the Poisson ratio, and $A = b.a = 0 \cdot 38$ cm². This formula applies when $w < d - \delta$, where δ is the deflection of R in mm. The following relation has been found for the pressure gauge: $P = 2 \cdot 23 \times 10^4 \times \delta$ kg. In the limiting case, $w = d - \delta$, and since δ is negligible compared

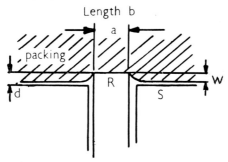

Fig. 4. The deformation of the packing during pressure measurement.

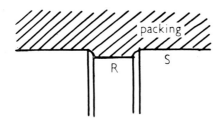

Fig. 5. Characteristic deformation of packing under pressure.

with d, the measurement error due to height difference (d) between R and S is given by writing $w = d$ in equation (1) with $v = 0$, and $m = 0 \cdot 5$. Thus

$$P = 2d \, E\sqrt{A} \text{ kg}$$

and the pressure p is given by

$$p = \frac{P}{A} = \frac{2dE}{\sqrt{A}} \text{ kg/cm}^2 \tag{2}$$

The packings were not subjected to static loads, but the compression of the packings at the printing speed of 1 m/sec may be calculated from Table 2 as $b^2/4D$ where D is the cylinder diameter (260 mm) and b is the width of the pressure nip. By division of this compression by the packing thickness a relative compression ϵ is found, and in Fig. 6 this has been compared with the maximum pressures for the packings IV and V. Only one curve has been drawn since there is only a slight difference in the packings, and the chord from

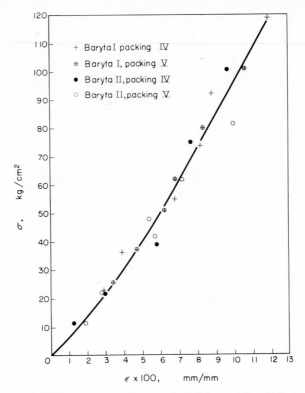

Fig. 6. Curve for the approximate estimate of the modulus of elasticity.

0 kg/cm² to 100 kg/cm² gives an approximate value for E ($E = \sigma/\epsilon =$ 9·5 kg/mm²). Similarly for the packings I, II, and III:

$$E_{\mathrm{I}} \simeq E_{\mathrm{III}} \simeq 14 \text{ kg/mm}^2$$
$$E_{\mathrm{II}} \simeq 5 \text{ kg/mm}^2$$

For $d = 3/1000$ mm the following error of measurement is arrived at from (2)

$$p_{\mathrm{I}} \simeq p_{\mathrm{III}} \simeq 1\cdot4 \text{ kg/cm}^2$$
$$p_{\mathrm{II}} \simeq 0\cdot5 \text{ kg/cm}^2$$
$$p_{\mathrm{IV-V}} \simeq 0\cdot9 \text{ kg/cm}^2$$

If the pressure gauge had been adjusted in such a way that the pressure sensitive part of R under no load was level with S, the pressure distributions in the packings would have differed from the above mentioned cases (cf Fig. 5). Under load the packing will be forced down in the recess in which the pressure sensitive part moves. Kallstenius and Bergau[2] have examined the case when the pressure sensitive part is cylindrical. Gravesen[3] has compared this case with that of Boussinesq where the cylindrical pressure die is pressed freely into the elastic medium (Fig. 4). It was found that the Kallstenius–Bergau pressure gradient was three times that of Boussinesq. That is

$$\left(\frac{dP}{dw}\right)_K = 3\left(\frac{dP}{dw}\right)_B$$

If this approach to the problem is applied to the situations shown in Figs. 4 and 5, the measuring error is presumably three times as big in the latter situation as in the first one. Consequently the first mentioned adjustment has been preferred.

The pressure gauge was calibrated statically, but by experiments its natural frequency has been found to be at least five times bigger than the biggest forced frequency during the printing. Thus the static adjustment can be considered satisfactory.

MEASURING THE SPEED

The speed of the bed was measured by means of a band which during the measurements was fastened to the bed and followed its movements back and forth. The band runs from a spring loaded drum, via a slip ring, which by rotation opens and closes a switch in an electric circuit. The current impulses are registered by an Schwarzer Oscillograph and the distance between the impulses will vary with the speed of the bed.

The motor regulator was calibrated for speed at 10 different settings; and the speed could be set with an uncertainty not exceeding $\pm 2\%$. Thus it was possible to determine the speed of the bed by adjusting the regulator irrespective of the printing.

The following speed steps were used during printing:
0·63 m/sec, 0·69 m/sec, 0·76 m/sec, 0·86 m/sec, 0·96 m/sec, 1·08 m/sec, 1·19 m/sec; and furthermore 1·00 m/sec.
On Fig. 7 the speed indicator is seen connected to the bed.

INK TRANSFER FROM FORME ROLLERS TO FORME

The weighable steel printing plate was imposed together with four other plates in a forme. The average type height from 20 measurements was $23\cdot610 \pm 0\cdot001$ mm. The inking rollers were made of rubber, and the quantity of ink on the forme was weighed before and after printing. It is not possible on this letterpress machine, as in a proofing press, to distribute the ink on the forme and weigh it immediately before printing, since subsequent printing will be preceded by a further inking of the forme. Consequently a new procedure was worked out. It was found that the ink transferred, after

Fig. 7. Speed measuring instrument.

about 20 inkings, settled down to a constant and reproducible quantity within acceptable limits. Thus two successive weighings did not differ by more than 50 mg/m². This must be considered an acceptable uncertainty in the amount of ink, and the method was therefore adopted. A further advantage was that printing occurred immediately after inking; thus the ink properties did not change between inking and printing. A prerequisite for the application of the method is that for each printing, the distribution must be made at the printing speed on the experiment, since the amount of ink transferred is somewhat dependent on the speed.

Figure 8 shows the interdependence of the amount of ink on the plate and the speed for various constant amounts of ink in the inking unit. Each box in Fig. 8 corresponds to a constant, but unknown, amount of ink in the inking unit.

At each speed the measurements were not made until the weight of ink on the plate had settled down to a value which did not vary outside the accepted limits. In order to avoid any influence of temperature rise on the interpretation of the results the sequence of experiments was such that after

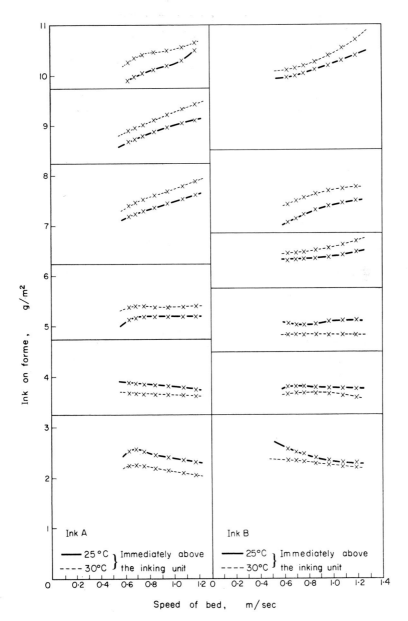

Fig. 8. Relation between ink on forme and printing speed at constant ink amounts in the inking unit. Composition of ink A: 23·4% carbon black; 73·6% linseed oil; 3·0% alkali blue. Composition of ink B: 20·5% carbon black; 76·6% linseed oil; 2·6% alkali blue.

C

measurement at a particular speed, a repeat measurement at the first speed
was made. Several weighings were also made at randomly repeated speeds.

The measurements were made at controlled temperatures of 25°C and
30°C. By way of comparison the experiment was repeated with a thinner ink
as shown in Fig. 8 (ink B). In order to get a clearer picture of the influence of
the temperature the two quantities of ink at 25°C and 30°C are compared in
Fig. 9 at 1 m/sec printing speed. As is seen from these curves, the amount

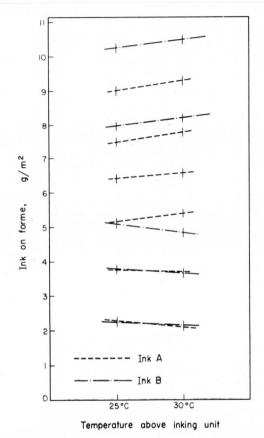

Fig. 9. Amounts of ink on forme compared with the temperature immediately
above the inking unit. Printing speed 1 m/sec.

of ink transferred falls with a rise in temperature for amounts of ink in the
inking unit, below a certain level and then increases with the temperature for
amounts above this level. The differences in the ink transfer from forme
rollers to printing plate suggest that the ink splitting between rubber and
metal in the inking unit does not remain constant in the whole speed range.

INK TRANSFER FROM FORME TO PAPER

(a) General

When printing on the two types of paper Baryta I and Baryta II, the printing was done simultaneously on the two packings. In Table 2, column 1 records the comparison, column 2 the cylinder packings. Comparison 1 has been treated in a previous paper,[7] and in comparison 2 some of the metal foil under the two sheets of acetate sheet has been removed and replaced by polythene foil of the same caliper.

Curves are drawn between the amount of ink transferred to the paper y and the original amount of ink on the plate x.

According to Walker and Fetsko[8, 9] the ink transfer y to the paper by an adequate amount of ink, x (i.e. a greater amount than is necessary for a sufficient coverage of the paper) can be expressed as follows

$$y = fx + b(1 - f)$$

where b is the amount of ink initially accepted by the paper at the moment of impression, and f is fraction of free ink split from the plate to the paper upon

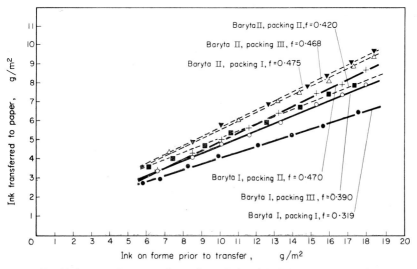

Fig. 10. Ink transfer curves for packings I, II and III. Printing speed 1 m/sec.

separation; b and f may be considered constants at identical pressures, paper, ink, packing, and plate. Thus the ink transfer curve appears as a straight line as shown in Fig. 10; f is determined from the slope of the curve, and b is calculated from their intercepts on the y–axis which are equal to $b(1 - f)$; the data for the curve are obtained at a printing speed of 1 m/sec. It will be noted that the measurements are made by printing with considerable amounts of ink. This is necessary in order to define the linear part of the ink transfer curve since somewhere on it lies the point corresponding to complete coverage—the coverage point.

(b) Comparisons 1 and 2

Figure 10 shows that under comparable printing conditions, using packings I and II at approximately the same linear pressure, the slope of the curves, or the f values, are quite different. Reference to Table 2 shows that the linear pressure on packing II is slightly below that on packing I, and in order to test the reversed conditions a comparative printing was done on the packings II and III, the latter only differing from I by the fact that the metal foil under the acetate sheets in packing I had been replaced by polythene foil of the same caliper. This apparently insignificant alteration under the hard acetate sheets did, however, effect a comparatively steep increase in the ink transfer and the f value as seen in Fig. 10. This result was obtained in spite of the fact that packing I, in the case of Baryta I, was adjusted to a greater linear pressure than packing III, and irrespective of the fact that the two packings did not show a substantial difference in pressure distribution. Furthermore the shore hardnesses were equal.

That it is a question of a difference in the flexibility of the two packings is evident, as we can assume that packing III gives improved contact between paper and printing forme. However, the results cannot be explained as due to lack of contact in the case of packing I, since the points of coverage for both packings is reached with amounts of ink on the printing papers corresponding to approx. $3 \cdot 0 \text{ g/m}^2$. In the case of completely failing contact between paper and forme a much steeper course of the ink transfer curves is to be expected so that the inclination of the curves becomes equal to or greater than the f value for packing II.

In consequence of these measurements which show that the ink transfer with these hard packings is very sensitive to small alterations in the composition of the packings, it would be desirable to separate the influence of the pressure distribution and the packing composition upon the ink transfer by printing upon two packings of a realistic composition in two machines with different impression cylinder diameters.

(c) Comparison 3

In comparison 3, Table 2, the printings were done on two packings, IV and V, and the ink transfer in the Polyautomat was compared with the printing in a Fogra-tester, which is a test printing device with a cylinder diameter of 65 mm. The cylinder is, in this case, the printing forme and the packing is mounted on a plane. Consequently special packing plates have been made for packings IV and V used here since the underlying material for the packings is aluminium. The first experiments were a comparison between ink transfer in the two machines under varying pressure inasmuch as the coverage point has been visually determined for each amount of ink.

Figures 11 and 12 show the ink transfer to Baryta I and Baryta II papers respectively on the two printing machines with differing amounts of ink on

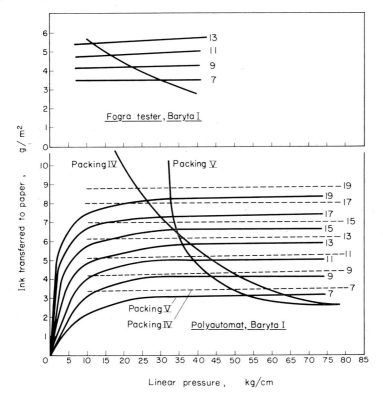

Fig. 11. Interrelation between ink on Baryta I and linear pressure for the packings IV and V at constant amounts of ink on the forme. The figures on the curves show the amount of ink on the forme in g/m^2.

the plate. Furthermore, curves have been drawn through the coverage points at different pressures. For the printing on the Polyautomat it will be seen that the ink transfer is different for the two packings IV and V for both Baryta I and II, and the curves for the coverage points are also different for the two packings. Thus it must be concluded, in the case of Baryta I, that the coverage at linear pressures of 35 kg/cm or above (i.e. in the practical pressure range) is better on the hard packing V. If the ink transfer is compared at the same amount of ink on the plate, this difference in coverage cannot, however, be read from the coverage point curves without due respect to the different ink transfers for the two packing types as appearing from the other curves in Figs. 11 and 12. Thus the difference in coverage point is somewhat compensated by the fact that packing IV transfers more ink than V. At 7 g/m^2 on the plate the linear pressure necessary to reach the coverage point for packing IV is thus actually reduced by about 7% compared with the

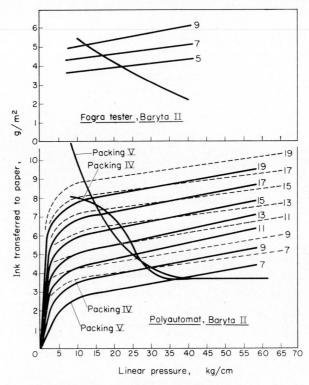

Fig. 12. Interrelation between ink on Baryta II and linear pressure for the packings IV and V at constant ink amounts on the forme. The figures on the curves show the amount of ink on the forme in g/m^2.

assumption that the two packings effect the same fraction of ink to paper. In the case of Baryta II it must be concluded that in spite of the slight difference in the coverage point curves, the soft packing IV gives the best coverage inasmuch as the curve for this packing intersects the ink transfer curves at lower pressures than in the case of packing V. At 7 g/m^2 on the plate the least pressure necessary to reach the coverage point for packing IV is thus actually reduced by about 20% compared with the assumption that the two packings effect the same fraction of ink to paper. Moreover, the comparison between the two papers shows for both machines that the total amount of ink transferred to Baryta I above a certain pressure is practically independent of it whereas the transfer to Baryta II shows some dependence on pressure.

While it is possible to show some difference in the ink transfer for the two packings IV and V, the curves for the ink transfer in the Fogra-tester show that the coverage point curves are identical. Consequently it is concluded that the type of packing is of less importance when printing with cylinders of smaller diameter.

A comparison between the ink transfer in the Fogra-tester and in the Polyautomat is interesting. To do so, the pressures required in each machine to reach the coverage point for the same amount of ink on the paper are compared. This relation can be deduced from Figs. 11 and 12, and the comparison is shown in Fig. 13.

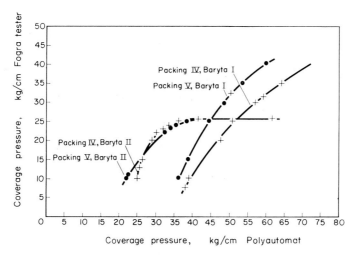

Fig. 13. Interrelation between covering pressures at two printing presses. Printing speed is 1 m/sec. Comparison of coverage pressures measured on the Fogra-tester and the Polyautomat at 1 m/sec.

As mentioned earlier the ink transfer can be characterized by the two constants b and f. Table 3 gives the b and f values for Baryta I and II at 7 printing speeds in the Polyautomat, and the difference between the linear pressures for packing IV and V is so small in these experiments that the b and f values may be considered to be at the same pressure on the two packings. This will be understood when estimating the influence of the pressure on these constants (compare table 4 and Figs. 15 and 17). Table 4 gives the b and f values for two printings in the Fogra-tester. As is shown in Table 2, printing was done in the Polyautomat at six different linear pressures, but b and f values have only been recorded for two pressures because it is only realistic to determine these figures when the coverage point is reasonably

TABLE 3

| Baryta I, Polyautomat | | | | | Baryta II, Polyautomat | | | | |
| Linear pressure 56 kg/cm. Packing IV | | Linear pressure 48·1 kg/cm. Packing V | | Speed | Linear pressure 42·8 kg/cm. Packing IV | | Linear pressure 36·9 kg/cm. Packing V | | Speed |
b g/m²	f	b g/m²	f	m/sec	b g/m²	f	b g/m²	f	m/sec
0·995	0·459	1·805	0·389	0·63	1·584	0·546	2·372	0·467	0·63
0·041	0·489	1·356	0·398	0·69	2·259	0·513	3·006	0·406	0·69
0·353	0·476	0·926	0·413	0·76	2·591	0·488	2·418	0·421	0·76
0·160	0·477	0·873	0·413	0·86	1·753	0·517	1·845	0·442	0·86
0·543	0·457	0·250	0·431	0·96	1·676	0·504	1·221	0·445	0·96
0·683	0·441	0·324	0·439	1·08	2·354	0·423	1·281	0·421	1·08
0·943	0·430	1·125	0·384	1·19	0·325	0·532	0·929	0·440	1·19

TABLE 4

| Baryta I, Fogra-tester | | | | | | Baryta II, Fogra-tester | | | | | |
| Packing IV (soft) | | | Packing V | | | Packing IV | | | Packing V | | |
b g/m²	f	kg/cm	b g/m²	f	kg/cm	b g/m²	f	kg/cm	b g/m²	f	kg/cm
1·711	0·345	10	1·791	0·330	10	2·957	0·368	10	3·112	0·341	10
1·292	0·368	15	1·988	0·321	15	3·660	0·328	15	3·915	0·296	15
2·077	0·351	20	1·745	0·353	20	3·380	0·366	20	3·398	0·364	20
2·077	0·340	30	1·736	0·360	30	3·650	0·375	30	4·102	0·320	30
1·846	0·361	40	1·938	0·360	40	4·481	0·371	40	4·875	0·315	40
Baryta I, Polyautomat						Baryta II, Polyautomat					
Packing IV			Packing V			Packing IV			Packing V		
0·683	0·441	56·0	0·324	0·439	48·1	2·354	0·423	42·8	1·281	0·421	36·9
0·960	0·430	77·6	0·601	0·415	69·7	3·127	0·439	63·2	2·226	0·416	50·4

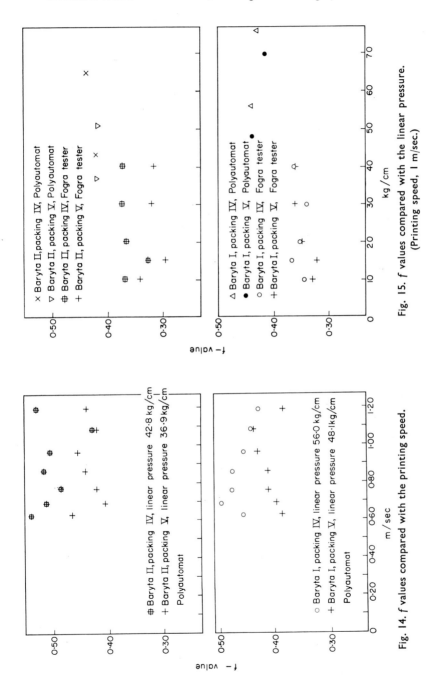

Fig. 15. f values compared with the linear pressure. (Printing speed, 1 m/sec.)

Fig. 14. f values compared with the printing speed.

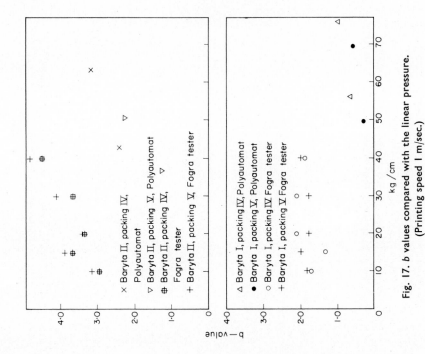

Fig. 17. *b* values compared with the linear pressure.
(Printing speed 1 m/sec.)

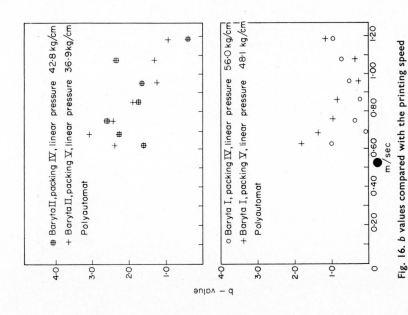

Fig. 16. *b* values compared with the printing speed

low (with high linear pressure); the b and f values were determined by regression analysis of the ink transfer curves.

Figure 14 shows the variation of f with the printing speed for the Poly-automat; and Fig. 15 the variation with the linear pressures for both machines. Similarly Figs. 16 and 17 show b values as a function of speed and pressure. It is clear that printing on packings such as IV and V gives a comparatively haphazard distribution of b and f values for varying speeds and pressures. Consequently for each paper and ink it is difficult to see any relationship between f value and pressure or speed, whereas the b values in the case of Baryta II show a tendency to decrease with increased speed and to increase with increasing pressure. The b values, on the other hand, are rather haphaz-ardly distributed in the case of Baryta I.

Comparing effects of different packings and machines distinct differences appear. Thus it is seen from Figs. 14 and 15 that when printing on packing IV, higher f values are obtained than when printing on packing V. Moreover, the f values are on the average higher on the Polyautomat than on the Fogra-tester; on the other hand, the b values on the average are considerably lower on the Polyautomat than on the Fogra-tester. Thus a decreasing f value and an increasing b value can be noted. In the case of Baryta I it is seen that the b value at 70 kg/cm has not reached the same value on the Polyautomat as the b value at 10 kg/cm in the Fogra-tester. As for Baryta I no b values are identical in the two machines even when compared at 10 kg/cm in the Fogra-tester and 77 kg/cm in the Polyautomat. Primarily this shows, for the materials examined, that the linear pressure is not the only determining factor for the two machines, and furthermore the great differences in pressure mentioned above show that not even identical maximum pressures lead to identical ink splitting in the two machines.

The conclusion drawn from the b and f values in comparisons 1 and 2 is that both the packing and the geometrical conditions during the printing have an independent influence upon the ink transfer.

SUMMARY

Ink transfer to two coated printing papers with different printability properties has been examined, a black standard letterpress ink being used. The printing was done on five different packings, and has been done simultaneously on two packings in order to get a standard of comparison as ideal as possible. The initial aim was a comparison of the ink transfer for two different pressure distributions at the same linear pressure, but the first experiments show that it is necessary to separate printing geometry (cylinder diameter) and type of packing since both factors seem to have influence upon the ink transfer. Therefore the subsequent experiments were concentrated on printing on packings of conventional composition on two machines with different cylinder diameters, the Polyautomat and the Fogra-tester. Printings were done at 6 pressures and 8 speeds in the Polyautomat and at 5 pressures and 1 speed in the Fogra-tester.

It was found that the soft packing in the Polyautomat transfers more ink than the hard packing at the same pressure and ink amount on the plate, but that the amount of ink transferred is independent of the packing in the Fogra-tester. On the Polyautomat the coverage for Baryta I was best on the hard packing, and the reason was sought in the nature of the packing. As for Baryta II the coverage on the soft packing was best for the same ink amount on the plate, and this was due to the fact that more ink was transferred with this packing. With the same ink amount on the two papers there was no appreciable difference between the two packings. In printing with the Fogra-tester no difference was found between the two packings. A comparison was made between the pressures necessary to obtain coverage in the two machines for the same amount of ink on the paper. Finally by regression analysis of the ink transfer curves at various pressures and speeds b values were derived from the theory of Fetsko. The b values obtained in the Polyautomat are considerably smaller than those obtained in the Fogra-tester, and only in the case of the very absorbent paper was it possible to obtain b values of a similar magnitude in the Polyautomat at much heavier pressure than in the Fogra-tester. The f value, on the other hand, was smaller for the Fogra-tester. Thus, for the papers and packings examined here, it was impossible to find any simple connection between b and f values, the linear pressure. Additionally, the same maximum pressure in the two machines does not lead to the same ink transfer. However, it can be recorded that a decrease of f means an increase of the b value. In summary, this study shows that both geometrical conditions and the composition of the packing independently influence the ink transfer.

The measurement of pressure and speed and a special procedure to determine the weight of the ink used has been explained. Incidental to this method of inking was the observation that the amount of ink transferred from inking unit to forme depends to some extent upon the printing speed, which again shows that the splitting between metal, rubber and forme is different at different speeds.

REFERENCES

1. S. TIMOSHENKO, Theory of Elasticity, p. 370, McGraw-Hill, New York (1951).
2. T. KALLSTENIUS and W. BERGAU, Investigations of soil pressure measuring by means of Cells, *R. Swed. Geot. Inst. Proc.* **12** (1956).
3. V. ASKEGAARD, The measurement of pressure between an infinitely rigid wall and a compressible medium, *Meddelelse nr.* 10, *Laboratoriet for Bygningsteknik, Danmarks tekniske Hojskole*, København (1959).

4. L. OHLSSON and L. PIHL, Undersökning rörande tryckfördelning pa formen vid tryckning i cylinderpress. *Medd. Graf. Forskningslaboratoriet*, **31**, 3–12 (1953).
5. L. NORDMAN, R. GINMAN, G. OLOFSON, V. ERAVUO, Piezoelectric measurement of printing pressures, *TAGA, Proceedings of the 11th annual meeting* (1959).
6. MARKERT, Druckverteilungskurven und Druckkraft bei Flachform-Hochdruckmaschinen, *Inst. für Druckmaschinen und Druckverfahren, Darmstadt* (1960).
7. A. FRØSLEV-NIELSEN, Estimating the quality of letterpress printing presses, *TAGA, Proceedings of the 12th annual meeting* (1960).
8. C. WALKER and J. M. FETSKO, A concept of ink transfer in printing, *Amer. Ink Maker*, (December, 1955).
9. A. C. ZETTLEMOYER, R. F. SCARR and W. D. SCHAEFFER, Influence of ink properties on transfer during printing, *Intern Bull.*, **80**, 88 (1958).
10. R. GINMAN and L. NORDMAN, Subjective estimation of the quality of solid prints, *Intern. Bull.*, **80**, 55 (1958).

DISCUSSION

CARLSSON: What conclusions of relevance to practical printing can be drawn from this investigation?

FRØSLEV-NIELSEN: It is very difficult to draw general conclusions relevant to practical printing from experiments with only two papers and one ink, but the experiments show that it is necessary to take care of the influence of printing geometry and packing when planning printing investigations. The most sure method will, of course, be to print with conditions as near to practice as possible, that means using realistic cylinder diameters, packings, speed and so on.

DÜRNER: You had to stop your testing machine in order to weigh the plate. Could you stop it immediately so that you did not re-ink the forme again under varied conditions?

FRØSLEV-NIELSEN: As mentioned in my paper, we found that after 20 distributions of the plate in the inking system the amount of ink on the plate remains constant and in the Polyautomat it is possible to stop the press immediately, so that the inking of the forme is done at constant speed during the whole distribution time.

ALBRECHT: In a paired comparison of the print quality of 49 machine coated and art papers at ink coverages of 1 g/m² and 2 g/m² we found good correlation between the results obtained on a Heidelberg cylinder automat and on the Fogra-tester. Why then do you not find any influence of packing materials when using the Fogra-tester?

FRØSLEV-NIELSEN: I do not quite know how to relate ink splitting problems to the quality measurements you have mentioned and so I do not know how to compare my results with yours. We have some ideas about the influence of the distribution of the tangential forces in the printing nip and maybe also the radial pressure distribution influences the ink splitting.

It is also possible that different cylinder sizes will provide differing compressibility of the packings, especially in the upper layers.

RUPP: We have made experiments with different packing material on our printability tester and have found a strong dependence. The softer the packing material the higher is the maximum of ink transfer and the greater the slope of the ink transfer curve. Our results are in qualitative agreement with those of the author.

MILLER: Mr. Frøslev-Nielsen has calculated a value of Young's Modulus for his cylinder coverings by relating his maximum measured compressive stress σ (the maximum pressure) and the maximum compressive strain ϵ (derived from his measurements of nip width). So that $E = \sigma/\epsilon$. This relation is true so long as ν (Poisson's Ratio) is zero, which he has assumed to be so.

If it is again assumed that $\nu = 0$ we may calculate the pressure distribution from the geometry in Fig. 1. If t is the packing thickness, d the maximum packing deformation and y the deformation at x units of length from the centre of the nip

$$y = d - \frac{x^2}{D} \text{ approximately}$$

where D is the diameter of the cylinder.

(This formula is also true if both printing elements are cylinders when $1/D$ is taken as $1/D_1 + 1/D_2$ where D_1 and D_2 are the undeformed cylinder diameters)

so $\quad y = \dfrac{b^2}{4D} - \dfrac{x^2}{D}$

$\therefore$ the compressive strain at x, $\epsilon(x) = y/t$

$\therefore \epsilon(x) = \dfrac{1}{t}\left(\dfrac{b^2}{4D} - \dfrac{x^2}{D}\right)$

$\therefore$ the compressive stress at x

$$= \dfrac{E}{Dt}\left(\dfrac{b^2}{4} - x^2\right)$$

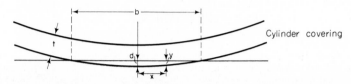

Fig. I.

When this function is plotted for different values of x the resulting curve appears to bear quite a close resemblance to the shape of Mr. Frøslev-Nielsen's experimental curve. The theoretical curve is constructed on the assumption that $v = 0$ and so the shape of the experimental pressure distribution curve would seem to indicate by itself alone that the cylinder coverings used should be characterized by saying Poisson's ratio is zero.

In this connection it may be useful to compare the pressure distribution curves given in Mr. Frøslev-Nielson's paper with those of G. J. Parish in *Brit. J. Appl. Phys.*, **9**, 158, (1958).

PRESSURE AND SPEED EFFECTS OF CYLINDER COVERING DURING PRINTING

by R. D. W. MILLER and S. R. C. POULTER

The Printing, Packaging and Allied Trades Research Association,
Leatherhead, Surrey, England

INTRODUCTION

A large proportion of printing involves rolling contact and the deformation of a cylinder covering. This deformation is generally an essential part of the process and produces a printing pressure controlled within a certain range by varying the constraint on the covering. This is often done by varying the thickness of the covering and printing " pressures " are frequently expressed in units of length. In practice this is not very important to the printer since the pressure in kg/cm² which a paper requires is not known precisely and the width of the nip and the pressure distribution across it will depend upon the covering. A number of investigators have measured the magnitude of printing pressures and the results, which are probably of greatest interest to machinery manufacturers, have been summarized in a publication by the Research and Engineering Council of the Graphic Arts Industry.

Alterations to the thickness of a cylinder covering, to adjust printing pressures or assist register, raise problems of rolling speeds since a synchronous movement between surfaces is desirable if print quality is to be achieved and maintained. The dangers of overpacking cylinders in letterpress and lithographic printing are generally understood but the conditions for correct packing are not well defined. The observation that the rolling radius of a deformable covering may not decrease as deformation increases is not new[1] and the relevance of this to printing has been considered by several investigators.[2-6]

The present paper is an account of recent work at PATRA on rolling speeds and pressure distributions for a number of materials.

THE EFFECT OF DEFORMATION ON ROLLING SPEED

Consider two cylinders coupled by gears to run in contact with the same angular speed. If one turns through an angle θ so does the other.

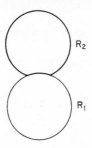

Fig. I.

The length of arc on the first (rigid) cylinder which passes through the nip will be

$$L_1 = R_1\theta$$

and the second (blanketed) cylinder

$$L_2 = R_2\theta$$

Thus, transferred print length

$$L_2 = \frac{R_2}{R_1}L_1$$

Suppose now only the first (rigid) cylinder is gear driven and that it drives the blanketed one by friction.

Over a certain distance in the nip the surfaces will be locked and in this region the strain in the blanket surface will be constant.

Suppose that unit length of surface outside the nip becomes length λ in the nip.

Then, transferred print length

$$L_2 = \frac{L_1}{\lambda}$$

If the angular speed of the lower roller is w_1 then

$$R_1 w_1 t = L_1$$

Similarly

$$R_2 w_2 t = L_2 = \frac{L_1}{\lambda}$$

whence

$$\frac{w_1}{w_2} = \frac{R_2}{R_1}\lambda$$

If now the cylinders are again coupled by gears so that $w_1 = w_2$ we consider the " true rolling " of Kuehn and Sites to exist when $R_1/R_2 = \lambda$. In general where cylinders are coupled by gears, facsimile print length cannot be obtained at one nip under true rolling conditions unless $\lambda = 1$.

This is not important in offset printing except to some degree in blanket to blanket perfecting, but a knowledge of λ for a given blanket will help determine the correct relation between plate and blanket cylinder diameters.

The value of λ is particularly important in letterpress printing not only because transfer is generally direct and print length errors cannot be compensated for at a second nip, but also because the packing is deformed by the image area only and differences in print length and rolling relations may exist between image and non-image areas giving rise to distortions of the packing and printed sheet. In addition, the value of λ must be considered when choosing the height of bed-bearers with respect to type height, although in many cases press stability may be an over-riding factor in this respect.

In gravure printing the significance of λ is not so obvious since the deformable impression roll is not geared to the plate cylinder but is driven through the web. Some preliminary experiments indicate, however, that friction between the paper and rubber is such that the increase with pressure of the surface strain of the rubber is to some extent transmitted to the paper.

MEASUREMENT OF λ

(a) Apparatus

In view of the importance of λ to the behaviour of cylinder coverings in printing, apparatus was constructed at PATRA so that λ could be measured for different materials.

This is shown in Fig. 2 and consists of two interchangeable rollers; one is of solid metal and the other can be covered either with a bonded layer of rubber or with typical printing blankets at a known tension. The tensioning mechanism was so designed that the upper roller can be driven continuously by the lower gear driver roller. The gap between the metal surfaces is continuously variable by screw adjustments and there is a clear view of the nip region from the side. The rollers are approximately 15 cm in diameter and length and these dimensions may be considered large in comparison with the thickness of the coverings tested.

The lower roller can be driven by the gear box at constant speeds in the range 0–200 rev/min. The speed is checked stroboscopically against the electric mains frequency. A disc bearing equiangular marks is mounted on the upper shaft. The apparent rate of movement of the marks when illuminated by a stroboscopic lamp which is triggered by a toothed wheel on the driving shaft measures the difference in angular speed between the two rollers. From this λ can be deduced according to the equation on page 36.

D

Other measurements which can be made are the vertical movements of the upper and lower rollers, any change in blanket diameter and the change in temperature of the blanket surface. Temperature rises are minimized by the forced circulation of air at constant temperature.

Fig. 2. Equipment for measuring rolling speeds of cylinder coverings.

(b) Results

The effect on λ of the change in gap between the metal surface for a number of roller coverings is indicated in Figs. 3 and 4. The graphs in fact show the percentage speed change in the nip which is 100 (λ − 1).

It will be seen that once overall slipping between rollers has ceased the relation between λ and the constraint on the roller covering is in most cases linear over the range normally encountered in printing. Thus the gradient is characteristic of a given covering and a knowledge of it helps in the choice of the correct blanket circumference for " true rolling " in printing.

For solid rubber coverings which are virtually incompressible, λ > 1 and increases as the gap decreases. The change of λ for a given change in gap is greater the thinner the covering but is not dependent upon the hardness of the rubber. Thus it is the constraint rather than the pressure which determines the magnitude of the speed change.

For roller coverings consisting of sheets of paper it is found that λ<1 and that (1 − λ) increases as the gap between the metal surfaces decreases. A similar result is given by a woven fabric blanket, the two materials giving a change of speed with change of gap roughly twice as great as would be expected from the reduction in radius. Both materials are compressible as compared with rubber, a volume change occurring in the constriction of the nip.

Cylinder coverings which consist of a combination of compressible and incompressible layers give values of λ which lie between the value for rubber

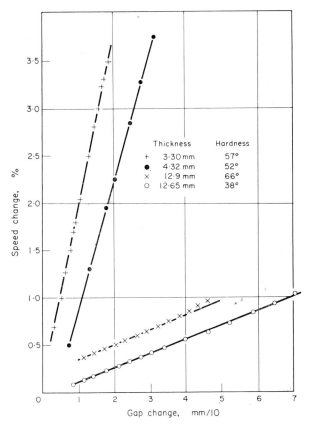

Fig. 3. Effect on λ of thickness and hardness of rubber coverings

of the same total thickness and the value for the compressible material. This is illustrated by the results for the two offset blankets. The exact value of λ will depend upon the relative thickness of the layers, their relative hardness and, in some cases, the extent to which different layers are free to move tangentially at the nip boundaries. The results for blanket 2 show the ideal combination as far as true rolling is concerned since the required blanket diameter will be the same for any amount of impression.

In the case of letterpress printing from a relief image, it is even more important for ($\lambda - 1$) to be as small as possible. This will help to minimize relative movement between paper and forme at the nip boundaries and at the edges of blocks. In fact, empirical methods have led to packing combinations which go far to achieving this end, as can be seen in the type of blanket combinations used in newspaper work and the common use of rubber sheeting with paper in cylinder packings for flat-bed presses.

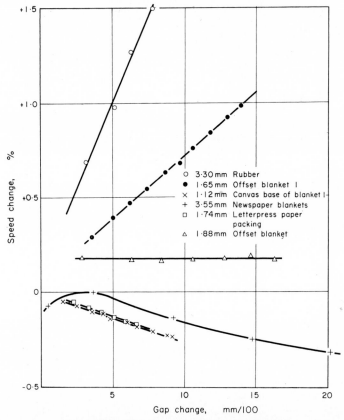

Fig. 4. Effect of λ of compressibility of covering.

Summarizing, the application of specific measurements to practical press conditions is unlikely to be of direct help except where coverings are fairly constant in make-up. In general, as far as the achievement of true rolling is concerned, cylinder coverings should contain a combination of compressible and incompressible layers and should be thick and comparatively hard rather than thin and soft.

THE CALCULATION OF PRINTING PRESSURE

Theoretical Considerations

It can be shown from the work of Hannah[7] that when a hard roller is pressed into one covered with a thin elastic layer, the difference in displacement between a point X (X half contact lengths) outside the contact region and the mid point of the contact region is given by

$$V(X)=\frac{h^2}{D}\left\{1-\frac{2M_0(K|X|)+(1-X^2)+|X\sqrt{(X^2-1)}|-\ln||X|+\sqrt{(X^2-1)}|+2\sum_{1}^{\infty}a_n(M_n(K|X|)-I_n(|X|))}{[C_1(K)]^2\left[1+\sum_{1}^{\infty}\frac{(-)^{n-1}8a_n}{(2n-1)\pi^2}\right]}\right\}$$

$$\text{for } |X| > 1 \qquad (1)$$

where $h =$ half the contact width, $X = x/h$. $K = h/2b$ where $b =$ the layer thickness, $1/D = 1/D_1 + 1/D_2$ where D_1 and D_2 are the roller

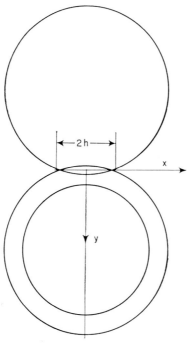

Fig. 5.

diameters and the coefficients a_n can be obtained from Hannah's equation (22). (A fuller account of this result will be published elsewhere.)

The assumptions of this formula are as follows:

(1) The strains are infinitesimal.

(2) The length of the contact region is small with respect to the roller diameters. This can be expressed numerically as

$$\frac{h^2}{D}\left(\frac{1}{D} - \frac{2}{D_1 + D_2}\right) \ll 1$$

(3) The layer thickness is small with respect to the roller diameters.

(4) The covering of the covered roller has linear elastic properties and is isotropic.

(5) The rollers are stationary.

(6) The surfaces of the rollers are smooth and no friction forces act between them.

(7) The inner boundary of the elastic layer is fixed horizontally and vertically.

If b, the layer thickness, is allowed to become infinite in (1) it can be shown that $V(X)$ reduces to

$$V(X) = \frac{h^2}{D}\left\{1 - [(1 - X^2) + |X\sqrt{(X^2 - 1)}| - \ln ||X| + \sqrt{(X^2 - 1)}|]\right\}$$

$$\text{for } |X| > 1 \qquad (2)$$

This result can be derived from Hertz's analysis.[7-9] The presence of the term $\ln ||X| + \sqrt{(X^2 - 1)}|$ in (1) and (2) means that the displacement of the centre of the contact region relative to infinite regions is infinite. This is an inherent drawback of this solution, which can be overcome fairly satisfactorily by relating the displacement at the centre of the contact region to a finite point on the boundary which is far enough away from the contact region for it to be reasonable to assume that, in practice, the displacement of the boundary due to the impression will have become negligible at this point. The point itself will be arbitrary, but it has been found that it makes only a small difference, if $X = 3$, is chosen in preference to $X = 4$ for the arbitrary point.

The expression (1) for $V(X)$ has been computed for $K = 1$, $0\cdot7$, $0\cdot4$, $0\cdot3$ and $0\cdot1$, at $X = 1, 2, 3$ and 4 with Poisson's ratio taken as $0\cdot5$. The expression (2) gives the value of $V(X)$ for $K = 0$ and $X = 1, 2, 3$ and 4.

These results have been plotted in Fig. 6, which is a representation of the boundary when the layer is considered flat for different values of K, and shows the effect of the elastic layer. (The results may also be applied to a slightly curved layer.) The point $X = 4$ is taken as having negligible displacement for all values of K and the difference in displacement between $X = 0$ and the points $X = 4$ on the boundary are plotted on the vertical axis in units of h^2/D^1 the horizontal axis being that of X. The figure then represents the effect of varying the layer thickness b, from $b = \infty$ to $b = h/2$ $(K = 1)$, for the same contact length $2h$.

The expression (1) may now be written

$$V(X) = \frac{h^2}{D}\left(1 + \delta(K,X)\right)$$

where $\delta(K,X)$ is only small for values of K greater than 0·4. The displacement downwards of the indenting cylinder may now be taken as

$$V(4) = \frac{h^2}{D}\left(1 + \delta(K,4)\right) = \frac{h^2}{D}\left(1 + \delta\right)$$

From the theoretical point of view, an improvement on this result might be possible if the general solution to the problem of a circular ring under given

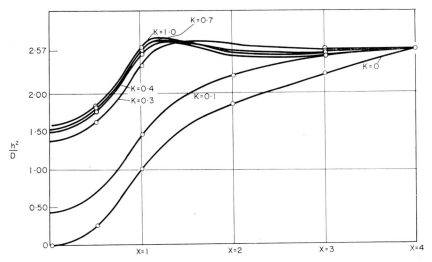

Fig. 6. Boundary profiles for Poisson's ratio $= 0.5$.

edge tractions and displacements[11] in cylindrical polar co-ordinates could be developed further. In this problem the boundary would not extend to x and consequently it might be possible to proceed to a point on the boundary where the displacements were inappreciable in theory as well as in practice when calculating the downward squeeze for a given h and D.

The Calculation of Printing Pressure in Gravure

Let $d = h^2/D$ so that d is the depth of the impression of the hard roller measured from the ends of the contact region: see Fig. 7.

Hannah's equation (24)[7] gives $h = h_0 C_1(K)$ where h_0 is the value of h for the same loading when the layer thickness is infinite. h_0 is related to W the loading per unit length on the roller by

$$h_0{}^2 = \frac{2WD}{\pi E}(1 - \eta^2) = \frac{3WD}{2\pi E}$$

when η is put equal to 0·5,
η being Poisson's ratio.

$$\therefore \frac{h^2}{D} = \frac{3}{2\pi E}W[C_1(K)]^2 = d$$

Whence

$$W = \frac{2\pi Ed}{3[C_1(K)]^2}$$

and

$$h = \sqrt{(dD)}$$

Now if $\Delta =$ the actual downward displacement under load W from first contact

$$V(4) = \Delta = (1 + \delta)d$$

Thus

$$W = \frac{2\pi E}{3[C_1(K)]^2}\frac{\Delta}{(1 + \delta)}$$

The following is a specimen calculation, and is actually that done for the results plotted on Fig. 9 which refer to roller 1.

To calculate W for any value of K we require $C_1(K)$. $C_1(K)$ has been computed for $\eta = 0·5$ at $K = 1$, 0·7 and 0·4 by Parish[10] and for $K = 0·3$ and

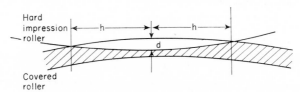

Fig. 7.

0·1 at PATRA. A plot of K against $C_1(K)$ is given in Fig. 8, which can be used to construct the following table of calculation, η being Poisson's ratio. For a pair of rollers 6 in. $= 15·2$ cm in diameter one having a layer of gravure rubber 0·13 in. $= 3·30$ mm thick of Young's Modulus of 436 lb/in.$^2 = 30·5$ kg/cm^2. The results for W are given in lb/in. in the table and kg/cm as well in Fig. 10.

The value of Δ has been determined at all values of d as accurately as can be done by constructing a graph, Fig. 9, of the number of units of h^2/D by which the edge of the contact region is below the point of zero displacement

Table 1.

d in.	$h = \sqrt{(dD)}$	$K = \dfrac{h}{2b}$	$C_1(K)$	$[C(K)]^2$	$\dfrac{d x 10^3}{[C_1(K)]^2}$	$W = \dfrac{2\pi E d}{3[c_1(k)]^2}$	δ	$1 + \delta$	$(1 + \delta)d$ in.
0·001	0·05477	0·2107	0·9078	0·8240	1·2136	1·1	0·50	1·50	0·0015
0·002	0·07746	0·2979	0·8561	0·7329	2·729	2·49	0·20	1·20	0·0024
0·003	0·09487	0·3649	0·8163	0·6663	4·503	4·11	0·10	1·10	0·00331
0·004	0·10954	0·4213	0·7802	0·6087	6·572	5·99	0·07	1·07	0·00428
0·005	0·12247	0·4710	0·7476	0·5589	8·946	8·16	0·058	1·058	0·00530
0·006	0·13416	0·5160	0·7167	0·5136	11·68	10·67	0·049	1·049	0·00629
0·007	0·14491	0·5573	0·6924	0·4793	14·6	13·31	0·042	1·042	0·00728

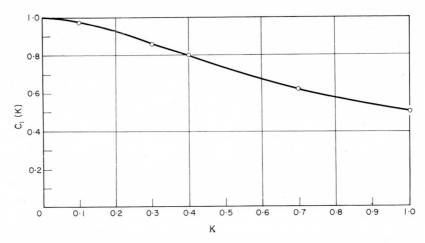

Fig. 8.

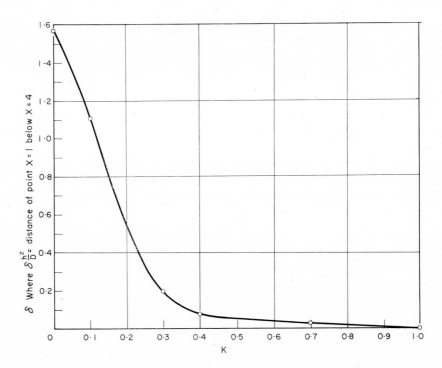

Fig. 9.

$x = 4$. The value of δ is read from this graph. The theoretical and experimental results for this roller and another with a slightly thicker cover are compared in Figs. 10 and 11, the theoretical result being a plot of W against Δ. There appears to be reasonable agreement between the theoretical and practical results at low deformations, but at high deformation the theory seriously underestimates the load or printing pressure. These tests were carried out at 50 rev/min.

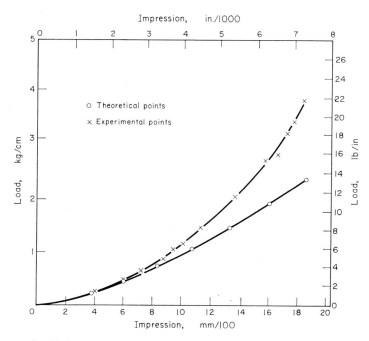

Fig. 10. Experimental and theoretical results compared or roller I.

The value of Young's Modulus used in the calculation was derived from hardness measurements made on an instrument which fulfils the British Standard requirements for rubber hardness testing.[12] The rubber covers were tested while bonded to the rollers and consequently the inner surface of the rubber was fixed. The British Standard requirement is for a free inner boundary. The indentation results were corrected for thickness, and the British Standard hardness value converted to its equivalent value for a sample 8 mm thick, using the correction graph supplied, whence Young's Modulus was determined from the known experimental relation between British Standard degrees of hardness for a sample of 8 mm thickness. The relation is given in.[12] The British Standard hardness results and Young's Modulus values are given in Table 2 below. In addition to this it was found difficult to obtain a very accurate estimate of the thickness of the rubber and some uncertainty must attach to the measurements made, as the rubber layers were bonded to a layer of ebonite, whose thickness could not be measured except at the edges of the covers. The covers of both rubber rollers were thin enough in relation to their axial width to justify the assumption of plane strain conditions.

TABLE 2.

	B.S.°	Young's Modulus (lb/in²)	Layer thickness (in.)	Diameter (in.)
Roller 1	57·5	436	0·130	6·012
Roller 2	52·3	346	0·173	5·989

The Calculation of Printing Pressure in Lithography

Some load displacement measurements were made on the apparatus previously described[5] on two samples of litho blanket and a news under-blanket of similar construction to a litho blanket initially tensioned at 50 lb/in. = 8·93 kg/cm round a cylinder of approximately 6 in. diameter

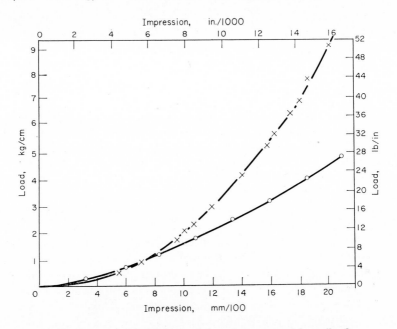

Fig. 11. Experimental and theoretical results compared for roller 2.

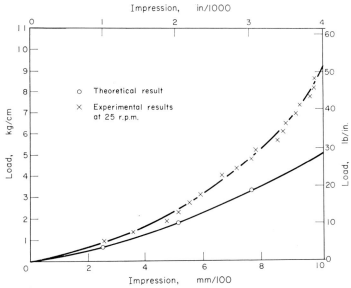

Fig. 12. Experimental and theoretical results compared for blanket 1 (strippable), tensioned at 50 lb/in.

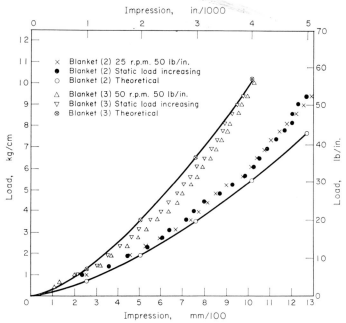

Fig. 13. Experimental and theoretical results for blankets (2) and (3) compared, also comparison with static tests.

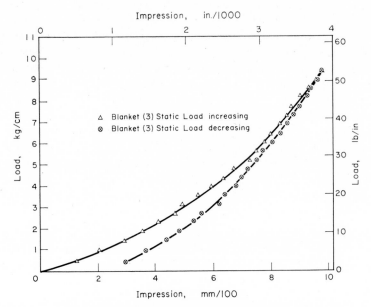

Fig. 14. Hysteresis under static loading for blanket (3).

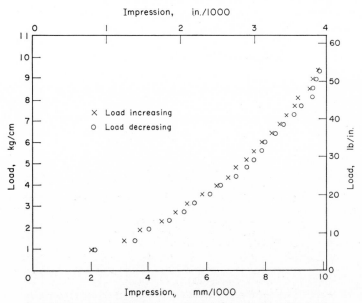

Fig. 15. Hysteresis under load on blanket (3) at speed of 50 rev/min.

and indented with one of exactly 6 in. diameter. Hardness measurements were made on all three blankets off the cylinder, and on the cylinder tensioned at 50 lb/in. initial tension. It was found that the hardness measurements made on the cylinder were considerably higher than on the untensioned blanket tested on the flat against a glass plate. These results are given in Table 3. The hardness results obtained in this way were used to calculate a " Young's Modulus " value which was inserted into a similar calculation to that made for the bonded rubber. Figs. 11 and 12 show a comparison of these calculations with the experimental results. The agreement for blankets 2 and 3 is quite good, while for blanket 1 it is poor. The value of K in these results was high, > 0.5, at all but deformations of less than 0.001 in., due to the lesser thickness of the blankets in comparison with the rubber; so d was assumed equal to Δ. The calculation is, of course, for Poisson's ratio $= 0.5$.

TABLE 3.

	Fully corrected B.S.° on cylinder	Fully corrected B.S.° off cylinder	Young's Modulus on cylinder (lb/in²)	Young's Modulus off cylinder (lb/in²)	Thickness (in.)
Blanket 1	75° B.S.	69° B.S.	1025	741	0·0635
Blanket 2	792° B.S.	75° B.S.	1282	1025	0·0725
Blanket 3	90·47° B.S.	75·2° B.S.	2222	1025	0·067

Tests were done under static and dynamic conditions on blankets 2 and 3 and it was found that there is little difference between the results obtained, see Fig. 13. Experiments were done with load increasing and decreasing statically and dynamically on blanket (3). The results of these are plotted in Figs. 14 and 15, and show considerable hysteresis for static loading and much less in tests at speed.

REFERENCES

1. O. REYNOLDS, *Phil. Trans. Roy. Soc.* **166** (1876).
2. A. T. KUEHN and B. L. SITES, *TAGA* **72**, (1953).
3. W. LENAARTS, *IGT Nieuws* **6** (1) 17 (1953).
4. H. A. BORCHARDT, R. H. BROMLEY and S. R. C. POULTER, *Printing Technology* **2** (2) 57 (1958).
5. R. D. W. MILLER, *Penrose Annual* **54**, 111 (1960).
6. L. J. LODEWIJKS, *IGT Nieuws* **13** (9) 130 (1960).
7. M. HANNAH, *Quart. J. Mech. Appl. Math.* **4**. Pt. 1 (1951).
8. H. R. THOMAS and V. A. HOERSCH, *Univ. Ill. Eng. Exp. Sta. Bull.* **212** (1930).
9. H. PORITSKY, *J. Appl. Mech.* **17**, *Trans. Amer. Soc. Mech. Engrs.* **72**, 191 (1950).
10. G. J. PARISH, *Brit. J. Appl. Phys.* **9**, 158 (1958).
11. M. G. SIMPSON, Ph.D. Thesis. Univ. Coll. Lond. (1955).
12. *British Standard*, **903**, Pt. 19 (1950).

DISCUSSION

DÜRNER: The value of Young's Modulus used in your calculation, you derived from measurements made by a British Standard hardness instrument. Could you explain the principle of this instrument?

MILLER: The hardness measurement is made by measuring the difference in penetration at two loads of a 3/32 in. (2·38 mm) diameter steel ball into a rubber test specimen 8 mm thick and at least 32 mm square. The first load to be applied is 30 g, the penetration being measured after 5 sec. The second load is 565 g, the penetration being measured after 30 sec. The test is conducted with gentle agitation provided by an electrically operated buzzer. Corrections for non-standard thickness of test specimens are given. The ball itself is fixed to the end of a dial micrometer which can be graduated in thousandths of an inch or hundredths of a millimetre. The load is applied to the top of the shaft and the body of the instrument is rigidly supported.

The relation between the difference in penetration and Young's Modulus has been determined experimentally for rubber and is given in British Standard 903.[12]

SCHAEFFER: Have you attempted to deduce the pressure distribution on the packing within the nip? The nip formed between two undeformed cylinders leads to a fairly unsymmetrical pressure distribution within a fluid in a nip. Deformation of the nip geometry can be expected to lead to considerable modification of the distribution of pressures.

MILLER: We have not attempted to calculate the pressure distribution. A pressure distribution on an elastic roller covering can be deduced using the same theoretical approach that leads up to the deduction of the line pressure in our paper. See references (7) and (10). In reference (10) it is found that the pressure distribution calculated on the basis of reference (7) gave some qualitative, but not such good quantitative agreement with measured values. We have so far only considered the effect of the properties of the packing on the pressure distribution without considering that the ink exerts a significant influence on the pressure distribution.

PRINCE: Have you measured a shift in the peak pressure from the centre line of the cylinder axes? We believe this shift of pack pressure can cause the short print-length which has been observed.

MILLER: We have not measured the pressure distribution across the contact region, but only the line pressure, and consequently cannot say anything about this.

HUNDERUP-JENSEN: We have made measurements on the dimensions of paper passing through a nip and found that the paper shortened and became thicker. Have you any explanation?

MILLER: At present I have no explanation for your observations of the shortening and thickening of the web on passing through the nip. Our tests were done without ink and have, up to the present, only included one newspaper blanket combination.

SCHAEFFER: Mr. Hunderup-Jensen's comment on the shortening and thickening of paper webs after transport through the printing nip parallels the experience in the U.S. of the calendering of plastic sheets. This problem has been treated theoretically by Finston at Brown University, who shows that the flow of plastic through a calendering nip is greater than expected on the basis of nip geometry and speed. The explanation is based on a non-symmetrical pressure distribution in the nip resulting in a pumping action within the region of minimum nip cross-sectional area. Recovery of the web at the nip exit is such as to produce a shorter and thicker web.

THE INFLUENCE OF THE PRINTING INTERVAL ON THE QUALITY OF MULTICOLOUR PRINTING

by K.-H. Schirmer

Institut der Deutschen Gesellschaft für Forschung im graphischen
Gewerbe, München, Bamberger Haus

Abstract—The suitability of a set of commercial inks for multicolour printing has been studied with the FOGRA printability tester. Ink transfer and set-off behaviour in single and multi-colour printing were measured for different printing sequences. The intervals between successive printings varied from 2 hr to one or more days. Studies were also made of wet-on-wet printing. The dried prints were examined for colour density, gloss and apparent trapping. Trapping deduced from transfer measurements differs from that deduced from density measurements (apparent trapping) because the latter is influenced by print gloss. The gloss of secondary colours depends on the printing interval because this influences the absorbency of the first ink film printed.

INTRODUCTION

Today, letterpress multicolour prints are not only produced in the usual manner with a printing interval of one or more days but, widely, also with printing intervals of 1 or 2 hr only. In this procedure the printed sheets are transferred stack by stack from one press to another. The development of two- and multicolour printing presses further diminished the printing interval which resulted in so-called wet-on-wet printing with a printing interval of a few seconds, the over-print being super imposed upon the first printing layer while it is still wet.

Inks for multicolour printing are required to print easily regardless of printing interval and increased printing speed; they must transfer well and have good trapping when overprinted; additionally they should penetrate sufficiently fast and lead to a print of good quality.

It therefore appeared to be of interest to develop methods which with the aid of a printability tester would test inks for these characteristics.

53

E

EXPERIMENTAL PRINCIPLES

An examination of printing inks for multicolour printing requires consideration of their behaviour in single colour and overprinting at printing speeds applied in practice. To this end a printability tester may be used to examine under definite conditions the ink transfer and set-off behaviour of sample prints in single and multicolour printing in relation to printing pressure, printing speed and ink film thickness. Absolutely dry sample prints of definite ink film thickness may be used to measure both colour density and gloss of single and multicolour prints and also, by photometric methods, the trapping of the second on the first ink film.

The experimental methods were based on the following principles:

1. Ink transfer is determined by the correlation between the amount y of the ink transferred to the paper and the amount x of the ink on the forme. In the inking range above complete coverage of the printing paper this correlation is linear and may be described by the factors f and b of the Walker–Fetsko equation.[1] Whereas factor f is affected by the rheological properties of the ink, b describes that proportion of the printing ink or printing ink compounds which at the moment of printing strike into the paper; the so-called immobilization factor.

The usual measurement of ink transfer with single colour prints of various ink film thicknesses may likewise be applied to overprints if on to the first layer of predetermined thickness ($ca.$ $1\cdot5\mu$) another layer is super-imposed at various thicknesses. Also in the case of overprints of various ink film thicknesses on to the initial ink film the values of factors f and b may be determined, and by comparison with the values of the single colour print it is possible to establish whether in overprinting as compared to the single colour print any changes take place with regard to the splitting of the free ink film (change of factor f) or of the quantity of the ink immobilized by the paper (factor b). Also, by weighing, conclusions can be drawn about ink trapping from the relation between the amount of ink transferred in overprinting on to the first print y_d and the amount of ink transferred to the paper in the first print y_p at equal amounts of ink x on the forme.

2. By examining the set-off behaviour the solidification of the printing ink film immediately after impression, which is initiated by the striking in of vehicle compounds, can be assessed. The principle of this method is that the fresh print (single colour or overprint) of definite film thickness is pressed against unprinted paper at various intervals after impression. The amount of ink transferred to the unprinted paper shows how far the solidification on the fresh print has proceeded.[2]

The set-off can be evaluated by photometric measurement of ink on the set-off strip and by plotting the measured values against the logarithm of time after printing. In this way the time for the set-off to show a just visible colour density can be made on the set-off strip. The inverse of this time may serve as a measure of the absorbing properties of the paper or of the first printing layer in the case of overprints.

3. The colour depth of the prints is established by photometrical measurements of the so-called colour density.

Colour density measurements were made with the Carl Zeiss spectrophotometer. In this the printing inks are illuminated by an incident monochromatic beam of light at an angle of 45°. The measurement as such is made against white paper with the measuring element set vertically against the printing sample. For the monochromatic light used in measuring colour densities the wave lengths of the relevant absorption maxima of the printing inks are chosen, i.e. for yellow 420 mμ, for magenta 530 mμ and for cyan 620 mμ.

4. Gloss was measured by an objective method. To this end the sample was illuminated by white light incident at 60° and the intensity of the specularly reflected light from the printed sample was compared with that from a polished black glass plate used as a standard (i.e. 100% gloss). By this method, as can be confirmed by visual impression, prints of various hues and depths of colour can be assessed with regards to paper gloss.

5. If D_2 is the colour density of the second ink (measured as a single colour on paper), D_1 that of the first ink and D_{1+2} that of the overprint of ink 2 on ink 1, then the trapping can be correlated with the following quantity

$$\text{Ink trapping} = \frac{D_{1+2} - D_1}{D_2} \cdot 100\%$$

The ink trapping values obtained from colour density measurement with reflected light can only then be brought into agreement with gravimetrically measured ink trapping values, using the relation between the amount of ink and colour density of the initial print, when the gloss of the first print and overprints are equal. If, however, the initial and overprint are of different gloss the colour density obtained affords no real measure of the amount of ink transferred on to the paper and the initial print. This is because measured values of colour density are strongly influenced by surface gloss when using surface illumination.

The influence of gloss in photometric measurement of film thickness can be avoided by making the measurements with transmitted light. This procedure, which, however, can only be applied with printing papers of equal transparency, has been mentioned by Borchers.[4] It affords a method of measuring the ink trapping value from relative values of film thickness and can also be used to obtain gravimetric ink trapping values from the correlation of colour density and amount of ink. According to Preucil the ink trapping value which affects the appearance of the overprint and which is computed from the colour density values in reflected light is termed " apparent ink trapping ".[5]

For the assessment of print quality in overprinting apart from ink trapping, colour density and gloss of the secondary colours as compared to the primary colours, the amount of ink required for sufficient coverage and the uniformity of the overprint has to be considered.[6]

The experimental methods applied are summarized in Table 1.

TABLE 1. SURVEY OF MEASURING METHODS

Property	Method	Parameter
Ink transfer	Plot film thickness transferred to paper vs. film thickness on plate	b, film immobilized by paper f, split of free film
Set-off behaviour	Smear-off of fresh print to paper	t_a, set-off period
Colour density	Diffuse reflectance for complementary wave length	D, colour density
Gloss	Specular reflectance (60°)	G, Gloss %
Trapping	Relation between colour density on first-down ink and colour density on unprinted paper	Trapping %
Lower practical limit	Minimum film thickness for full coverage	Ink film thickness, g/m^2

TEST PROCEDURE

An ink set for multicolour printing (DIN ink set yellow, magenta, cyan by Messrs. Kast and Ehinger, Stuttgart-Feuerbach) was used for studying the behaviour of two inks each when superimposed. Thereby both the printing interval and printing sequence in overprinting were varied. The printing paper used was a commercial coated art paper (APCO II/II by Messrs. Scheufelen, Oberlenningen). Prints were made with the FOGRA printability tester at a " linear " pressure of 20 kg/cm and a speed of 2 m/sec.

The printing interval between both printing operations was varied within a wide range, from wet-on-wet conditions to 24 hr and 1 week.

The sequences used were those usually applied in wet-on-wet printing, i.e. cyan and yellow as first and second colours, and the reversed sequence yellow–cyan, as well as the sequence used in multicolour printing, i.e. yellow–magenta.

Printing inks were used at the consistency as delivered by the manufacturer. The rheological properties of the printing inks were determined by measuring the flow curves with the Ferranti Viscosimeter at a temperature of 20°C. For measurement of the flow curve the range of the shear rate of 0–450 sec^{-1} and 450–0 sec^{-1} was covered several times, the curve of descending shear rate being taken as the true flow curve if, after another cycle, no further changes were observed. Yield values S_0 and the values of plastic viscosity U taken from the flow curves of printing inks as well as values of shortness according to Zettlemoyer have been compiled in Table 2.

TABLE 2. RHEOLOGICAL PROPERTIES OF INKS (ink set acc. to DIN 16 508)

	Yield Value S_0	Plastic viscosity U	Shortness S_0/U
Yellow	15,000	215	70
Magenta	29,000	253	115
Cyan	16,500	150	110

The printing speed of 2 m/sec corresponds to that of a single revolution press with a cylinder diameter of 54 cm (Heidelberger OHZ) printing 4000 sheets/hr. A further increase of the printing speed in the experiments was impossible without adding a thinner although according to practical experience inks may be printed at speeds up to 4 m/sec without picking. The reason for this is that, as compared to printing presses, on the printability tester owing to its smaller cylinder diameter ($D_p = 6.5$ cm) at equal circumference speed a greater stress occurs in ink splitting. Picking is not only influenced by the circumference speed but likewise by the speed of the separating action.

At the point of separation of a cylinder from a printing plate, the acceleration b_t is related to the circumferential speed V and cylinder diameter D by[7]

$$b_t = \frac{2V^2}{D}$$

From which it follows that for two cylinders of diameter D_m and D_p, equal values of separating action and hence stress require the circumferential velocities V_m and V_p to be related by

$$V_m = V_p \frac{D_m}{D_p}$$

with $D_m = 54$ cm (the diameter of the OHZ machine) and $D_p = 6.5$ cm (the printability tester)

$$V_m \approx 2.9 V_p$$

and it follows that inks which can be printed in the tester at a speed of 2 m/sec are equivalent to 4 m/sec on a normal press.

To start with, the inks were used for examining ink transfer in single colour prints at various ink film thicknesses as well as their set-off behaviour, at a film thickness of approx. $1 \cdot 5\mu$. In order to study the dependence of ink transfer on printing speed the printing experiments were made at speeds of 2 m/sec and 1 m/sec. For measurement of ink transfer in the case of over-printing, a large number of single colour prints of a definite ink film thickness of $1 \cdot 5$ g/m² were printed with the first ink. Then, after various printing intervals the second printing was made with various film thicknesses upon the first print. In this way each print was completely covered with the second ink. In other cases, only one half was overprinted so that finally the complete printing strip was made up of an overprinted portion and two parts each, with one of the two colours. Between two overprints each of the described sort, single colour prints of the second-down ink were inserted in order to be able in the same printing operation to use the ink transfer of the single colour print for comparison and from this comparison deduce ink trapping values gravimetrically. Overprints with the second ink were made at various film thicknesses from 5 to 1 g/m² by starting with 160 mgs of ink in the inking unit of the tester and allowing the gradual exhaustion of ink to produce a series of progressively thinner films.

Prints at an ink film thickness of approx. $1 \cdot 5\mu$ of the second-down ink were selected for studying the set-off behaviour.

After the sample prints were completely dry their colour density and gloss were assessed. Their measurements covered both single colour and overprints at various ink film thicknesses. Furthermore, on the strip containing both first-down and second-down colour, separate and superimposed ink trapping was measured photometrically.

RESULTS

(i) Single prints on paper

The measurements made on the three printing inks, yellow, magneta and cyan, of the ink set are recorded in Table 3. The prints were made at a linear pressure of 20 kg/cm and a speed of 2 m/sec; in addition, transfer measurements were also made at a speed of 1 m/sec, and these results are given in parentheses in Table 3. It appears that with increasing printing speed the values for b decrease whereas those for f show an increase. This means an improvement in ink transfer at greater printing speeds and larger ink film thickness.

In the cases reported the value of the factor b for the primary colour yellow is very low, whereas primary colours magenta and cyan, even at a printing speed of 2 m/sec, show considerable values for *b*. The gloss and set-off results refer to films of thickness 1·5 g/m².

TABLE 3. PROPERTIES OF INKS (ink set acc. to DIN 16 508)

	Yellow	Magenta	Cyan
Ink transfer *f*	0·440 (0·420)	0·460 (0·380)	0·490 (0·400)
b	0·105 (0·130)	0·380 (0·440)	0·370 (0·600)
Set-off period t_a	2 min	1·8 min	1·4 min
Gloss %	27	25	20

(ii) Superimposed colours

Compared with printing on unprinted paper, ink transfer on to paper covered with an ink film of definite thickness shows, as can be expected, a change in the factor *b*. Apart from a decrease of *b* which was particularly noticeable in the case of long printing intervals, an additional clear increase

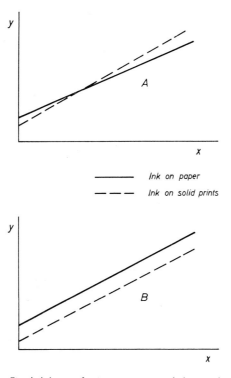

Ink on paper
Ink on solid prints

Fig. I. Ink transfer in overprinting (schematic).

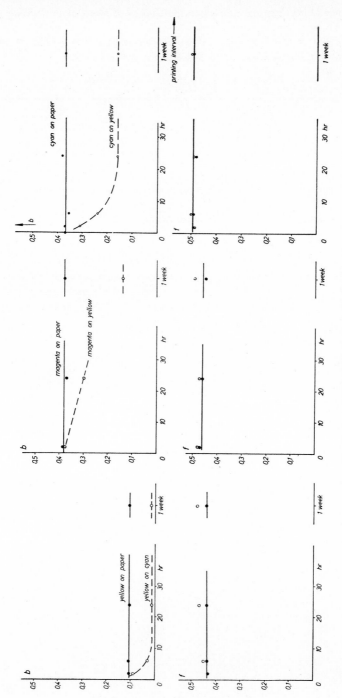

Fig. 2. b and f for different printing intervals.

of the value f was observed, particularly with magenta upon yellow and yellow upon cyan (compare Fig. 1, Case A). In the case of cyan being printed upon yellow, however, only b underwent a change (Fig. 1, Case B).

Whereas in case A good ink trapping may result in the medium range of ink film thickness, ink trapping in case B shows changes corresponding with the value of b. The extent of the change of factors b and f depends upon the printing interval. This becomes clear from the experimental results recorded in Table 4 and graphed in Fig. 2.

TABLE 4. b AND f FOR DIFFERENT PRINTING INTERVALS
(Printing sequence: yellow–cyan, cyan–yellow, yellow–magenta)

Yellow–Cyan				
	Cyan on yellow		Cyan on paper	
Printing interval	f	b	f	b
wet over wet	0·530	0·405	0·480	0·370
2 hr	0·484	0·310	0·488	0·370
6 hr	0·500	0·240	0·490	0·355
24 hr	0·488	0·154	0·480	0·380
1 week	0·498	0·160	0·494	0·370
Cyan–Yellow				
	Yellow on cyan		Yellow on paper	
Printing interval	f	b	f	b
2 hr	0·435	0·090	0·435	0·110
6 hr	0·450	0·032	0·435	0·109
24 hr	0·471	0·017	0·438	0·107
1 week	0·478	0·020	0·445	0·105
Yellow–Magenta				
	Magenta on yellow		Magenta on paper	
Printing interval	f	b	f	b
2 hr	0·480	0·380	0·470	0·385
24 hr	0·474	0·300	0·462	0·370
1 week	0·495	0·140	0·450	0·382

Whereas the low value of b in the case of yellow has decreased to its final value after only a 10 hr printing interval when printed on cyan, the decrease in the case of magenta upon yellow proceeds very slowly. Correspondingly the ink transfer factor f changes in the former case after only 6 hr whereas in the case of magenta upon yellow it only starts to rise after a printing interval of a week (Case A). Yellow-cyan overprints show a particularly strong decrease of b with increasing printing intervals. As in this case factor f

remains practically constant (Case *B*), ink trapping corresponding with the decrease in *b* is diminished. The overprint for this printing sequence will, therefore, deserve closer examination.

For the overprint of cyan upon yellow Fig. 3 shows the values of ink trapping computed on the basis of colour density measurements by incident

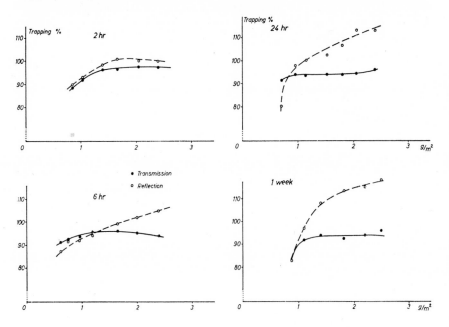

Fig. 3. Apparent trapping for different printing intervals (printing sequence: yellow–cyan).

and transparent illumination with reference to cyan printed at various film thicknesses upon yellow of constant film thickness. Obvious differences between ink trapping values measured by incident and transparent illumination occur especially in the case of long printing intervals and large ink film thicknesses. They result from the gloss of the secondary colour green growing in proportion with the increase of the printing interval.

The variation in the gloss of the secondary colour green can be seen from Fig. 4 which shows the dependence of gloss on ink film thickness when cyan is printed on a yellow print of constant film thickness. This dependence on film thickness clearly depends on the printing interval. For low ink film thicknesses the curves move towards the gloss values of yellow prints (*ca.* 27%). In the case of long printing intervals the gloss values of the secondary colour surpass those of the cyan single colour print, and thus causes differences in ink trapping values. The differences grow in proportion to the increase of gloss of the secondary colour green compared with the gloss of cyan prints.

The variation in gloss of the secondary colour green is due to the effect of the printing interval on the absorbency of the yellow prints. The differences in absorbency, after different intervals, are due to increasing solidification with age of the film.

Figure 5 shows the variation of set-off after different printing intervals. The minimum set-off time is shown by prints after an interval of two hours. Longer printing intervals and shorter intervals of wet-over-wet printing both give increased set-off period.

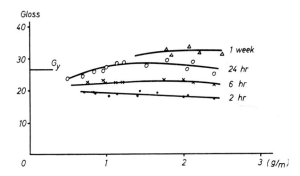

Fig. 4. Dependence of gloss on ink film thickness for yellow + cyan print.

As the absorbency of the first-colour prints is higher the shorter the set-off periods, gloss can be compared with the reciprocal of the set-off period.

Figure 6 shows that a linear correlation exists between the gloss of overprints and the absorbency of the first-down ink (expressed as the reciprocal of set-off time).

Table 5 referring to a cyan print of 1.5 g/m², compares the values of ink trapping at various printing intervals computed from colour density measurements by incident and transparent illumination with values

TABLE 5. INK TRAPPING FOR PRINTING SEQUENCE YELLOW + CYAN

Printing interval	Apparent trapping Reflection Transmission		Calc. true Trapping	Gravimetric Trapping	G %	D
wet over wet	104	104	108	110	28·0	1·26
2 hr	100	97	96	98	18·5	1·23
6 hr	98	96	95	97	22·5	1·26
24 hr	105	94	92	93	28·5	1·36
1 week	110	94	92	93	31·5	1·41

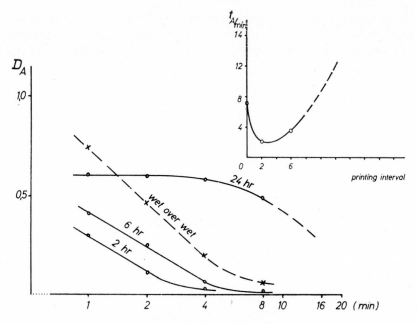

Fig. 5. Evaluation of set-off behaviour for different printing intervals (printing sequence: yellow–cyan).

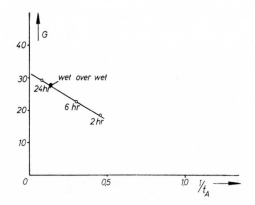

Fig. 6. Dependence of gloss of yellow + cyan prints on absorbency of first-down ink (yellow).

obtained by direct weighing. Data for gloss and colour density in incident illumination are also given. It appears that the ink trapping values obtained by measurements with transparent illumination are quite close to the true ink trapping values.

Moreover, gravimetrical ink trapping has been computed from the correlation between ink film thickness on the paper and colour density in transparent illumination. The differences as compared to the values computed on the basis of ink transfer are caused by the relative uncertainty of measurements by transparent illumination. The reasons therefore are not only the inexactness of photometrical measurements but likewise the lack of uniformity regarding the transparency of printed paper.

In principle, such measurements by transparent illumination cannot fully coincide with the true ink trapping value, since although the correlation between ink film thickness and colour density in transparent illumination is linear, direction does not touch point zero. Consequently, colour density in transparent illumination does not directly indicate the true ink trapping value as this would be the case with a correlation running through point zero. For compution sequent, D_0 must be taken into account which results in:

$$\frac{y_D}{y_P} = \frac{D_{1+2} - D_1 - D_0}{D_2 - D_0}$$

which means that only in the case of $D_0 = 0$ the measurement indicates the true ink trapping value.

(iii) Wet-on-wet printing

As the results in Table 4 show, cyan printed on yellow in the wet-on-wet procedure shows an increase of both the b and f values. This results in an ink

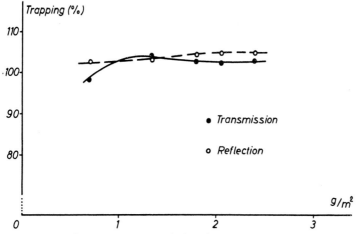

Fig. 7. Trapping for wet-over-wet printing (printing sequence: yellow–cyan).

trapping of over 100% (see Fig. 7), and as shown in Fig. 6, the development of gloss is connected with the absorbing properties of the initial print.

As in the examined sample of wet-on-wet printing of cyan upon yellow there exists a considerable uniformity of gloss (see Fig. 8), the differences in ink trapping values obtained by measurements with incident and transparent illumination are small (Fig. 7). Their transformation into true gravimetric ink trapping values shows good agreement with the values determined on the basis of ink transfer (compare Table 5).

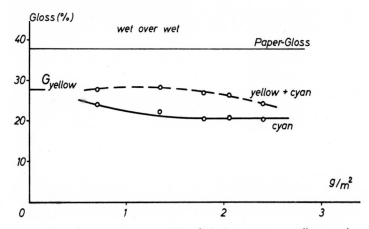

Fig. 8. Gloss for wet-over-wet printing (printing sequence: yellow–cyan).

For overprinting at various printing intervals the properties characteristic of printing quality are summarized in Figs. 9–11. From them the following conclusions can be drawn.

1. The true ink trapping value is satisfactory in the case of short printing intervals whereas the value of apparent ink trapping which affects the optical impression increases with an increasing printing interval.

2. In the range of short printing intervals the gloss of the primary and secondary colours is almost uniform, whereas in the case of large printing intervals the gloss of the secondary colour surpasses that of the primary colour.

3. In the range of normal ink film thicknesses, coverage of the overprint may be considered very good. Only with printing intervals of a week's duration good coverage requires somewhat higher ink film thickness, whereas in wet-on-wet printing complete coverage can be obtained with as little as 1 g/m².

Uniformity of the overprint may be considered good, and independent of the length of the printing interval.

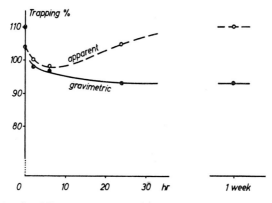

Fig. 9. Trapping for different printing intervals (printing sequence: yellow–cyan).

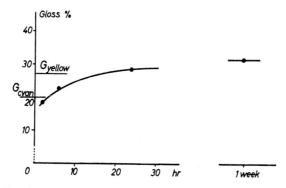

Fig. 10. Gloss for different printing intervals (printing sequence: yellow–cyan).

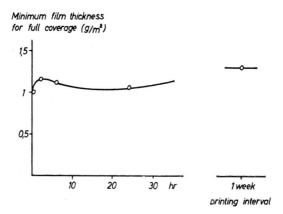

Fig. 11. Lower practical limit for different printing intervals (printing sequence: yellow–cyan).

CONCLUSIONS

The measurements described have confirmed the advantage of a short printing interval, in agreement with practical printing experience and in addition it has been established that:

1. The true ink trapping value can be established on the basis of ink transfer in overprinting as compared to the single colour print.
2. The difference between the true ink trapping value and the apparent ink trapping value derived from measurement by incident illumination is due to the influence of gloss with secondary and primary colours.
3. The development of gloss of the overprint depends not only on the gloss of first-down ink but also on the printing interval, or rather the absorbency of the first colour print. This latter can be assessed from the set-off behaviour of the overprint. There exists a linear correlation between gloss and the absorbing properties of the first colour print.

REFERENCES

1. W. C. WALKER and J. M. FETSKO, A concept of ink transfer in printing. *Am. Ink Maker* **33**, No. 12, 38 (1955).
2. J. ALBRECHT and K.-H. SCHIRMER: Über die messtechnische Druckgütebeurteilung schwarzer Illustrations-Buchdruckfarben. Deutsche Gesellschaft für Forschung im graphischen Gewerbe Instituts-Mitteilung Nr. 1/1 (1955).
3. F. PREUCIL, Color hue and ink transfer, *TAGA Proceedings* 102–109 (1953).
4. C. H. BORCHERS, *Printing Inks and Color*, Pergamon Press, London (1961) (discussion remark).
5. F. PREUCIL, Color and tone errors of multicolor presses, *TAGA Proceedings*, 175–180 (1958).
6. J. M. FETSKO, *Problems in measuring the quality of black solid prints*, NPIRI Project Report Nr. 35, April (1956).
7. E. RUPP and K. RIECHE, Beiträge zur Bedruckbarkeit von Papier und Folien, Inst. für Graphische Technik, Leipzig (1959).

DISCUSSION

ROGERS: The term " trapping " has been applied to printing of " wet " ink over " wet " ink. " Ink transfer " is the term applied to application of ink to paper.

Should we not be more consistent to confine " trapping " to the relatively short time intervals between inks; and " ink transfer " to either paper or " dried ink on paper."

SCHIRMER: If in describing experimental work we make it clear to what we are referring, I do not think it matters.

" Trapping " is the transfer of one ink film on to another when printing multicolour. I think it difficult to decide when the previous ink is dry or not, and therefore when it is " wet-on-wet."

" Ink Transfer " is the general term to be used when ink is transferred to some surface.

LASSEUR: In the description of your experimental conditions you do not say whether the ink contained driers.

SCHIRMER: The ink used was delivered ready-to-print for coated art paper, No further drier was added.

BANKS: The influence of the first film printed on the trapping of a second film will be influenced by the changing wettability of the first film due to changing oxidation. For this reason one cannot discuss the effects from the point of view of the Fetskoe Walker type of explanation.

SCHAIFFER: Will you please explain the source of the curves labelled " transmission " in several of the plots on trapping.

SCHIRMER: With the given curves the ink trapping was calculated from values of colour density in transmission. These are independent of gloss.

TOLLEMAN: Can there exist a linear relationship between densities and an ink film thicknesses over a wide range of transmission.

SCHIRMER: The linear relationship of transmission densities has been established over a range of ink film thicknesses.

BANKS: This would be expected if Lambert–Beer's law held.

LARAIGNOU: What was the time interval between the wet-on-wet prints?

SCHIRMER: The intervals were about 5 sec.

FINK: (1) Having tested only one set of three inks, do you believe that other inks show the same behaviour.
(2) Have you studied the influence of the composition of the inks on the results of your proposed testing methods.

SCHIRMER: (1) If these inks have similar composition, I think yes.
(2) Not yet—this will be considered later.

F

LABORATORY EXPERIMENTS WITH HIGH SPEED PRINTING OF NEWSPRINT

by G. E. CARLSSON and R. GINMAN

The Graphic Arts Research Laboratory, Stockholm, Sweden

THE GFL ROTARY-PRINTING PRESS

It seems to be generally accepted that the most reliable method of predicting the printability of paper is by test-printing under fully controlled conditions. Vandercook proof-presses and other similar printing presses have accordingly been extensively used in printing and paper research laboratories all over the world. Many investigations of the printability of newsprint have also been performed with the aid of such presses. But in the case of newsprint such methods deviate considerably from the practical printing conditions. On one hand the rotary printing principle is set aside, on the other the printing speed is considerably smaller than under practical conditions.

The use of speeds other than those used in practice may introduce errors in view of the great influence of printing speed on the transfer of ink to the paper.

These differences in speed have probably contributed to the often low correlation between the results obtained when newsprint was printed under laboratory conditions and when it was printed in ordinary rotary presses.

Work on the construction of a rotary press, in which newsprint could be printed with a speed and pressure fully corresponding to practical conditions, has been going on at the Graphic Arts Research Laboratory for about 10 years. Among other things we aimed to produce an accurately known and controlled variation of pressure. Another important requirement raised, especially by paper-makers and printers, was that the printed specimens should be as large as possible in order, on the one hand, to provide an area large enough to afford a number of determinations of optical properties of the printed surface, and on the other to facilitate a visual inspection of the print, which is considered to be a very valuable supplement to optical measurements. A larger area of print has the added advantage of reducing ink weighing errors in the determination of the ink transfer.

A number of different models of the printing press have during the years been developed and after much experimental work a definite design now exists. A small number of GFL printing presses have now been manufactured and have been ordered by most of the Scandinavian newsprint mills.

A short description of the GFL rotary press will now be given. The apparatus consists of two separate main parts; an inking unit and the rotary press proper.

The size of the paper specimen is 10×36 cm. On this are four solid areas, each of the size 6×9 cm, printed in one operation.

The four printing formes, which consist of $0 \cdot 1$ mm thick steel plates, are inked in the inking unit and then after weighing easily fastened with spring clasps to the plate cylinder of the printing press.

Depending on how the inking procedure is carried out, it is possible either to print the four solids with the same amount of ink or to print a set of solids with different amounts of ink.

If the latter method is used it is possible in one printing operation, supplemented with weighings and optical measurements, to get four points on each of the curves representing the relationships: amount of ink on the forme—amount of ink transferred to the paper, amount of ink on the paper—blackness contrast, and blackness contrast—strike-through, which gives rather complete information about the most important printing characteristics of newsprint.

The printing pressure in the press can be varied continuously up to values of the same order of magnitude as the highest pressures used in production.

The standard model of the press can be run at two speeds, $1 \cdot 7$ and $4 \cdot 6$ m/sec. By changing the gear box the number of possible speeds can be increased.

The press prints according to the rotary principle, and the cylinder covering is of the same type as in newspaper rotary presses.

The plate cylinder A in the rotary press (Fig. 1) has clasps, similar to those on the forme cylinder in the inking device, for fastening the printing plates. The impression cylinder B is covered with a rotary packing about 1 mm thick.

The pressure is switched on by pneumatic means which is rather unusual but which experience has proved to be most suitable in view of the special conditions under which the press prints and which subject the machinery to very heavy mechanical strains.

The press is started and run up to full speed without pressure between the cylinders, and then the pressure is switched on. The pressure is exerted only during one cylinder revolution; it is then automatically cut off.

With a hand pump an overpressure is created in a pressure chamber. The pressure is read on a manometer D. The air pressure works through a self-sealing piston H on a lever system through which it presses the impression cylinder against the plate cylinder when the pressure is thrown on. To control the manometer, it is possible by means of a balance arrangement to counterbalance the pressure by placing a weight in the hook *E*. A lamp is lit when equilibrium is reached.

The load between the cylinders can be varied continuously between 50 kg and 150 kg corresponding to maximum pressures of 20·5 kg/cm² and 42·5 kg/cm². At the latter pressure the pressure zone is about 5 mm wide.

The paper to be printed is fastened to the impression cylinder with tape at the front and back edges.

When the press is started, the cylinders rotate without pressure between them at the selected speed which can be measured with the tachometer *C*. The cylinders are driven through adjusted and matched gears at both ends

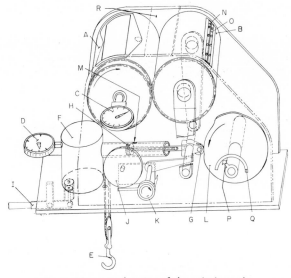

Fig. 1. Schematic drawing of the printing unit.

of the cylinders. The gears are of steel on cylinder *A* and of fibre on cylinder *B*. Cylinder *A* has a certain degree of freedom of movement in the direction of rotation in relation to its gears in order to ensure a true rolling against cylinder *B* during impression. Because of this papers of different thicknesses ranging from 0·04 to 0·11 mm can be printed.

The printing pressure is independent of the paper caliper, which is a very important advantage over flatbed proof presses, in which the pressure depends very much on the thickness of the paper printed.

The pressure is switched on by turning a handle on the side of the press which releases a hook holding the piston *H*. The compressed air will then, through the lever system, press the impression cylinder with the paper against the plate cylinder with the inked plates. To diminish the mechanical strains when the pressure between the rapidly rotating cylinders is operative, the lever movement is directed by a cam. This gives an even pressure increase even at the highest speed.

The pressure between the cylinders reaches its full value about 10 cm before the point where the paper meets the first printing plate.

To damp vibrations, the moving parts are made as light as possible consistent with the necessary structural strength. The cylinders are statically

Fig. 2. The complete press, the printing unit to the left and the inking unit to the right.

and dynamically balanced. The pressure chamber is filled with coarse steel wool to diminish the pressure wave which arises when the pressure is operated.

A photograph of the printing press is seen in Fig. 2.

SOME PRELIMINARY EXPERIMENTAL WORK

Comparison test printings of newsprint samples from a great number of paper mills has already been carried out with our rotary press parallel with the usual physical determinations of paper properties. A number of news inks have also been printed on different makes of newsprint and the ink coverage and strike-through were compared.

We shall now briefly report some of the results, obtained in the fundamental investigations of the press, as an example of the variable conditions which are attainable.

The experiments have also thrown light on some of the effects which the various printing conditions have on the ink transfer to newsprint and the ink requirement of the paper. The results seem, as will be shown later, to have

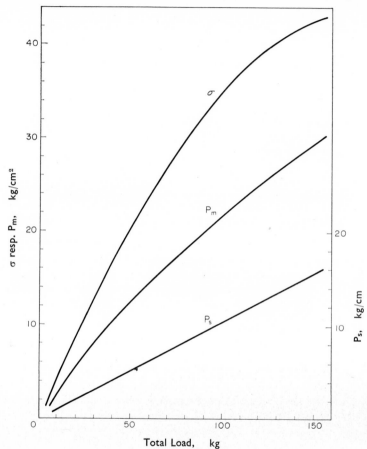

Fig. 3. The relationship between total load, maximum pressure, mean pressure and linear pressure.
σ = pressure in center of the pressure zone
P_m = average pressure over the pressure zone
P_s = linear pressure

general application when printing newsprint in this press and presumably also in other rotary presses.

The external printing variables in these experiments were the load between the cylinders, the printing speed and the amount of ink on the plate.

The load between the cylinders can be expressed as the total load in kilograms or as linear pressure in kg/cm (P_s). For comparison with practical conditions it is also of interest to know the pressure per unit area.

As the pressure varies over the width of the printing zone it can be calculated either as the maximum pressure which is prevailing in the middle of the printing zone (σ) or as the average pressure over the whole printing zone (P_m).

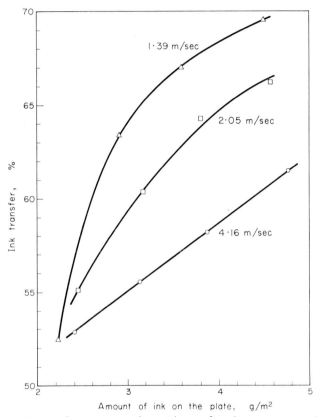

Fig. 4. Influence of printing speed on ink transfer. Linear pressure 17 kg/cm.

How the line pressure, the average pressure and the maximum pressure vary with the total load between the cylinders is shown in Fig. 3. The values of average pressure and maximum pressure which can be attained in the press are of the same order of magnitude as those in an ordinary rotary press for newspaper printing. In such a press the line pressure, however, is considerably larger but, since the width of the printing zone is larger, the pressure will be smaller in relation to the line pressure.

The printing speed is given in m/sec and is accordingly the velocity of the paper passing through the printing zone.

The printing speeds used in these experiments were 1·39, 2·05 and 4·16 m/sec. Compared with the speeds of the paper web which can be attained in modern rotary newspaper presses, 7–11 m/sec, the experimental speeds may at first appear to be insufficient. But for most of the effects at the transfer of ink to paper in printing which are caused by the speed, the time of contact between paper and printing forme is certainly of greater importance than the real speed of the paper.

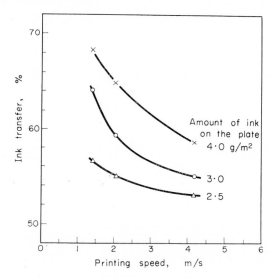

Fig. 5. Ink transfer as a function of printing speed for different amounts of ink on the plate. Linear pressure 17 kg/cm.

In a big rotary printing press the width of the printing zone using normal cylinder coverings and pressure is 15–20 mm. In the laboratory press this width is only about 5 mm. At the same paper velocity the time of contact in the laboratory press is only 1/4–1/3 of the time of contact in a normal rotary press. The velocity of the paper in the laboratory press should accordingly be multiplied by 3 or 4 in order to get a value more comparable with the printing speed of a normal rotary press.

The range within which variations of printing pressure and speed can be brought about in the laboratory rotary press seems thus to cover well the conditions of practical newspaper printing.

In an investigation of how the ink transfer to a certain sample of newsprint varies with the amount of ink on the plate at different printing speeds at constant pressure (15 kg/cm) the results shown in Figs. 4 and 5 were obtained. Principally these results do not imply anything new and they are in good agreement with results from earlier research of the transfer of ink to paper in printing

A matter which, however, may attract special interest is the quantitatively great influence of the printing speed on the ink transfer. The fact that the ink transfer decreases so markedly with increased printing speed seems not to have been clearly shown earlier, but quantitative determinations of the ink transfer at the high velocities as here used may not have been performed.

In Fig. 6 the influence of printing pressure on the ink transfer at two

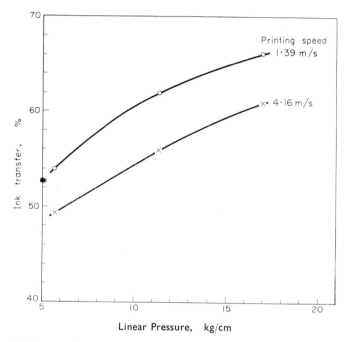

Fig. 6. Influence of pressure on ink transfer at two different printing speeds. Amount of ink on the plate about 5 g/m².

different printing speeds but with the same amount of ink on the plate (5 g/m²) is shown.

A result of great interest obtained in these preliminary experiments was the fact that the ink requirement of the newsprint tested decreased with increased printing speed. The ink requirement is the amount of ink on paper which under the prevailing printing conditions is required to give a certain blackness contrast or relative density of the print. This condition is evident from Fig. 7, which shows the blackness contrast of the paper as a function of the amount of ink on the paper at two different printing speeds, 1·39 and 4·16 m/sec, respectively.

This observation seems not to have been reported before and is of great interest not only with regard to the laboratory printing of paper but also to practical printing conditions. A high printing speed must in consideration to the lower ink transfer be considered as disadvantageous, but if the ink requirement of the paper decreases with rising printing speed this disadvantage will be more or less compensated for.

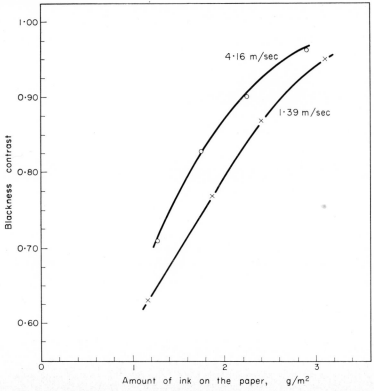

Fig. 7. Influence of printing speed on blackness contrast as a function of amount of ink on the paper.

In order to establish whether this observation was valid for newsprint in general and not just for the special sample investigated an extended study was made.

INVESTIGATION OF THE INFLUENCE OF PRINTING SPEED, PRESSURE, AND INK VISCOSITY ON THE INK TRANSFER AND THE INK REQUIREMENT OF THE PAPER

The following variables were chosen:

    Ink: I_1, viscosity 15 poise

                     I_2, viscosity 34 poise

TABLE 1. PAPER PROPERTIES

Sample	Basis weight g/m²	Caliper mm	Bulk cm³/g	Porosity Bendtsen 75 mm wc ml/min	Smoothness Bendtsen 150 mm wc		Surface oil absorbency 11·0 P oil sec	Pr. opacity filter FMY/C %	Luminance filter FMY/C %
					Load 1 kg/cm² ml/min	Load 5 kg/cm² ml/min			
S1	52·0	0·085	1·63	210	133	45	24	91·8	70·7
S2	52·7	0·082	1·56	129	52	20	21	93·8	73·5
S3	53·5	0·094	1·76	283	130	50	16	92·4	72·3
S4	53·8	0·085	1·58	158	95	39	20	95·4	68·7
S5	53·7	0·085	1·58	373	118	50	10	94·1	67·7
S6	61·4	0·067	1·09	53	38	15	64	96·3	70·8
S7	66·0	0·060	0·91	7	42	17	> 300	93·4	74·2

Printing speed: V_1, 1·39 m/sec

                      V_2, 4·16 m/sec

Printing pressure: P_1, 11·5 kg/cm ($P_m = 20\cdot5$ kg/cm^2)

                      P_2, 17 kg/cm   ($P_m = 29$ kg/cm^2)

Paper: $S1$, Scandinavian newsprint

                      $S2$, Scandinavian newsprint

                      $S3$, Scandinavian newsprint

                      $S4$, Scandinavian newsprint

                      $S5$, Canadian newsprint

                      $S6$, Magazine paper for rotogravure printing

                      $S7$, Machine-coated rotogravure paper

The two inks used were ordinary commercial news inks chosen only with regard to their viscosities. They were also quite different with regard to other properties. It is therefore not possible to draw any conclusions from the difference between the printing results obtained with the two inks with the exception of the ink transfer values. These must primarily depend on the ink viscosity, other printing conditions being the same.

The newsprint samples covered a very wide range of standard newsprint qualities. The magazine paper was included to provide an opportunity of studying the effects of the printing variables on a paper different from newsprint but yet with relatively high absorbency. The special behaviour of this paper made it desirable to include another type of paper in the investigation. For that reason some supplementary printing runs were made on a machine-coated rotogravure paper (S7).

Some of the more usual properties of these papers are given in Table 1.

Primarily 72 printing runs were planned in accordance with the scheme in Table 2.

TABLE 2. SEQUENCE OF PRINTING RUNS

Ink	I_1				I_2			
Printing speed	V_1		V_2		V_1		V_2	
Pressure	P_1	P_2	P_1	P_2	P_1	P_2	P_1	P_2
Paper								
$S1$	1 49	25 61	37	13	43	7	19 55	31 67
$S2$	2 50	26 62	38	14	44	8	20 56	32 68
$S3$	3 51	27 63	39	15	45	9	21 57	33 69
$S4$	4 52	28 64	40	16	46	10	22 58	34 70
$S5$	5 53	29 65	41	17	47	11	23 59	35 71
$S6$	6 54	30 66	42	18	48	12	24 60	36 72

Later the investigation was completed with 32 supplementary printing runs in accordance with Table 3.

TABLE 3. SEQUENCE OF SUPPLEMENTARY PRINTING RUNS

Ink	I_2						
Printing Speed	V_1				V_2		
Pressure	P_1		P_2		P_1		P_2	
Paper								
S3	73	85	79	91	82	94	76	88
S4	74	86	80	92	83	95	77	89
S5	75	87	81	93	84	96	78	90
S7	97	101	99	103	100	104	98	102

For each printing run four prints on the same paper sample with different amounts of ink were obtained.

The printing plates were weighed without ink, and with ink before and after printing and thus the ink transfer to paper was determined.

The light reflection of the printed areas was measured with an Elrepho reflection meter, 24 hr after printing, and the blackness contrast between the printed and unprinted paper was calculated in the usual way.

The strike-through of the print was obtained in similar way by measuring the back of the printed paper.

For each printed specimen, the following three curves were drawn:

(*a*) Amount of ink on the print as a function of that on the plate.

(*b*) Blackness contrast of the print as a function of the amount of ink on the paper.

(*c*) Strike-through of the print as a function of the amount of ink on the paper.

From these curves the following parameters were taken:

Ink transfer,　percentage of ink amount on the plate, (when this is 6·0 g/m²), transferred to the paper.

Ink requirement, the amount of ink on the paper which gives a blackness contrast of 1·00.

Strike-through,　the blackness contrast of the back of the paper when the print has a blackness contrast of 1·00.

These three parameters, which relate only to one point on each of the three curves, may be considered to characterize the principal printing properties of the paper. Accordingly they give by no means a complete picture of the printability of the paper. It is very probable that another ranking of the papers might have resulted if the parameters had been taken at lower amounts of ink.

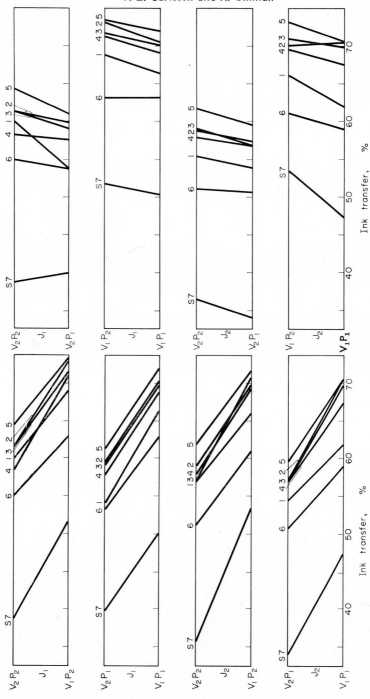

Fig. 9. Influence of pressure on ink transfer for the two inks I_1 and I_2 at printing speeds V_1 and V_2..

Fig. 8. Influence of printing speed on ink transfer for the two inks I_1 and I_2 at pressures P_1 and P_2.

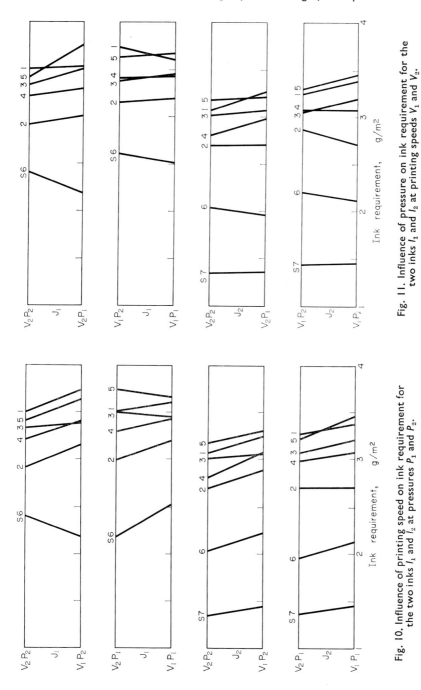

Fig. 11. Influence of pressure on ink requirement for the two inks I_1 and I_2 at printing speeds V_1 and V_2.

Fig. 10. Influence of printing speed on ink requirement for the two inks I_1 and I_2 at pressures P_1 and P_2.

The reason why these particular parameters were chosen is that they correspond to the conditions of maximum density in practice. It is here that troubles with poor paper in regard to set-off, filling-in and strike-through are most disturbing.

How the various printing conditions affected these parameters can be studied in Tables 4–8 and Figs. 8–11.

The values in the tables are mean values of the parameters, obtained from the different printing runs according to Tables 2 and 3.

TABLE 4. INK TRANSFER IN % TO THE PAPER AT 6·0g INK/M² ON THE PLATE

Ink	I_1				I_2			
Printing speed	V_1		V_2		V_1		V_2	
Pressure	P_1	P_2	P_1	P_2	P_1	P_2	P_1	P_2
Paper								
S1	66·4	68·9	54·0	60·0	62·0	66·2	54·0	55·5
S2	70·3	73·0	59·8	61·5	70·4	70·0	57·4	59·0
S3	70·0	71·7	59·2	61·6	69·9	71·0	57·0	59·2
S4	69·0	71·2	57·8	58·4	67·5	69·6	56·9	58·0
S5	71·9	73·5	61·2	64·4	70·7	73·1	59·7	61·8
S6	63·1	63·1	53·3	55·1	59·1	61·2	50·7	51·2
S7	50·3	51·8	39·9	38·8	47·4	53·5	34·2	36·5

TABLE 5. INK REQUREMENT IN G/M² OF THE PAPER FOR A BLACKNESS CONTRAST OF 1·00

Ink	I_1				I_2			
Printing speed	V_1		V_2		V_1		V_2	
Pressure	P_1	P_2	P_1	P_2	P_1	P_2	P_1	P_2
Paper								
S1	3·60	3·73	3·52	3·50	3·38	3·24	3·27	3·07
S2	3·19	3·14	3·00	2·91	2·71	2·88	2·70	2·69
S3	3·44	3·38	3·49	3·33	3·20	3·05	3·07	3·00
S4	3·42	3·40	3·29	3·21	3·07	3·07	2·98	2·80
S5	3·66	3·62	3·74	3·41	3·45	3·30	3·21	3·17
S6	2·51	2·60	2·18	2·40	2·12	2·21	1·96	2·03
S7	—	—	—	—	1·45	1·44	1·36	1·34

From Table 4 and Figs. 8 and 9 it is evident that increased speed causes decreased ink transfer and that increased pressure gives increased ink transfer. This applies generally to all the papers tested. The influence of the change in speed is much bigger than that of a pressure change. It should, however, be pointed out that $V_2 : V_1 = 3$ but $P_2 : P_1 = 1.5$. But, even if this circumstance is taken into consideration, it is still evident that in the range covered here the printing speed has a more marked influence on the ink transfer than the pressure.

TABLE 6. STRIKE-THROUGH OF THE PRINT AT A BLACKNESS CONTRAST OF 1.00

Ink	I_1				I_2			
Printing speed	V_1		V_2		V_1		V_2	
Pressure	P_1	P_2	P_1	P_2	P_1	P_2	P_1	P_2
Paper								
S1	0·107	0·113	0·109	0·110	0·097	0·092	0·094	0·082
S2	0·074	0·077	0·071	0·076	0·064	0·074	0·062	0·064
S3	0·094	0·095	0·092	0·095	0·084	0·081	0·081	0·087
S4	0·077	0·076	0·070	0·073	0·065	0·066	0·065	0·060
S5	0·089	0·084	0·080	0·103	0·075	0·076	0·070	0·070
S6	0·051	0·054	0·044	0·046	0·035	0·039	0·035	0·038

The effects will be clearer from the mean values of the ink transfer at the different speeds and pressures as seen in Table 7.

TABLE 7. MEAN VALUES OF INK TRANSFER IN %

	V_1	V_2	P_1	P_2
Newsprint	69·8	58·8	63·2	65·4
Magazine	61·6	52·6	56·6	57·7
Machine-coated	50·7	37·4	43·0	45·2

The low ink transfer to the machine-coated paper at high printing speed is very remarkable. The most plausible explanation is that the time of contact between paper and ink at the high speed is too short for a complete wetting of the paper by the ink.

The principal purpose of this investigation was, however, to establish whether or not the earlier observation of the lowering of ink requirement of the paper with increased printing speed was generally valid for newsprint. The data in Table 5 and shown in Fig. 10 show that this is the case not only for newsprint but also for the two other papers tested.

The influence of the pressure on the ink requirement of the paper is not uniform but the discrepancies between the papers in this regard are so small

G

and the magnitude of the effect so slight, that it may be concluded that pressure has in general no practical influence on the ink requirement within the range covered by this investigation.

The effects of printing speed and pressure upon the ink requirement of the papers is more clearly shown by the mean values of this parameter at the different speeds and pressures summarized in Table 8. Each value is a mean from 42 printing runs, each of which comprised four printed areas.

TABLE 8. MEAN VALUES OF INK REQUIREMENT IN G/M^2

	V_1	V_2	P_1	P_2
Newsprint	3·31	3·17	3·27	3·21
Magazine	2·36	2·14	2·19	2·31
Machine-coated	1·45	1·35	1·41	1·39

The printed samples of newsprint were of different make and covered a wide range of standard newsprint qualities. The effect shown here must therefore be significant.

The values for the magazine and machine-coated papers are means of results from 6 and 4 printing runs respectively. As the effects were very similar for each printing run the values can be considered quite reliable.

The influence of the external printing variables on the strike-through is very small as can be seen in Table 6. The differences caused by paper as well as ink properties are of a much bigger order of magnitude.

DISCUSSION

This investigation has shown that the ink transfer to paper decreases markedly at high printing speed. For one paper tested the ink transfer falls below 50%. Increased pressure only slightly increases the ink transfer at high speed. The conclusion which may be drawn from these facts is that the time of contact is too short at the high speed to allow proper wetting of the paper by the ink.

It has also been shown that the amount of ink on the paper, which is required to give a certain blackness of the print, decreases with increasing speed. It is not so easy to find a plausible explanation for this fact. At first one would assume that the ink is not pressed so deeply into the paper at high speed and thus gives a better coverage when it stays on the surface. Against this idea is the fact that the effect is more marked for papers with lower porosity than newsprint and that increased pressure does not increase the ink requirement. It seems possible that the effect is caused by divergencies in the ink splitting mechanism at high and low speed which may give rise to differences in the ink distribution on the paper surface.

A conclusion which may be drawn from this investigation is that in order to get the right magnitude of the parameters chosen for characterizing the printability of paper, when printing in laboratory presses, the printing conditions, especially the speed, should be as like the practical printing conditions as possible.

It is also evident how important it is to have the external printing variables under full control.

It may, however, also be observed that the ranking of the papers with regard to ink transfer, ink requirement and strike-through as well as the relative magnitude of these parameters is, with a few exceptions, the same for all the combinations of speed, pressure and ink used.

We have, however, established that appreciable changes of the ranking occurred when comparative printings of a great number of newsprint samples were performed in the GFL rotary press and in a Vandercook press, as can be seen in Appendix A.

APPENDIX A

COMPARATIVE TEST-PRINTING OF NEWSPRINT IN VANDERCOOK PRESS AND GFL ROTARY PRESS

A number of newsprint samples from practically all Scandinavian newsprint mills were printed in a Vandercook press and also in the GFL rotary press.

Printing conditions

Vandercook: speed, 1·0 m/sec
pressure, 10 kg/cm ($P_m = 10$ kg/cm^2)
ink viscosity, 23 poise

GFL rotary: speed, 4·16 m/sec
pressure, 17 kg/cm ($P_m = 29$ kg/cm^2)
ink viscosity, 33 poise

24 different newsprint samples were printed. In the Vandercook press were on average 7 specimens of each sample printed with different amounts of ink.

In the rotary press two printings of each sample gave 8 printed specimens with varying ink amount.

From the curves representing the amount of ink transferred to the paper as a function of the amount of ink on the plate, and the blackness contrast and the strike-through of the print as functions of the amount of ink on the paper, the following three parameters were taken:

Ink transfer in % at an ink amount of 4 g/m² on the plate.

Ink requirement for a blackness contrast of 0·90.

Strike-through at the blackness contrast of 0·90.

The values obtained for these parameters from printing in the two presses are seen in Table A1 and in Fig. A1 they can be more easily compared.

TABLE A1.

Paper	Ink transfer %		Ink requirement g/m²		Strike-through	
	V	GFL	V	GFL	V	GFL
A	61·0	55·7	2·65	2·65	0·097	0·090
B	64·3	56·2	2·85	2·80	0·110	0·099
C	61·8	55·5	2·70	2·65	0·103	0·092
D	64·3	59·8	2·65	2·62	0·085	0·078
E	63·5	57·8	3·00	2·59	0·095	0·081
F	55·0	58·5	2·45	2·61	0·067	0·068
G	63·0	56·4	2·62	2·59	0·070	0·077
H	53·8	53·7	2·87	2·82	0·095	0·089
J	58·0	49·9	3·25	2·85	0·110	0·092
K	55·5	54·1	2·87	2·85	0·108	0·100
L	55·0	53·6	3·07	2·89	0·100	0·104
M	55·5	57·3	2·72	2·41	0·094	0·079
N	58·0	54·9	2·98	2·45	0·112	0·094
O	58·2	55·7	2·90	2·47	0·105	0·093
P	55·0	55·8	2·65	2·62	0·075	0·075
Q	69·5	59·8	2·37	2·50	0·060	0·066
R	58·3	58·7	2·55	2·66	0·057	0·059
S	63·8	58·7	2·30	2·58	0·060	0·067
T	62·0	60·3	2·46	2·48	0·080	0·067
U	58·5	54·8	2·53	2·47	0·085	0·081
X	59·0	55·3	3·14	2·75	0·090	0·077
Y	56·3	58·8	2·66	2·57	0·100	0·086
Z	53·3	54·4	2·77	2·72	0·087	0·089
Å	57·8	55·8	2·55	2·58	0·084	0·084

It is very evident that the correlation between the ink transfer and ink requirement of the paper calculated from the printing in the two presses is very poor. This fact must be due to the divergence in mechanical printing conditions which exists between the two printing presses.

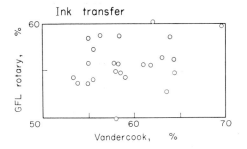

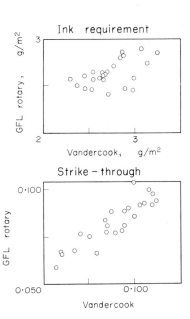

Fig. A1. Relationships between results obtained in the Vandercook proof press and in the GFL rotary press. Ink transfer at an ink amount of 4 g/m² on the plate. Ink requirement and strike-through at blackness contrast 0·90.

DISCUSSION

HUNDERUP JENSEN: In your paper you state that the ink requirement of newsprint decreases with increasing printing speed. Using an I.G.T. print tester at speeds of 0·42, 1·1 and 2·2 m/sec and working with different makes of Scandinavian newsprint we find an opposite effect. Can you offer any explanation?

CARLSSON: I am sorry that you cannot agree with our statement, but I can assure you that I have only reported results of a rather exhaustive experimental work carried out under carefully controlled conditions. I would assume that the divergence between our results, of which we do not know any more details than the few which you have mentioned, is to be explained by differences in printing conditions, most likely to the much lower printing speeds you have used.

NORDMAN: There might be a reason why the results of Carlsson and Jensen differ and that is the definition of blackness contrast employed for the comparison of the ink requirements.

Which was it in both cases?

CARLSSON: In our case it was 1·00.

HUNDERUP JENSEN: We have measured the ink requirement for a blackness contrast of 0·85.

FETSKO: It is not a matter of distrusting results. There was a time when we preached the superiority of the printability of an ink-paper combination in contrast to rating a series of papers with one ink or a series of inks with one paper. It is now apparent that one must also consider the press. Based on results we are hearing at this conference, it is apparent that the influence of speed depends on the geometry of the press and that this matter must be studied further.

BANKS: We do not in general know much about the real pressures operating during impression. Certainly if a press is adjusted to a given pressure at a given speed, any increase in speed can be expected to increase the pressure in the ink film during impression for hydrodynamical reasons. These can attain very high values which will depend on the geometry of the nip and the viscosity of the ink.

PRINCE: We have observed on a newspaper press the same results shown by Mr. Carlsson in Fig. 5 of his paper, that is, that while ink transfer decreases with increase in printing speed the absolute amount of ink transferred increases with speed.

ROGERS: Does the use of the solid plate permit the trapping of air in the film at the time of contact between ink and paper? Would a halftone plate tend to give more nearly uniform results?

CARLSSON: I would think that when printing such a porous paper as newsprint, very little difference would occur between solid and halftone plates with regard to the trapping of air.

GINMAN: With regard to Mr. Hunderup-Jensen's remarks concerning the influence of speed on ink requirement, I would like to draw attention to Fig. 2 in Mr. Prince's paper, which shows that printing quality reaches a minimum at a certain speed. It may well be that Mr. Hunderup-Jensen has worked in a speed range lower than the speed corresponding to this minimum point while our speed values were on the higher side.

STUDIES OF THE PRINTABILITY OF NEWSPRINT PAPERS AT VARIOUS SPEEDS AND PRESSURES

by E. RUPP

Institut für grafische Technik, Leipzig

FROM studies of the relationship between paper properties and printing results, newsprint papers and the effect of pressure and speed on (i) ink transfer, (ii) variations in width of lines, and (iii) the printing tolerance of halftone dots will be discussed.

INK TRANSFER

The ink transfer coefficient

$$V = \frac{y}{x - y}$$

(x = amount of ink on the forme before impression, y = amount of ink transferred to paper) was measured as a function of x, with printing speed s, and printing pressure p as parameters for various newsprint papers. Solid areas were printed with a news ink of low viscosity on the printability tester. A soft cylinder packing with a silk rubber sheet was used.

The results were evaluated by means of a modified form[1] of the Zettlemoyer Fetsko formula, in which their exponent Kx is replaced by x^2/D^2. D is a coefficient closely related to the quantity of ink required for full coverage. V_m is the maximum ink transfer coefficient in the curves relating V and x, with s and p as parameters. x_m is the value of x giving V_m. The quantities x, y, D and b are given in g/m^2.

The oil-based rotary news ink (Rotary black) had a viscosity of 1600 centipoise at 50°C.

When comparing the printing speeds of a printability tester and a rotary printing press consideration has to be given to the time of contact in the nip between paper and ink. Assuming, in general agreement with others, a width of the printing line in the nip of $4°$ which is independent of speed s, a contact time of 0·001 sec is found for the printability tester (cylinder diameter 10 cm) at a speed of 4 m/sec. With a rotary cylinder of 60 cm diameter the contact time at the same speed is 0·005 sec (calculated geometrically). Therefore, the speed of 4 m/sec of the printability tester would correspond to a speed of 20 m/sec for the rotary printing machine.

The measurements were made with machine glazed newsprint papers (Bekk-smoothness about 15 sec) from seven paper mills and with a calendered paper (Bekk-smoothness about 200 sec) from one mill. Three examples of the results are given in Tables 1–3 and Figs. 1 and 2. The conclusions which are reached, for the effects of speed and pressure, are derived from the average values of all papers and will now be summarized.

Conclusions

Variation of speed S

$$p = \text{const.}$$

For both kinds of paper: $V_m \cdot \sqrt{s} = \text{const.}$
For machine glazed papers: $x_m = \text{const.}$, independent of s.

In this case $y_m = \dfrac{x_m}{1 + \sqrt{(s/c)}}$, dependent on s.

For machine glazed papers: $D = \text{const.}$, independent of s.
For calendered paper: D increases, linearly with s.
For machine glazed papers: b decreases with s.
For calendered paper: b decreases, linearly with s.
For both kinds of paper: $f \cdot \sqrt{s} = \text{const.}$
For machine glazed paper: b increases with V_m.
For machine glazed papers: D is independent of s, when x_m is independent of s.
For calendered papers: D increases, linearly with x_m.

Variation of pressure p

$$s = \text{const.}$$

For both kinds of paper:
   V_m increases, linearly with p.
   D decreases with p
   b increases, linearly with p
   f is const., independent of p
   b increases, linearly with V_m
   D increases with x_m.

It may be premature to discuss these empirical results with other paper and ink properties, but most remarkable is the independence of f on pressure p,

TABLE 1. NEWSPRINT PAPER Z 14, MACHINE GLAZED.
(Rotary black; $p = 50 \text{ klb/cm}^2$)

s	V_{max}	x_m	D	b	f
1	1·44	6·2	3·45	4·7	0·26
2	1·16	6·2	3·45	3·8	0·21
4	0·84	6·2	3·45	3·3	0·14

$s = 4 \text{ m/sec}$

p	V_{max}	x_m	D	b	f
25	0·70	6·4	3·56	2·9	0·14
50	0·82	5·6	3·45	3·3	0·14
75	0·89	5·2	3·04	3·6	0·14

TABLE 2. NEWSPRINT PAPER Z 11, MACHINE GLAZED.
(Rotary black; $p = 50 \text{ klb/cm}^2$)

s	V_{max}	x_m	D	b	f
1	1·29	7·5	4·35	4·7	0·26
2	1·04	7·5	4·35	4·0	0·19
4	0·74	7·5	4·35	3·4	0·12

$s = 4 \text{ m/sec}$

p	V_{max}	x_m	D	b	f
25	0·62	7·7	4·75	3·2	0·12
50	0·73	7·0	4·35	3·4	0·12
75	0·79	6·0	3·34	3·6	0·12

TABLE 3. NEWSPRINT PAPER Z 9, CALENDERED
(Rotary black; $p = 50$ klb/cm²)

s	V_{max}	x_m	D	b	f
1	1·21	3·8	2·12	1·6	0·35
2	0·98	4·0	2·21	1·4	0·29
4	0·66	4·4	2·38	1·0	0·21

			$s = 4$ m/sec		
p	V_{max}	x_m	D	b	f
25	0·56	4·5	2·63	0·8	0·21
50	0·66	4·0	2·38	1·0	0·21
75	0·75	3·8	1·96	1·2	0·21

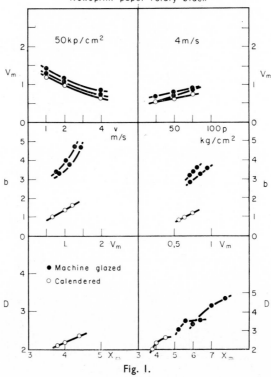

Fig. I.

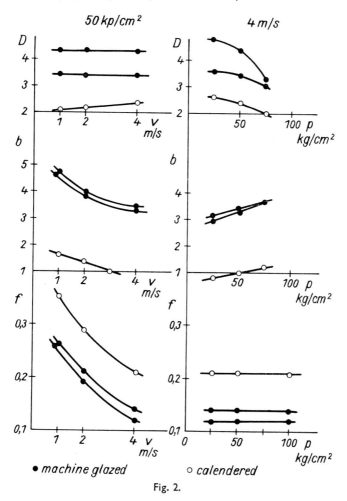

Fig. 2.

and for machine glazed papers the independence of x_m and D on speed s. For both ink transfer characteristics V_m and f, the same mathematical expression involving $\sqrt{s}$ is valid. Since rather simpler relationships may be observed with inks of low viscosity it would be useful to study all kinds of papers using such inks.

VARIATION IN WIDTH OF PRINTED LINES

When an etched line screen is printed with rectangular profile in letterpress printing, a squeezing of the ink around the border and diffusion beyond the border is observed. This diffusion is greater with low viscosity ink, and with high porosity paper as is the case with newsprint. For varying printing speed *s* and pressure *p* the differences in width of printed lines may be taken as a quality test. But the method is not very sensitive to variations in paper properties. When a line screen with circular profile is applied the differences in width depend predominantly on porosity and hardness of the paper. These differences are greater and the method shows improved discrimination of papers.

A line screen made by coiling a thin steel wire around the rims of the forme wheel of the printability tester was used. The strands of the wire (diameter 0·6 mm) were arranged parallel to the axis of the wheel. They were inked with the same amount of rotary black ($x = 2·5$ mg) for all measurements. This amount is less than the quantity for complete coverage since a large quantity does not discriminate papers so well.

Machine glazed and a calendered newsprint paper were used for printing at different speeds and pressures and the widths of the printed lines in different sections vertical to the lines were measured with a measuring microscope in units of the ocular scale (1 unit $= 22\mu$). The error of a series of 10 measurements is ± 2 units. The results are shown in Table 4 where the pressure is given in units of klb/cm.

TABLE 4. VARIATION IN WIDTH OF LINES
(Wire forme; Rotary black; $x = 2·5$ mg)

p klb/cm	s m/sec	Newsprint paper	
		m'gl. *Z* 14	cal. *Z* 9
25	1	15·2	14·8
	2	15·7	16·0
	4	15·7	14·7
50	1	17·7	18·8
	2	17·8	17·8
	4	18·0	17·7
75	1	19·0	20·3
	2	19·0	20·4
	4	18·6	19·4
Growth in width 75 : 25		22%	32%

These results show that there is no growth in width of line with printing speed. The differences for both kinds of paper at the same printing pressure are small and cannot be used for paper testing. But if we compare the width of line at $p = 75$ and $p = 25$ for both papers we find a clearly greater value

(32%) for calendered paper than for machine glazed paper (22%). The greater value belongs to the harder paper with fewer pores.

TABLE 5. VARIATION IN WIDTH OF LINE AT DIFFERENT PRESSURES
(Wire forme; Rotary black; $x = 2 \cdot 5$ mg; $s = 1$ m/sec)

p klb/cm	Paper	
	m'gl. No. 60	cal. No. 2
10	15·0	14·3
30	18·6	19·2
50	19·6	20·1
70	20·5	21·3
Growth in width 70 : 10	36%	49%

This effect of printing pressure is confirmed by measurements with two book papers (Table 5) using rotary black. The width of line is markedly increased at higher pressure on the harder and less porous paper. Further work is necessary to investigate the possibilities of the method for paper testing.

PRINTING TOLERANCE OF HALFTONE DOTS

By varying the printing pressure with a constant amount x of ink on the forme a good reproduction of a grey scale is found only in a limited range of pressure. This range is called the tolerance of printing pressure. At very low values of p the solid of a grey scale will show incomplete impression, at high values the dots in the highlights will show ink squash. Therefore, as the first limit, I, of pressure tolerance that pressure is taken at which the solid impression is complete, and as the other limit, II, that pressure at which the beginning of ink squash is observed in the highlight dots. A grey scale of 8 steps is used (step 8 is a solid), and screen distance of 48 lines/cm mounted on the forme wheel of the printability tester (without makeready). At the same total printing force the printing pressure on step 1 in the highlights is 6 times greater than on step 8.

Increased printing force was used on machine glazed and calendered papers using rotary black as above. The amount of ink for inking the grey scale forme was 5 mg for machine glazed and 2·5 mg for calendered paper. As there was much slur in printing the grey scale, there was some uncertainty as to the onset of ink squash. As an average result the same values were found at printing speeds of 1, 2 and 4 m/sec.

For machine glazed paper limit I 60 klb/cm²   Z 14 limit II 180 klb/cm²
For calendered paper   limit I 25 klb/cm²   Z 9   limit II 110 klb/cm²
These results are in agreement with our former experiments [1] as to the behaviour of machine glazed and calendered paper, where we used a speed of 1 m/sec.

It is proposed to repeat the experiments with a coarse screen of 14 lines/cm, so as to minimize the effect of slurring.

REFERENCE

1. E. RUPP and K. RIECHE, "Beiträge zur Bedruckbarkeit von Papier und Folien," *Inst. grafische Technik*, *Leipzig*, (1959).

DISCUSSION

SCHAEFFER: Has your transfer equation been able to reproduce the exact shape of your transfer curves obtained at different apeeds? Experience with the NPIRI transfer equation has shown that, for *b* values greater than approximately 6, the assumptions made in the linear form of the equation are not justified. Calculations for *b* and *f* should include the term $(1 - \exp(-x/b))$ since *b* is large in comparison with the *x* values generally used in determining per cent. transfer.

RUPP: Our values of *b* for newsprint were below 5, but the whole problem as to the exact transfer equation is not settled yet.

FETSKO: We are not surprised that pressure has little effect on the ink splitting coefficient because the final film split takes place at the end of the nip where the influence of pressure is at a minimum.

ROGERS: Is it possible for you to calculate the degree of plate makeready necessary for a plate, when the cylinder packing materials are known?

RUPP: The apparatus for making the prints is used without makeready.

LASSEUR: Dr. Rupp states that a speed of 4 m/sec on his printmaker corresponds to 20 m/sec on a production press. On the assumption that it is mainly the time of contact which governs the ink transfer the possible influence of differences in shearing velocity with different cylinder diameters is not taken into account. This seems to me to be not entirely justified.

Further we have experience from which it appeared that in estimating the relation between the cylinder diameters and the width of the contact area, mere geometrical considerations are not adequate. We measured pressures and contact areas on two large gravure presses and on our proof press with the following results:

Image cylinder	Production press	Proof press
Length	150 cm	22 cm
Diameter	40 cm	10 cm
Impression cylinder		
Diameter	50 in.	11 in.
Thickness of rubber ..	1 in.	1 in.
Shore hardness ..	80°	80°
Pressure	20 kg/cm	20 kg/cm
Printing area	1·1 cm	1·0 cm

So it is clear that in spite of considerable dimensional differences between the cylinders the contact areas were equally wide. Scale-effects as found here, which we have not yet been able to explain, raise doubts about geometrical calculations.

SPEED AND PRESSURE CONSIDERATIONS ON A NEWSPAPER PRESS

by R. W. Prince

ANPA Research Institute, Inc., Easton, Pa., U.S.A.

Abstract—Newspaper press speed and impression setting have been studied relative to measurable printing quality resulting from the use of news ink and newsprint. At practical production speeds, with any practical impression setting, it was found that printing quality increased with press speed. Also, at any speed tried, the printing quality improved with increased printing impression.

INTRODUCTION

It is believed that many factors involved in printing are individually affected by speed and pressure. Therefore, we have elected to study first the over-all effect of these parameters on measurable printing quality so that the ultimate relationship of speed and pressure can be defined in terms of desirable results, viz. printing quality.

As part of a study to determine the degree of correlation between the Larocque proof press printing quality test [1] and printed results obtained from a newspaper press, an investigation was made of the effect of speed and impression on printed samples from a newspaper press.

The Larocque printing quality test was designed to duplicate, on a proof press, conditions existing on newspaper presses. In this test, only one ink is used and ink-film thickness and pressure are quantitatively controlled. It enables the classification of various newsprint samples according to their printing quality. The measurement of printing quality is based on reflectance measurements of printed and unprinted newsprint samples. Using these reflectance measurements, the per cent. printing quality of a sample is defined by the following equation:

$$\% \text{ Printing Quality} = 100 - \frac{R \text{ (ink corrected)} \times 100}{R \text{ (paper)}}$$

R (ink corrected) is the average reflectance of a printed sample corrected for the amount of standard ink used. R (paper) is the average reflectance of the unprinted paper sample.

According to this definition, a completely black surface would be rated as 100% and unprinted paper as 0%.

For comparative purposes, the data herein reported relate speed and impression (pressure) to per cent. printing quality as defined above rather than to ink transfer or some other parameter which, in itself, may be singly affected by speed or impression.

GENERAL PROCEDURES

Since we have no humidity control in our pressroom, each roll of paper was handled in the same way. This was done to minimize the effect of humidity. Ink used on the Hoe Printmaster was the same ink used in proof press testing.

The proof press procedure utilizes a 6×7 in. magnesium plate for printing a solid area. For the Hoe press run, a 6×15 in. magnesium plate was curved and mounted on a magnesium saddle to duplicate the type of plate used on the proof press.

Each newsprint roll was marked at 6 in. intervals from the core. These levels were marked to determine where tears were to be pulled.

The first runs on each roll were identical. Ink feed (quantity) and impression (pressure) were set to produce a normal printed page. At a speed of 790 ft/min, each roll was run to the first marked level. Fifty consecutive tear sheets were pulled from the delivery, identified as to order, and rushed to the temperature- and humidity-controlled room. This sampling procedure, from press to test room, required less than two minutes.

Under controlled temperature and humidity conditions (71·5°F–45% r.h.), the tear sheets (each essentially an eight-page paper) were divided and numbered consecutively. Reflectometer readings were made immediately on the fifty printed solids. Ten blank pages, adjacent (along cylinder axis) to the printed solid, were chosen randomly from the fifty papers and wrapped in moisture-proof paper for later testing on the proof press.

Whereas the Larocque printability is calculated from a measured amount of ink, for these tests measurement of the amount of ink laid down by the Hoe Printmaster was not possible. Therefore, no ink correction was applied to the reflectance measurements of tear sheets pulled from the Hoe press. It was assumed that the ink-film thickness on the printing plate remained relatively constant for a given ink setting. Printability was calculated for Hoe press prints on the basis of this assumption.

RESULTS

With the ink fountain adjusted to a given setting, tear sheets were pulled at web speeds of 316, 633, 950 and 1266 ft/min. Figure 1 shows the effect of speed increase and impression change on the printability of a roll of newsprint. It can be seen that at all speeds the printing quality improves with increasing impression.

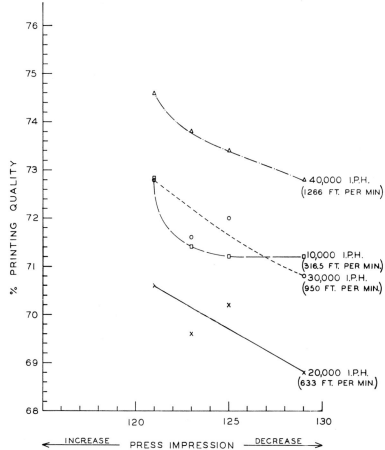

Fig. 1. Relationship of newspaper press speed and impression and newsprint printing quality.

Figure 2 shows the relationship found between press speed and printing quality. The apparent inversion of the proportionality may be a function of the ink pumping system on the press, centrifugal forces which could affect the impression, or, perhaps, experimental error.

DISCUSSION

Yelmgren[2] has noted that, on the same newspaper press, the absolute amount of ink transferred increases to a slight extent with increasing speed, although the percentage of ink transfer decreases. It has been observed that

H

a change in inking level on the newspaper press greatly affects the blackness of the printed sample measured by a reflectometer. Figure 3 shows the relationship for four rolls of newsprint. The abscissa is plotted in thousandths of an inch and represents ink key settings measured by a feeler gauge.

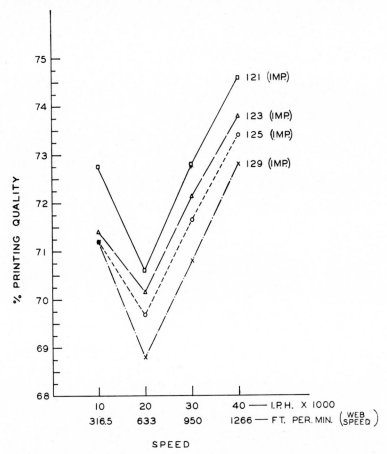

Fig. 2. Printing quality variation with newspaper press speed for different press impressions.

It is not known how much additional ink is transferred for a change in ink key setting of 0·001 in. We do know, however, that, on representative samples of newsprint printed on the proof press, a change in inking of the plate from 2·0 g/m² to 2·5 g/m² increases the Larocque printability number by 6 to 8 percentage points of printing quality. Such a change is easily discernible to the naked eye. Figure 4 shows this relationship for a variety of newsprints. Figure 5 is a photograph of one particular newsprint where " A " was printed with an ink density on the plate of 2·0 g/m² and " B " printed with an ink density of 2·5 g/m². This is an extreme case where the difference in printing quality number between " A " and " B " is 19 percentage points.

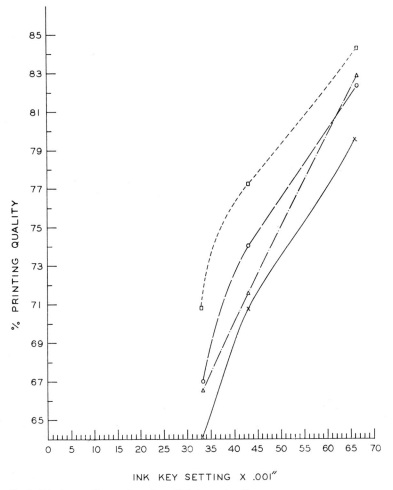

INK KEY SETTING X .001″

Fig. 3. Printing quality as a function of ink fountain adjustment on a newspaper press.

It is felt that more studies of the dynamic behaviour of blankets during the printing operation may yield information pertinent to a better understanding of the effect of speed on newspaper press printing. What has been explored and reported here serves only to illustrate the effect of speed and pressure on printing quality in terms of practical printing results. It is hoped that other experimenters who have studied such things as plate distortion due to

R. W. Prince

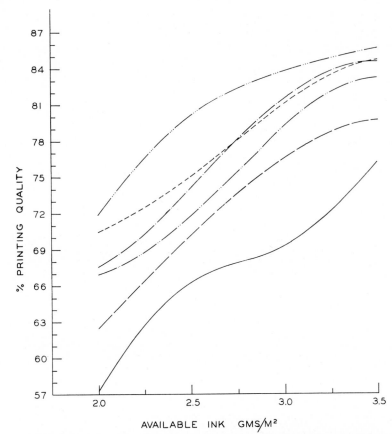

Fig. 4. Variation in printing quality of newsprint with increased inking on proof press.

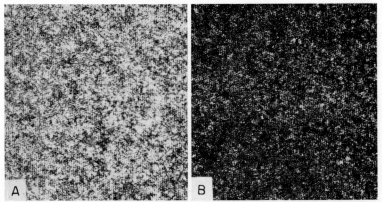

Fig. 5. Photograph of newsprint sample printed from plate with ink density of 2·0 g/m²(A) and an ink density of 2·5 g/m²(B).

centrifugal force, dynamic blanket compression, and high-speed ink transfer can offer an explanation for the characteristic printing quality–speed relationship shown in Fig. 1.

ACKNOWLEDGMENT

The writer would like to thank Mr. F. J. Stanczak and Mr. S. W. Mabus, who were responsible for most of the experimental work.

REFERENCES

1. G. LAROCQUE, B. AXELROD, and S. CLARK, Measuring the printing quality of newsprint, *Pulp Paper Mag. Canada* **52**, No. 3, 166–174 (February, 1951).
2. A. E. YELMGREN, A technique for measuring high-speed ink-film transfer, *Advances in Printing Science and Technology*, Vol. 1, Pergamon Press, Oxford (1961).

DISCUSSION

LASSEUR: Mr. Prince's paper raises difficult questions of a general nature for me. In order to estimate printability he uses the Larocque method in which a quality factor is derived from reflection density measurements. Now a number of investigators are not convinced that the density of a print is its main quality defining property but rather the microscopic density distribution is important. Six years ago at the 3rd Conference we came to a generally accepted concept of printability. Since then we have developed all over the world tests for the estimation of this printability and methods for the interpretation of the test results—tests and interpretations that differ widely from place to place. The question I ask is this: Is it not time that we tried to reach some uniformity about the carrying out of tests and their interpretation?

NORDMAN: Would you care to give an explanation of the fact that in Fig. 4 there is an inflection point in some of the curves?

PRINCE: (communicated) I have no conclusive explanation to offer but it may be significant that the newsprint papers exhibiting the inflection are all relatively rough.

THE RISE OF TEMPERATURE OF RUBBER AND INKING ROLLERS ON A HIGH-SPEED ROTARY PRESS AND ITS INFLUENCE ON THE INK AND THE PAPER

by Ib Hunderup Jensen

The Joint Purchase Association of the Danish Newspress, Copenhagen, Denmark

IN CONNECTION with a press-room extension at one of our big newspapers it proved important to combat the generation of heat in the inking devices during the run. As already theoretically proved by Funk[1] in the late twenties, and as has been mentioned several times in the ANPA Mechanical Bulletins[2], the inking devices consume a considerable part of the entire power used by a rotary press. Some state that it amounts to 40%, others to 60% and it is transformed into heat.

Miller[3] recently published some laboratory experiments with rubber covered and steel rollers with measurements of the width of the nip at different speeds.

However, as far as I know a closer examination of how big the rise of temperature is on the rollers of an inking device has never been made. Furthermore, information about the correlation between the rise of temperature and the width of the nip between the rubber covered inking roller and the underlying steel roller or the influence that this heating has on the tendency of the column rules to cut into the inking rollers is not available in the literature. Neither is there any published work on how these rises of temperature influence the printing ink and dry out the surface of the newsprint as it passes between the inking devices of an ordinary unit-press.

In our studies the rise of temperature on the rollers was measured initially with a copper-constantan thermo-element trailing in the ink film on a steel roller during the run and later with a resistance-thermometer (SWEMA) on rubber and inking rollers during the stops that always occur during a run. It was expected that the first method might give too high readings due to frictional heat being generated between the element and the roller, but as good agreement was found between the results from both methods this source of error may be excluded.

In Fig. 1 is shown a typical record of the rise of temperature on different rollers in the enclosed inking device of a rotary press running at 40,000 c/hr corresponding to a paper speed of 381 m/min. The measurements were made with the resistance thermometer on stationary rollers.

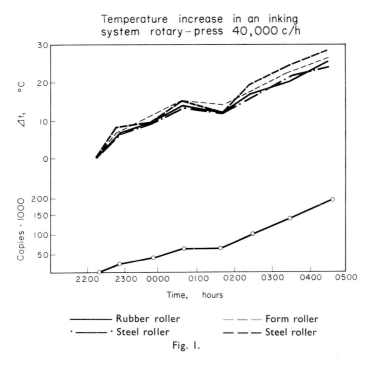

Fig. I.

It appears that the rise of temperature is rather gradual during the run and that only a very moderate decrease of the roller temperatures takes place during the 50 min stop about one o'clock. Furthermore it can be seen that the increase is biggest on the inking roller and a little less on the other rollers.

Figure 2 shows the rise of temperature on the bottom steel roller of a covered-in inking device in relation to the actual running time and the average speed during this period.

In none of these measurements has the width of the nip between the rubber covered and the steel rollers been measured. So-called normal setting has been used but the measured temperatures suggest that the nip pressure might have been rather high.

Figure 3 shows the influence of an enclosure on the rise of temperature of

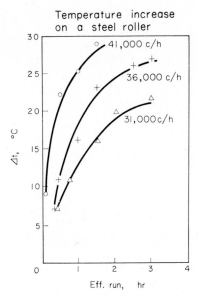

Fig. 2.

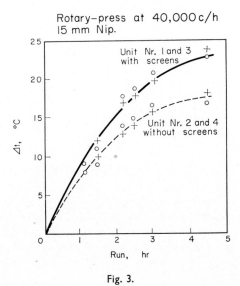

Fig. 3.

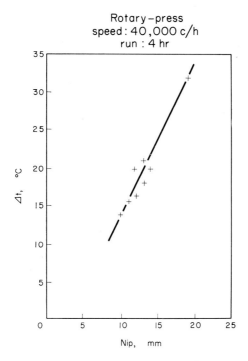

Fig. 4.

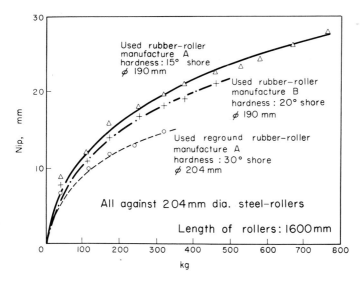

Fig. 5.

the inking roller when the width of the nip is adjusted to 15 mm before printing. The speed of the rotary press was 40,000 c/hr.

Finally Fig. 4 gives some measurements of the rise of temperature on the inking roller after 4 hr running at 40,000 c/hr using different starting widths of the nip. Unfortunately the measurements are rather few but the trend is unmistakable and does not justify further experiments which are rather destructive of rollers.

In order to find the correlation between the width of the nip and the load on a rubber covered roller of known Shore-hardness some rollers were

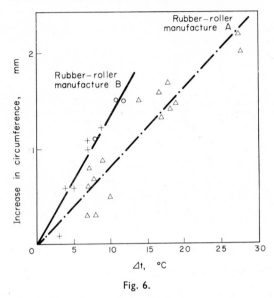

Fig. 6.

statically loaded and the corresponding width of the nip was measured. As Fig. 5 shows the impression increases markedly when the width of the nip exceeds 10 mm.

The increase of the circumference of the inking roller with rise of temperature was measured and is shown in Fig. 6.

In this particular press-room the Shore-hardness of the rubber rollers lies between 15 and 25° and the initial width of the nip between the inking roller and the steel roller is adjusted to 15 mm. As a rule it increases to 21–22 mm during the run, corresponding to a doubling of the initial pressure between the rollers. The radial impression increases simultaneously from 0·4 to 0·8 mm causing the column rules to cut into the inking roller.

This rise of temperature of the rollers during the run is likely to be to some extent self-intensifying because of the increasing width of the nip and the corresponding pressure increase between the various rollers.

From these investigations it might be concluded that it is possible to reduce the rise of temperature in the rollers of the inking device by keeping the width of the nip as small as possible, but a reduction of the coefficient of thermal

Fig. 7.

expansion might probably be most effective. The roller manufacturers state that the coefficient of thermal expansion of the rubber rollers lies between 1.5×10^{-4} and 2.5×10^{-4} °C^{-1}.

That a reduction of the rise of temperature of the rollers is advantageous in other respects is shown by the following:

First of all, the part of the total power consumption used by the inking devicess increases from *ca.* 40% at the start to *ca.* 50% during the run. This can probably be reduced.

Further, the rise of temperature causes a decrease in the flow of ink through the inking device during the run. By marking the adjusting ink screws it was found that they had to be opened half a turn during a 4 hr run at 40,000 c/hr causing a 20°C rise of temperature on the inking rollers. Figure 7 shows the

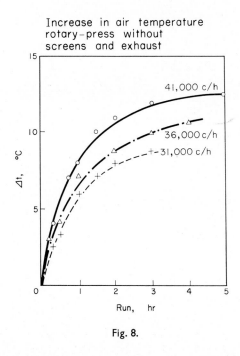

Fig. 8.

opposite regulation performed on a 25°C warm inking system. The drop in the blackness of the print is considerable.

The heat generated in the inking device during the run is partly removed by convection of the air between the two inking devices.

Figure 8 shows some measurements of the air-temperature between such two inking devices in relation to the running time and speed. The measurements were made with the dry bulb of an Assman psychrometer (Lambrecht, Göttingen) and reveal that these increases of temperature can be rather large if nothing is done to remove the heat. The wet bulb was also read but only a slight increase of about 0·8°C during the run was found here, corresponding to a decrease in the relative humidity from about 50% to about 25%. This will cause a loss of moisture from the paper during its passage through the unit.

In order to find out whether it was possible to prevent this by letting the paper pass through a humid zone before it ran between the inking devices of the unit, water-atomizers were placed in the roll stand space in such a way that the whole width of the paperweb for 2 m was subjected to 90% relative

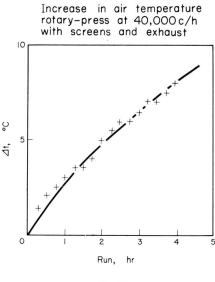

Fig. 9.

humidity just before it entered the unit. This was, however, ineffective. The effect of enclosing the inking system completely with screens both on the outside of the roller train and on the innermost side and drawing air through the channel at different speeds was noticeable.

Comparisons of Figs. 8 and 9 show that by exhausting at 300 m³/hr, the rise of temperature during the run is not as steep as without this exhaustion and screening, and the measured increase in the air-temperature is only about 8°C with exhaustion against 12°C without it. Unfortunately this exhaustion has no influence on the temperature of the rollers.

Following the methods of Voet,[4] tests were made on the effect of screening on the spread of ink-mist into the room. The screen was found merely to reduce the rate at which the mist escapes into the room.

It was found to be impossible to prevent the ink-mist from penetrating into the press-room by the screening alone.

However, by exhausting the space between the screens at 300 m³/hr about 95% of the ink-mist is kept from penetrating into the press-room. Finally an increase of the relative humidity around the inking device from 38% to 52% caused 80% decrease in the amount of ink-mist with the same ink and at the same speed.

Further tests of ink-misting were made comparing full screening with exhaustion with the effect of exhaustion without screens.

Such tests showed that even exhaustion without screens removed 80% of the ink-mist that otherwise would diffuse into the press-room.

Most of these results have been obtained through close co-operation between our Association and the Berlingske Tidende. I am grateful for this valuable support and for the permission to publish the results of a supplementary investigation carried out by the Berlingske Tidende.

Further I am indebted to A/S Sadolin and Holmbald for skilled assistance.

REFERENCES

1. G. Funk, Triebkraft und Drehmoment bei Hochdruck-Rotationsmaschinen; Ein Beitrag zur Theorie des Rollwiderstandes an Walzenpaaren. Deutsche Zentraldruckerei, Berlin SW. 11 (1938).
2. ANPA Mech. Bull. No. 524/54 and No. 656/58 and ANPA Res. Bull. No. 142/1957.
3. R. D. W. Miller, The nebulous nip, *PATRA J.* (1960).
4. A. Voet, Ink misting and its prevention, *Int. Bull. Printing and Allied Trades* No. 73 (1956).

DISCUSSION

Rogers: Have any measurements been made of the energy input to the drive of the inking system? These values will be helpful in providing a heat-balance for the system, and an understanding of the parts of the system into which the energy is dissipated.

Hunderup Jensen: Yes we have, but only for the presses in this printing office. As stated in my paper the fraction of the total power consumption of the press, which is used in the inking system, will increase from about 40% to about 50% during the run. Of course there will be a decrease in the total power consumption of the press during the run due to the heating of the lubrication in the bearings. This accounts for about 10% but as you see there will be a higher consumption of energy in the inking system at the stop than at the start which, as far as I can see, is caused by the increasing nip width and pressure between the rollers.

Reid: It is difficult to explain why the temperature of the steel roller and that of the rubber roller should increase at so nearly the same rate as shown in Fig. 1. Because of the huge difference in thermal capacity of the steel roller and the rubber one, it would be expected that the steel roller would lag thermally behind the rubber roller. Is it possible that the temperature-measuring system is showing only the temperature of the ink, and not of the rollers? It would be most interesting to make a heat-balance on the press to determine the exact distribution of energy in the inking system.

Hunderup Jensen: I quite agree that it might be difficult to explain the uniform temperature increase on the different rollers of an inking system as shown in Fig. 1. The only explanation I can offer is that such a system is not a simple one from a thermal transmission point of view. This can be illustrated by the following:

(1) In the nip both the ink film and the rubber roller generate heat which is transferred to the steel roller.

(2) All the rollers are covered by an ink film which will cause a huge reduction in the heat transmission to the surrounding air.

We expected that it would be possible to get rid of a large fraction of the heat generated in the rubber rollers during the run by increasing the exhaustion from the inking system. Therefore we increased the suction from 300 m³/hr to 1400 m³/hr. As a matter of fact we got no reduction in the temperature rise of the rollers.

The ink film is very thin on the rollers and I believe the ink temperature is the same as the surface temperature of the roller. It has been impossible to get differences higher than a fraction of a °C by wiping the ink film off the roller surface.

Nevertheless I think a heat balance study would be most interesting.

LARAIGNOU: Is the temperature difference you indicate in your report the difference between the ink temperature on the roller and the room temperature or is it the difference between the ink temperature on the roller and the temperature in the ink duct?

In fact you may have an increase of the temperature of the ink itself before it gets on the rollers due to the fact that the machine is getting warm.

HUNDERUP JENSEN: The ink duct on the press is continually supplied from a big tank containing a quantity varying from half a ton to 4 tons of ink the temperature of which is the same as the room temperature. I agree that the press is getting warmer during the run but the temperature rise is only a small fraction of that of the rollers. Therefore I think that the increase in temperature on the rollers during the run corresponds to the temperature rise in the ink from the duct to the ink film on the forme rollers.

MEASUREMENTS OF PAPER ELONGATIONS ON FAST RUNNING PAPER WEBS DURING PRESS RUN

by IB HUNDERUP JENSEN

The Joint Purchase Association of the Danish Newspress, Copenhagen, Denmark

AT THE PATRA conference for newspaper technicians (Harrogate, October 1957) Mr. N. J. E. Haglov presented a paper on web tension, reel stands and reel changing.[1] After having mentioned the investigations of the visco-elastic properties of newsprint, made by Professor B. Steenberg and his collaborators in 1947–50, the author briefly referred to the various brake devices for paper reels which are used on rotary presses, and how they work. Finally he concluded that it would be desirable to examine more closely the influence of the tension in the paper between the reel stand and the plate cylinder on the paper tension in the rest of the press.

As this is a very interesting question to which an answer—as far as I know—has not yet been given, I should like to mention some very preliminary investigations of paper elongations we have made on running rotary presses.

The first problem in such a measurement is to procure a measuring instrument with sufficient accuracy. As it is impossible mechanically to measure the length of a running paper web it was decided to print a pattern of lines 1.5×12 mm with about 610 mm intervals on a paper web, and then by means of phototubes measure the elongations at various tensions and speeds as differences of time.

The apparatus consists of 2 phototubes with a very narrow field of vision connected with an electronic measuring instrument which with precision can measure the differences of time when the printed marks are " seen " by the two tubes.

These phototubes are arranged in such a way that the marks arrive simultaneously if no elongation takes place, while the marks, in case of elongation, turn up too early before one of the phototubes.

The interval between the time the first mark passes the front tube to that when the second mark passes the rear tube depends on the paper elongation.

The apparatus consists of a rigid framework upon which is fixed two photomultipliers, connected with an optical system permitting a field of vision of 2·0 mm along and 60 mm across the paper web. The distance between them was 614·3 mm and this length is represented by *b*.

The electronic measuring apparatus consists of a condenser chronograph with a blocking box so that the chronograph normally is blocked and only operates when a pair of measuring marks passes. Thereafter it is automatically blocked again.

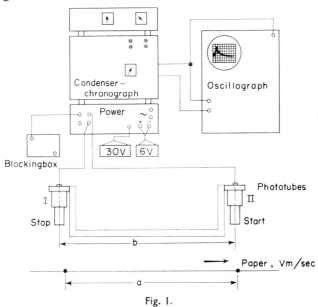

Fig. 1.

Furthermore a double beam oscillograph is connected so that the shape of the curve from the phototube signals can be studied as well as controlling and suppressing the electronic noise level if necessary. The arrangement is shown in Fig. 1.

The measured difference of time, Δt, is determined by the following equation:

$$\Delta t = \frac{(a + \Delta a) - b}{v} \text{ msec.}$$

a, is the distance in mm between the measuring marks in the unstrained paper.

Δa, is the elongation in mm.

b, is the basis length in mm.

v, is the paper speed in m/sec.

J

From this

$$\Delta a = v.\Delta t + b - a$$

From which the elongation can be determined knowing a, b, v and Δt.

V can be measured with sufficient precision either with the newspaper counter and a stop watch or with a stroboscope, while it is more difficult to obtain a sufficiently exactly.

By unrolling on a rewinder and controlling various parts of the reel we have found that the distance a varied from 610·9 mm to 608·2 mm, further that the mean value of a decreased slowly through the reel with a random distribution around the mean value and a maximum dispersion of 0·7 mm.

It was surprising that a varied as much as these measurements revealed. Further investigations have, however, shown that the marking out of a 5000 m/reel can be done with 0·3 mm as maximum dispersion on the distances between the marks. This of course will facilitate these measurements of paper elongations.

The first elongation measurements were carried out on a rewinder in a paper mill. This was done by marking out definite distances on the reel-ends of the unrolling reel where the mean length and the dispersion interval is measured, and then taking a sufficient number of measurements within these to calculate the mean value of Δt with adequate certainty. This can be done only if the dispersion of all other measurements is negligible.

The apparatus for time measurement has an uncertainty of ± 1 μsec. corresponding to an error of $\pm 0·01$ mm in $v.\Delta t$ when $v = 10$ m/sec. The measurement of v can be made within plus/minus 1 m/min, i.e. an error of $\pm 0·02$ mm on $v \times \Delta t$. Finally the measurement of b can be performed with an accuracy of 0·05 mm. Compared with this it is only possible to measure a with an exactness of 0·1 mm from an average of 25 measurements. This uncertainty is therefore dominant.

Table 1 gives some measurements and calculations of paper elongation at fairly constant paper tension for various speeds.

TABLE 1

a mm	b mm	v m/sec	Δt μsec	$v \times \Delta t$ mm	$b - a$ mm	Δa mm	Δa %	P kg/cm
609·5	614·3	3·33	−1110	3·7	4·8	1·1	0·180	0·8
610·2	614·3	4·16	− 701	2·9	4·1	1·2	0·195	0·8
610·4	614·3	5·0	− 509	2·6	3·9	1·3	0·215	0·8
608·5	614·3	5·8	− 769	4·5	5·8	1·3	0·215	0·8
608·6	614·3	6·67	− 649	4·3	5·7	1·4	0·230	0·8
608·4	614·3	7·5	− 594	4·5	5·9	1·4	0·230	0·8
608·2	614·3	8·3	− 550	4·6	6·1	1·4	0·230	0·8

Results from such measurements are graphed in Fig. 2 showing the interrelation between the elongation, the paper speed, and the paper tension.

After having ascertained the possibility of measuring the paper elongation at speeds of 30,000 c/h (4·65 m/sec) at which the paper is running in a rotary press, the apparatus was placed between the reel stand and the plate cylinder on a modern WIFAG-press, where the paper tension can be counter-balanced by a weight.

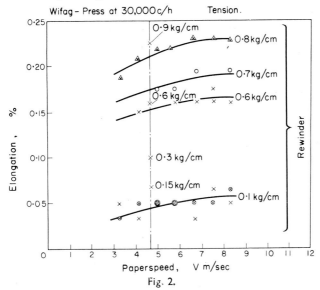

Fig. 2.

The elongation at constant speed at varying paper tension was measured— using the same paper as in the first series of measurements. Further, ordinary stereos were placed on the plate cylinder and from this printed paper web a folder made newspapers with an average length of 570·8 mm. For every level of tension a suitable number of newspapers was sampled for subsequent measurement. The values of the paper tension are given in Table 2 together

TABLE 2

	Before the plate cylinder				Measurement of the printed newspapers	
v m/sec	Δt μsec	Δa mm	Δa %	P kg/cm	Δc mm	Δc %
4·65	− 835	0·4	+ 0·067	0·15	− 0·9	− 0·160
4·65	− 800	0·6	+ 0·100	0·30	− 0·5	− 0·090
	− 712	1·0	+ 0·165	0·60	+ 0·02	+ 0·001
	− 644	1·3	+ 0·215	0·91	+ 0·2	+ 0·030

with the average elongation of a sample of 25 copies measured after the printing (Δc).

As can be seen from Table 2 the elongation takes place in the first section of the press caused by the brake tension, while a substantial part of this elongation seems to be " absorbed " in other places in the press, even resulting in a shortening of the paper when only small tensions are used.

It is, however, at present too early to say whether these observations generally hold true, but a continuation of the investigations is planned, and it is our intention also to measure the elongation caused by reel brakes before the plate-cylinder and the positive or negative elongation that takes place between the plate-cylinder and the folder.

I am indebted to Berlingske Tidende in Copenhagen and Holmens Bruks och Fabriks Aktiebolag in Norrköping for co-operation in this work.

DISCUSSION

CARLSSON: Is the contraction of the paper after the elongation only related to mechanical conditions or do you think that it is partially due to loss of moisture?

HUNDERUP JENSEN: As long as paper is stored in reels there will be no exchange of moisture between the paper in the different turns because moist paper is wound on top of moist paper and vice versa. In rewinding there will only be an exchange of moisture between the surface of the sheet and the surrounding air. Even if the moisture content of the paper is far from equilibrium with the relative humidity of the surrounding air most of the moisture in the interior of the sheet will be unaltered during the fraction of a second in which the paper passes from the unwinding to the rewinder or from the reelstand to the folder on a rotary press. Thus it is impossible to measure differences in the moisture content of the sheet before and after printing or rewinding with known measuring devices. Therefore, I think that the contractions given in Table 2 are only due to the mechanical conditions in the nip between the blanket and the plate cylinder during the printing.

POULTER: I should like to follow Mr. Carlsson's question on moisture content, by asking for a further explanation of the results in the last column of Table 2. I do not think the negative extension at low values of P so remarkable as the increase in extension with increase in P.

HUNDERUP JENSEN: If you plot the results given in Table 2 you will find that the curve showing the variation with speed of elongation under tension before the printing nip will be parallel with the curve connecting the change in length of the print after the folder and not under tension, and the curves will be displaced by about 0·175%. This corresponds to a contraction of 1 mm for a cut-off on the folder of 570·8 mm. This contraction is due to the mechanical conditions in the printing nip without any relation to the tension in the paper before this point. I think this is quite remarkable.

RHODES: You stated that the paper was wound and stored with uniform tension. How can this be done? Presumably the newsprint flows under tension and relaxes tension. Also, when newsprint is wound under constant tension, there exists a force component along the radius of the roll. Each wrap around the roll produces a small force, but the total force (force of one wrap × number of turns) must be very great. Such forces should compress the newsprint, thereby reducing the radius and circumference. This effect should tend to relax tension.

HUNDERUP JENSEN: Yes I did but I did not say that the tension under which the paper was wound is the same as the tension in the sheet in the stored reel. As far as we know up till now the fibre bonds will be drawn out in the first moment of tension and later will shift to a new position tending to reduce the tension and giving a flow. This has been known by papermakers for years. As an example of this, if a jumbo reel has been wound under too high a tension causing breaks in the rewinder, it is put aside for one or two days. From experience it is known that after this time the flow has caused a reduction in the tension of the sheet and the reel can be rewound safely.

Your question about the force component along the radius of the reel I can answer in this way. Every papermaker knows that a reel wound under uneven tension from the core of the outer sheet will be wavy where it is loosely wound. Further it is known that if a reel is wound from a sheet with an uneven thickness across the sheet the diameter of the reel will be small where the paper is thin causing a reduction in length of the sheet at these places during the store. Also it is known that paper, due to the tension in the sheet when stored in reels, will show a reduction in surface roughness and an increase in surface hardness.

RHODES: Do you have stress-strain information for loading speeds?

HUNDERUP JENSEN: Yes, we have. In the measurements on the rewinder referred to in my paper we also tried to split the elongation up into a reversible and an irreversible part by different speeds of the sheet. The result was that of a total elongation of 0·22% caused by a tension of 0·8 kg/cm paper width about 0·14% was reversible and 0·08% was irreversible.

INFLUENCE OF PACKING OF THE CYLINDER PRESS ON PRINT QUALITY

by Dr. P. FINK

Eidg. Materialprüfungs- und Versuchsanstalt, St. Gallen, Switzerland (EMPA-C)

INTRODUCTION

A number of materials are used for the packings of cylinder presses in the letterpress process. For the man in the pressroom it is often very difficult to decide whether a new material brings him the success hoped for. There are also quite different opinions about the usefulness of a given packing. So the Swiss printers were searching for a method for the characterization of a cylinder packing and also wanted to know whether it was necessary for good print quality to use so many different cylinder dressings. A certain standardization in the field of cylinder packing is the aim of this work.

The first step in this direction was a study of the function of the packing and the development of an appropriate test method. As a further step the printing results with quite different cylinder packings were compared, and also the effect of makeready on printing pressure was studied by these test methods. The main function of the packing is the regulation of printing pressure. In a certain way the packing is an element of the press, but the printer can adapt it to his needs. With the packing the printer can give the cylinder the necessary hardness or softness, and the elasticity too may be improved by an appropriate packing. The regulation of printing pressure by the cylinder packing is to increase the contact between the forme and the paper. Little variations in the thickness of the paper or the forme have to be equalized. The packing has to be an elastic element between the rigid elements of the press (cylinder and bed). The possibility of building up the cylinder packing separately allows the printer to adapt his press to the forme to be printed and to the paper. So, the composition of a packing may be determined mainly by the press and the forme (faces, types, blocks).

Another function of the packing is to take up the makeready, which allows a local variation of the pressure. Here it is important that the packing materials allow localized printing pressures.

A short summary of the testing methods is given in this report and the results of printing experiments with different cylinder packings are discussed.

TESTING OF CYLINDER PACKINGS

For an informative characterization of a cylinder dressing it is necessary to test various properties. Of course, the static and dynamic measurement of printing pressure is very important, but they do not give all the information needed. Attempts were made to replace tiresome and costly pressure-measurements on the running press by appropriate printing experiments. This method has the advantage of being used by any printer on his presses without a lot of testing apparatus. The single components needed for building up a packing were tested for only some important properties, whilst most tests were made on the packing as one unit. Only the top layer of the packing has to conform to special tests.

Testing of single components of the packing

Thickness. The thickness and also thickness variations in one sheet are very important qualities for the characterization of packing components. Measurements on a number of materials (paper, plastic, board, blanket, special materials) showed that the materials normally used have variations in thickness between 5 and 10% of their average thickness.

Elongation and recovering power after elongation. Strips of the materials are given a certain load and the elongation is measured. Afterwards the load is taken off and after some time the length of the unloaded strip is measured again. So the elastic and the plastic deformation of the material can be assessed. This test affords additional information about the behaviour of plastic and other special materials. It shows how much a given material can deform and recover in the direction of the circumference of the cylinder.

Additional tests on the top layers. It was found that the friction coefficient between the top layer and the paper to be printed is important. High friction between the paper and the packing brings difficulties in printing, especially slur. Experiments have shown that smooth papers normally have higher friction coefficients. The relatively high frictions between smooth papers and certain plastic or special packing components explain to a certain extent the printing difficulties caused by such materials as top layers.

The resistance of the top layers to different washing and cleaning solutions has to be tested.

A further test gives some information about the tendency to electrostatic charging of the packing and the printed sheets.

Testing of the cylinder packing

Cylinder packings are built up of several components which influence one another and, according to their position in the whole packing, have a more or less distinct effect on the properties of the packing. The relations between the properties of the single components and those of the whole cylinder dressing are very complex and it is therefore much easier to test the behaviour of the packing as one unit for getting the required information.

Compressibility. This important property is determined by the thickness of the packing as a function of the pressure. Such diagrams, where the thickness of a packing is plotted against the pressure of measurement, give much more information than only one compressibility factor, which depends very much on the measuring conditions.

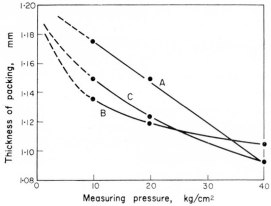

Fig. 1. Compressibility diagram of cylinder packings.

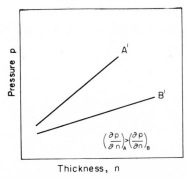

Fig. 1a.

Figure 1 shows some compressibility curves. Packing *A* containing different paper sheets and a blanket, and representing a usual composition, has a linear curve showing that at between 1 and 40 kg/cm² the loss of thickness is proportional to the pressure. Packing *B* contains 2 plastic sheets and a blanket and gives a characteristic curve for a packing which can be compressed to a relatively high extent under very little pressure, but is less compressible as the pressure is increased. At pressures normally used in printing such a packing has only a poor compressibility. Packing *C* is a composition recommended for mixed printing formes and lies between the samples *A* and *B*.

Comparing packings of different thickness it is important to know the absolute values of compressibility in mm and not the percentage loss in thickness. For the regulation of the printing pressure and to accommodate local high pressures* one must know how much the cylinder packing is compressed by a given pressure or which pressure is obtained if the packing has to be compressed by a certain amount.

For choosing appropriate makeready it is advantageous to know the compressibility curve. Thus, for example, an increase by makeready in the thickness of the packing giving an increase in printing pressure within the range of 30 to 40 kg/cm^2 will cause a larger increase in printing pressure with packing *B* than with packing *A*.

Hardness. The Shore-D-hardness was determined. This test does not give as much information as the compressibility diagram. The curves show that—with some exceptions—the compressibility is not proportional to the pressure. The measurement of hardness being made only under a well-defined pressure therefore gives only one point on the curve. The determination of Shore-D-hardness of the packings *A*, *B* and *C* gave the following results:

Packing	Shore-D-Hardness
A	77
B	66·5
C	73·5

These results show that corresponding conclusions cannot always be obtained from the compressibility diagram and the Shore-D-hardness. Packing *B* is soft in accordance with the Shore-D-hardness, but the compressibility diagram shows that packing *B* is hard in the range of normal printing pressures.

Static printing pressure. With the aid of a strain gauge measuring-head the pressure of the cylinder on the bed was determined when the press was

* B^1 is better than A^1 because accidental change in *n* can be accommodated (Überspannung).

still. This can be done before the beginning of the run, but measurements made after running are interesting too. Therefore the static printing pressure was determined in different sections of the forme corresponding to a 30%, 60% and 100% tone-value after a run of 2000 copies. Such measurements on various packings showed a quite different behaviour of the packings. Some results are given in Fig. 2.

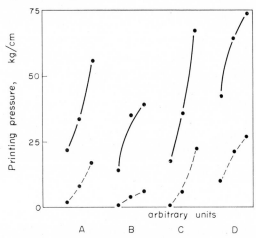

Fig. 2. Static pressure measurements after a run of 2000 copies using packings A, B, C, D. Pressure for correct printing of the 30%, 60% and 100% tone-value with (full line) and without (dotted line) printing sheet of 0·08 mm. The 3 points of each curve represent, reading left to right, 30%, 60%, 100% tone-values.

For good quality printing quite different pressures are needed for each tone-value with the different packings. Pressures between 0 and 40 kg/cm are found for the 30% value. The 60% value needs between 35 and 65 kg/cm and the 100% value between 40 and 80 kg/cm.

Further, the influence of one paper sheet (paper to be printed) on the pressure is of interest. A sheet of 0·08 mm raised the pressure differently at the 3 tone-values ; on the average it was found

for the   30% value   18 kg/cm pressure increase
for the   60% value   32 kg/cm pressure increase
for the 100% value   40 kg/cm pressure increase.

Additional tests. Other tests for characterizing a packing are the determination of elasticity, for instance the rebounding way of a ball. The formation of electrostatic charge can be measured also on the running cylinder.

Influence of makeready. The local increase of thickness and pressure by makeready is studied. The position of the makeready is also important for the pressure increase on the packing surface, but it is better to study this point by practical printing experiments. Thickness measurements at different pressures on packings containing overlay of definite thickness have been made. Figure 3 gives the results of such determinations.

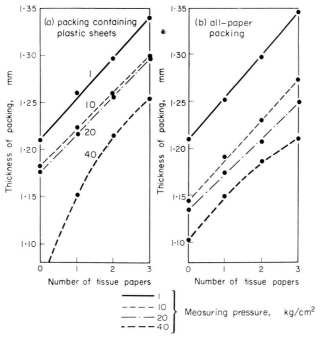

Fig. 3. Influence of an overlay of tissue paper on the thickness of packings at various pressures.

Thin tissue-papers (0·043 mm thickness) were laid in the packing and the increase of thickness was measured. It is seen that the packing containing plastic sheets is much harder than an all-paper packing at higher printing pressures; that means that makeready has much more effect on the plastic sheet packing than on the all-paper packing.

Printing tests

A printing test combined with some measurements allows a very comprehensive evaluation of a packing. On a cylinder automat a printing forme made up as shown in Fig. 4 was used.

The long halftone-field affords a measure of the print length. Between different papers there are marked differences. Very poor fidelity of length reproduction occurred with packings with plastic sheets uppermost. In these

cases there is also a tendency to slur. A further test is needed to get information about the pressure-regulating power of the packing. The press is
adjusted for a paper of 100 g/m². Prints are now made on papers of different

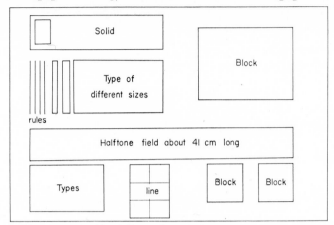

Fig. 4. Forme for printing tests.

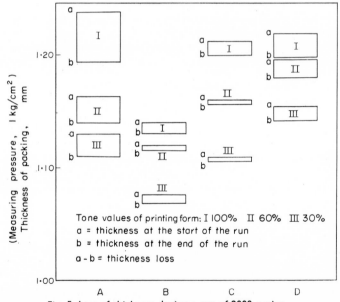

Tone values of printing form: I 100%   II 60%   III 30%
a = thickness at the start of the run
b = thickness at the end of the run
a - b = thickness loss

Fig. 5. Loss of thickness during a run of 2000 copies.

weights and the fidelity of reproduction as well as the printing quality are
evaluated. Printing experiments gave some relations between this regulation
power and the compressibility curves. It is found that packings with steep
compressibility curves are better able to equalize minor aberrations.

Of course, the print-quality is evaluated too. Here especially the long halftone field affords a very good measure of the tendency to slur.

The loss of thickness during the run is also compared for the different tone-values. Figure 5 shows diagrammatically the relative thickness losses of some packings after a run of 2000 copies.

The results show marked differences between the packings. Packings having a high loss of thickness should be constructed more elastically, so that the deformations during printing may recover.

PRINTING EXPERIMENTS WITH VARIOUS PACKINGS
Influence of thickness of packing in the printing process

3 packings were tested:

packing D: paper sheets and 1 blanket

packing E: 2 different plastic sheets (one as uppermost layer) 1 blanket, paper sheets

packing F paper sheets and special samples.

The compressibility curves of these 3 packings are given in Fig. 6 for a thickness of 1·20 mm. These diagrams show that packing D has a compressibility which is nearly linear with pressure in the range of 10 to 40

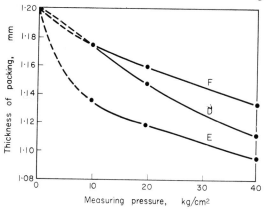

Fig. 6. Compressibility diagram of cylinder packings D, E and F.

kg/cm². The packings E and F are harder in this range, but they are quite different from each other in behaviour between 1 and 10 kg/cm², where sample E has a very high compressibility.

Static pressure-measurements by the strain gauge method on packings of an original thickness of 1·00 mm increasing by steps of + 0·04 mm to 1·20 mm gave different printing pressures for each packing. Figure 7 gives the results of these experiments, which show that packing D is softer than F and E. Makeready in packing D will not increase the pressure so much as the same makeready does in *F* or *E*. Printing experiments confirmed this conclusion. These experiments show that the effect of a given makeready can be very different according to the packing it is built in. It is necessary that the printer consider the type of packing within close limits of thickness. Diagrams like Fig. 6 or 7 may give him the required information for pressure regulation.

The position of an overlay in the packing is also an important factor. Two types were used in the packings: MKZ-overlay of 0·08 to 0·14 mm

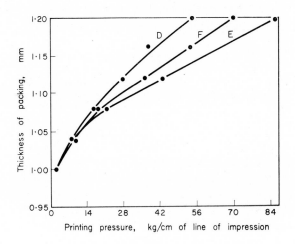

Fig. 7. Printing pressure as a function of the thickness of the cylinder dressings
D, E, F.

and a tissue-paper overlay of 4 thicknesses from 0·08 to 0·20 mm. The MKZ was prepared for different type sizes while the tissue-paper overlay was taken for printing a solid.

The printing experiment gave the following results:

Packing *F* always showed the best effect of the overlay, followed by packing *D*. With packing *E* type matter is thickened and not so sharp as with the other packings. The position of the overlay always has the same effect.

An overlay in the lower parts of the packing gives a broader and less sharp reproduction of the type matter and the 4 steps of the tissue-paper overlay are also not so sharp. Small defects in the overlay or the steps in a tissue-paper overlay have little effect on the print. An overlay in the upper parts gives a very sharp and clear reproduction and is more effective. The results show that the position of the overlay and the type of packing have an influence on the effect of a given overlay. Thus a characterization of a packing is possible by such simple tests which can help the printer.

After removing the overlays, printing experiments showed that the packings *D* and *F* had deformed permanently, while packing *E* showed no essential permanent deformation. This confirms other experiments, which showed that packing *E* had a better elastic recovery than the other two. Sample *E* was less deformed after a run of 2000 copies than the samples *D* and *F*.

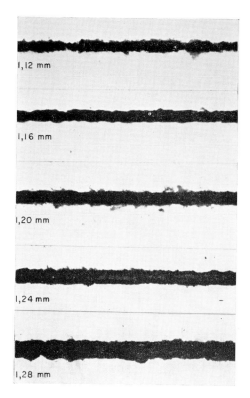

Fig. 8. Reproduction of a fine face with various thicknesses of cylinder packing *E*. Thickness of packing inclusive of printing sheet of 0·08 mm: magnification 60 ×.

The relation between the print quality and the thickness of the cylinder dressings was studied by some printing experiments. A forme containing rules, types of different sizes and blocks of different tone-values was printed with packings of various thickness. Some results may illustrate the usefulness of these experiments.

A very fine rule (0·04 mm), one of 2 points and one of 12 points were printed at various thickness of dressing and the precision of the reproduction was evaluated by measuring the breadth of the printed rules and by examination with a microscope. Figure 8 shows the influence of an increase of packing thickness on the rule reproduction. The control for the breadth of the rules shows that with the correct packing for good printing all rules have the same breadth, independent of the type of packing. The reproduction of the types is seen in Fig. 9. The sharpness of the reproduction depends on the packing. So sample *F* gives a very clear image.

The influence of the packing-thickness on the halftone-dot reproduction is shown in Fig. 10. A 20% tone value is printed with packing *E* of 1·04 mm

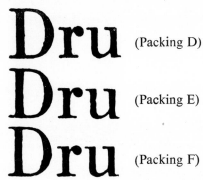

Fig. 9. Reproduction of types by 3 different packings. Magnification 20 ×. Types—6-point size.

Thickness of packing	1·08 mm
Thickness of paper	0·08 mm
Total thickness	1·16 mm

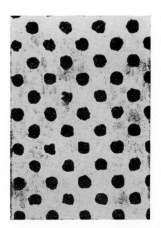 

Fig. 10. Influence of printing pressure on halftone dot reproduction. Print with packing *E* on halftone paper, 48 metric screen, 20% tone-value, magnification 60 ×.

1·04 mm	Thickness of packing	1·12 mm
0·08 mm	Thickness of paper	0·08 mm
1·12 mm	Total thickness	1·20 mm

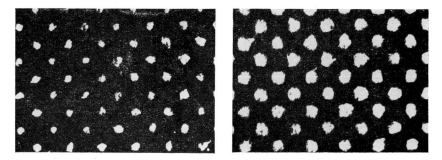

Packing D

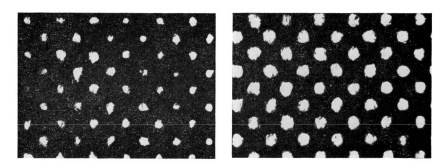

Packing E

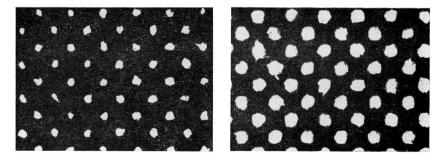

Packing F

Fig. 11. Halftone-dot reproduction by 3 different cylinder packings. 48 metric screen, magnification: 60 ×.

80% tone-value		60% tone-value	
Thickness of packing	1·16 mm	Thickness of packing	1·12 mm
Thickness of paper	0·08 mm	Thickness of paper	0·08 mm
Total thickness	1·24 mm	Total thickness	1·20 mm

K

TABLE 1. CORRECT THICKNESS OF CYLINDER PACKING FOR REPRODUCTION OF VARIOUS PRINTING ELEMENTS

Thickness of packing	Correct printing of		
	Packing D	Packing E	Packing F
1·00 mm	Dotted rule and fine faces	Dotted rule	Dotted rule and fine faces
1·04 mm	20% tone-value	Fine lines, 20% tone-value	20% tone-value, medium face
1·08 mm	Medium face 6-point and 12-point types 40% tone-value	Medium face 6-point and 12-point types 40% tone-value	6-point types
1·12 mm	2-point face 24-point and 48-point types 60% tone-value	2-point face 24-point and 48-point types 60% tone-value	2-point face 12-, 24- and 48-point types 40% tone-value
1·16 mm	6- and 12-point face 72-point types 80% tone-value and solid	6- and 12-point face 72-point types 80% tone-value and solid	6- and 12-point face 72-point types 60%, 80% tone-values, solid

and 1·12 mm thickness. By increasing the thickness (or pressure) the dots become larger. This test determines the correct thickness of packing for the various tone values and type-sizes. Table 1 gives the correct packing thickness for various elements of a printing forme, and in Table 2 the printing pressures are measured for the 3 packings tested and the various elements of a forme.

Table 1 shows that there are no very marked differences between the 3 packings. Only packing *F* needs greater thicknesses for halftone-reproductions in the 40% and 60% tone-values. Visual inspection of the prints showed that all packings work satisfactorily with 1·16 mm, except for the 20% tone-value. A thickness of 1·20 mm results in all cases in an over-pressure. Working with 1·16 mm, the pressure for the 20% value is not so marked when printing with packing *D*, which is to be expected from the compressibility diagram.

Table 2 shows that the hard packings need more pressure than soft ones. Therefore packing *E* gives, at the same thickness, a much higher pressure than packing *D*, and sample *F* lies between the two (see also Fig. 7).

TABLE 2. CORRECT PRINTING PRESSURE FOR THE REPRODUCTION OF VARIOUS
PRINTING ELEMENTS

Packing	Printing pressure in kg/cm for						
	Fine faces	Types		Halftone (48 metric screen)			Solid
		6-point	24-, 48-point	20%	40%	80%	
D	3	15	27	7–8	15	39	39
E	6	22	42	7–8	22	62	62
F	3	18	37	7–8	26	53	53

Finally the photomicrographs of Fig. 11 show the reproduction of halftone-dots by 3 tested cylinder dressings. The sharpness of reproduction is influenced by the packing. Thus sample *F* gives a very sharp reproduction, but small defects in the forme or makeready are also reproduced. Sample *E* has a slight tendency to slur, which can also be seen from the photomicrographs.

These experiments have shown the effect which certain properties of a cylinder dressing can have on the printing result.

PRINT QUALITY EVALUATION

A standardization of cylinder packings should attempt to reduce the great variety of packing compositions. It was therefore important to know the influence of quite different cylinder dressings on the printed results.

A combined forme containing types, faces, halftone blocks and line blocks was printed on a cylinder automat (Original Heidelberg cylinder automat) with 5 different packings. Without any special preparations, but with the usual care, it was printed on a smooth halftone paper. The packings had quite different components:

Packing G: top manilla sheet, 1 blanket and paper sheets.

Packing H: top tympan sheet, 1 blanket and paper sheets.

Packing I: all paper packing.

Packing K: soft packing with plastic sheets, top: plastic sheet and another plastic sheet in the packing.

Packing L: hard packing with plastic sheets, 2 plastic sheets of the same quality at the top.

In a second experiment a forme containing tables and types was printed on a book paper, using the cylinder packings H, I and L. Here too it was made ready and printed in the usual way without any special preparations.

In both cases, the press and packings were adjusted in such a way that the printer felt that he was working under the best conditions for good print quality. The prints were then examined by 50 letterpress-printers by the pair comparison method. Very obvious differences could not be detected, either between the 5 prints of the first forme or between the 3 prints of the second forme.

The estimation of the print quality by the pair comparison method, where the quality-points given by all 50 observers were summed, gave the following results:

Prints with a combined forme:

Packing G: 213 quality-points.

Packing H: 190 quality-points.

Packing I: 233 quality-points.

Packing K: 242 quality-points.

Packing L: 112 quality-points.

37 observers estimated the prints as good, 9 as satisfactory and 4 as medium.

Prints with a forme containing types and tables:

Packing H: 116 quality-points

Packing I: 71 quality-points.

Packing L: 113 quality-points.

39 observers estimated the prints as good, 3 as satisfactory and 8 as medium.

These results show that all of the 5 packings tested, which were estimated by the printers to be essentially different from one another, give good print quality and show no very marked quality differences. A more critical quality estimation shows that for the printing of a combined forme the packing L

gives inferior results. The common packings *G* and *H* give good results and are not very different from each other. The good result of the all-paper packing is surprising and is rated with 233 points—slightly higher than the samples *G* and *H*. Packing *K*, a special combination for such formes, had the most quality points, but was estimated only very slightly better than the all-paper packing.

For the reproduction of tables and type matter all 3 cylinder dressings tested can be used too. A more critical quality estimation shows here that the all-paper packing *I* was estimated as inferior to the others. Packings *H* and *L* are considered equal.

The results of these printing experiments showed clearly that it is possible to do good work with only a few standard cylinder packings, which simplifies the work very much. Significant quality differences cannot be seen between prints from different packings.

It is to be concluded from these experiments that the printer should choose his packings in relation to certain properties of the packing, but that cylinder packings should afterwards be reduced to a few standard types. The use of a great variety of different packing materials and combinations adapted to individual runs brings no advantage and complicates the work in the press-room.

SUMMARY

A test method comprising tests on single components and on the whole of cylinder packings by the way of printing experiments is described. These tests make it possible to characterize a packing in different ways, especially the compressibility behaviour in various ranges of printing pressure. The effect of makeready and the fidelity of reproduction too are important characteristics. The printing pressure need only be determined on the stationary press. All tests are simple and need no complicated testing equipment. Many of these tests can be made by the printer.

The influence of the cylinder dressing on the printing process and especially on the print quality was studied. The pressure correction by an overlay depends on the compressibility behaviour of the packing and of the forme to be reproduced. The correct thickness of the cylinder packing and the printing pressures for good printing are determined for various elements of a printing forme. The influence of the packing on the reproduction of faces, types, halftones and solids is demonstrated also by photomicrographs.

Finally it is shown, by 2 printing tests with 5 and 3 packings, that the influence of the packing composition on the print quality is not great. Good printing results were obtained on the same paper with very different cylinder dressings from the same forme. Therefore a reduction of packings to a few standard types is proposed.

DISCUSSION

LASSEUR: The main conclusion of your paper is that packing composition does not have a large influence on print-quality, but what is your opinion about the influence of the cylinder packing on forme-wear?

FINK: We have not studied this matter since our printing tests never involved runs of more than 2000 copies so that no significant wear could be observed. I think that the packing may have such an influence. We found that for good printing we needed approximately the same thicknesses of packing but that these thicknesses correspond to quite different printing pressures (see Tables 1 and 2). Thus it is likely that packings needing a higher printing pressure for good reproduction of the forme will also result in greater wear.

PASZKIEWICZ: Can you say if there is any correlation between experiments made on a proof press and on a letterpress, in regard to the different properties shown by a packing?

FINK: The experiments mentioned in the paper were made on a Heidelberg cylinder automat with runs of up to two thousand sheets. We have not verified our results on a proof press because the conditions are different from those used in practice.

PASZKIEWICZ: One of the most important characteristics of a packing is the resistance to permanent deformations during a long run. Have you made any studies of this point?

FINK: We intend to study the matter with the help of a printer who will provide practical results obtained from a long run. In this way we shall compare packings from the viewpoint of constancy of characteristics. Standardization of packings will not be possible before such studies have been carried out.

BANKS: How did you measure the coefficients of friction?

FINK: We measured the friction using the inclined plane principle. The packing was fixed to the plane and by slowly increasing the angle of inclination of the plane the angle at which a paper sample just began to move under load was measured.

FRØSLEV-NIELSEN: I would like to ask Dr. Fink if it is possible and valuable to supplement the compressibility measurements with measurements of the flexibility of the packing. This flexibility may influence the printing of adjacent elements in a forme. This influence is not obviously taken into account by compressibility measurements.

FINK: The testing methods reported can supply information on this point. The study of the influence of makeready on the printing result will show how far and in what manner a local increase of packing thickness by makeready will be transferred to the printing surface. Especially through variations in the position of the makeready on the packing it is possible to discover whether the effect of makeready is very clearly localized or not. In our experiments packing F gave a very sharp transfer of the local thickness increase in the presence of makeready. Whether at the top or bottom of the packing, this results in a good reproduction of the printing forme without broadening of lines or halftone dots.

SOME REQUIREMENTS FOR LETTERPRESS PRINTING PLATES USED IN HIGH-SPEED PRINTING

by Marvin C. Rogers

Photoengravers Research Institute, Flossmoor, Ill.

IN THIS paper we shall be concerned primarily with physical characteristics of letterpress printing plates intended for use on modern rotary presses producing multi-color reproductions at relatively high rates of speed. We shall further limit this discussion to the printing of publications or similar printed matter, on coated paper, or other paper having a relatively high finish. The printing inks used for this kind of printing process may be any of the usual typographic ink formulations, but where perfecting equipment is used, the inks usually will be of the heat-setting variety, where drying is accomplished through evaporation of solvents from the inks as they rest on the paper after printing.

Modern high speed production imposes many rigorous requirements on the printing plate. In principle at least, these same requirements are also placed on plates for slower operations, but they do not carry the same importance. High quality work from sheet-fed presses must be done with well made engravings just as they are required for rotary press work. The attainment of high quality reproduction on high speed equipment, requires the utmost in skill, control, and engineering understanding.

Broadly speaking, high speed printing done on rotary equipment, and using heat-setting inks, places some obvious requirements on the plates from which the printing is to be done.

1. Letterpress Engravings—the engravings used as the original plates for this work must, of course, be so prepared that halftone areas represent the original subject. These requirements are assumed, and are obvious to the reader.

   In addition, engravings must be capable of being readily molded for the electroforming processes in Electrotype manufacture. Details of these special requirements are discussed later.

2. Duplicate plates, such as electrotypes, must be capable of reproducing the images contained in the original engraving, but in addition, they must have physical characteristics i.e. strength, dimensional accuracy, and wear resistance, sufficient to withstand the loads imposed on them by the presses on which they are used.

3. The original plates and their duplicates must be capable of producing an acceptable result when printing four colors " wet." These are broad requirements, and cover many characteristics of the printing plates.

The study of these requirements by a theoretical approach, or through controlled laboratory experimental work, becomes extremely complicated and time consuming. Such an approach must contain elements of the many printability factors such as rheology, paper surface, printing pressures and similar partially indeterminate factors; physics, chemistry, and physical chemistry of original platemaking (engraving); and the chemistry and physics of duplicate platemaking. One must also add the mechanics of the printing operation at the printing presses. So far, as is known no one has attempted any such single comprehensive program, but there have been many separated and isolated attempts to study a part of the problem, most of which have never reached the stage of publication.

The writer has been a supporter of those who would examine the " practical results " obtained under uncontrollable but average production conditions, and then attempt correlation or decision based on the theoretical examination of a practical problem. In most commercial situations, this is the only solution to the important and immediate problems. It does have disadvantages, but it gets at the heart of the problems and many times the causes for failure of the work to meet quality requirements are rather quickly determined by this semi-empirical approach.

Some of the disadvantages are related to the uncertainties of uncontrollable experiments, and the disproportionate amount of effort which is required by the scientist or engineer making the study. The advantages however are great, since it is by this method that optimum conditions are ultimately attained through trial and error methods, and in production work, all of the subjective controls on quality and skilled effort are in effect. Production equipment producing saleable work must be operated in a manner such as to produce the best result possible. Even though the number of variables is great, the likewise high number of trials made under production conditions compensates partially for them.

The majority of the requirements for printing plates discussed in this paper have been determined under production conditions, and they represent very closely the optimum properties possible from existing materials. In most instances, it would be difficult by any theoretical approach to arrive at specification values.   It is for these reasons that this paper should have some value in a conference of printing research workers.

PHOTOENGRAVED RELIEF PRINTING PLATES

The most important single factor in determining the ultimate quality of the printed letterpress result is related to the quality of the photoengraved plates used by the printer.   It is assumed that the printing surface areas will reproduce the original subject, and we shall devote no attention to color separation, tone rendition, or halftone theory here.   Our prime concern is with physical character of the printing plate.   In this respect, there is no difference between any of the processes for printing, since each is expected to reproduce copy as closely as is theoretically and practically possible with the inks and other materials available.

As a practical matter, the proper transfer of printing ink from the press plate to paper, and the ability of the printer to produce uniformly high quality reproductions from a set of letterpress engravings, depends on physical phenomena, control over which may only be attained through the proper construction of the printing plate.   As a basis for discussion here, a portion of the specified qualities of engravings for use in United States publications is given below.   These are based on the data in Report No. 4[1] of the AAAA-MPA Joint Committee on Magazine Advertising, and it is believed that they were developed largely from experiences over nearly twenty years of quality printing on machine-coated papers using heat-setting inks.   Portions only, of these specifications are given here, because some of them bear no relation to the problems being discussed.

(a) Screen ruling—120-line screens have been found to be very satisfactory for both coated and super-calendered paper.   (Some publications specify the use of 133 line yellow plates.)

(b) Etching depth—see Table 1 below:

TABLE 1.

Ruling	Depth					
	Highlights		Middletones		Shadows	
lines/in.	μ	in.	μ	in.	μ	in.
100	96·5	0·004	66·0	0·003	45·7	0·002
110	88·9	0·004	61·0	0·002	40·6	0·002
120	81·3	0·003	55·9	0·002	38·1	0·002
133	73·7	0·003	50·8	0·002	35·6	0·001

(c) " Shoulders " and undercutting of halftone dots must not be present. High connectors between dots must be avoided.

(d) Hand correction by burnishing or tooling must be minimized or carefully done.

(e) Plate area total for four colors must not exceed 240%, and only one solid color plate should be used. Maximum screen density for any single color should not exceed 85%.

(f) Vignetted edges should be used sparingly.

(g) Powderless etched plates should not be etched excessively deep. (No specific depths are stated.)

Examination of these requirements reveals several points, each suggesting to the experimental worker that the satisfactory plate cannot be produced, or that the specifications have no scientific basis. Those with experience in examining engravings will usually agree with this concept, because seldom are plates made which meet all of these requirements, but their effect on the industry has been good.

It was requirements such as those reported above that were responsible for the incentive to development of powderless etching processes such as the Dow-Etch,* and PERI-Etch† (Jones—U.S. Patent 2, 746, 848).

High quality halftone engravings for letterpress printing in the United States are produced on copper. This is true almost 100% with color plates, and to a large extent with the single color engravings. A major requirement in the United States is that these engravings must usually be molded and duplicated by the electrotyping process which requires a durable material. Newspaper color must be matted and stereo types produced from them.

The Jones† method of powderless etching of copper involves the addition of thiourea to an iron chloride etching bath, and the use of the bath under controlled conditions of temperature, paddle speed, and time. Halftones of 120-line ruling are etched in 22 min to a depth of 0,0025 in., with virtually no loss in surface area. Sidewalls are vertical, and undercutting seldom takes place. Modifications of the thiourea bath, not yet revealed because of patent applications, permit etching of line work (type and line illustrations) to 0·020 in. in 17 min, with no powdering with fusible powder required. Some typical conditions for halftone etching require a machine paddle speed of 500 rev/min, temperature of 78°F, 30°Be iron chloride, and approximately 2 g of protective additive per liter.

Shoulder problems do not exist when this etching method is used, and consequently, the molding of powderless etched plates results in few of the former defects, but the straight sidewalls sometimes make it difficult to remove the molding materials from the original engraving. In powder etched plates, when shoulders are present, slight variations in the impression on the plates during printing result in the shoulders contacting the paper,

* Dow Chemical Co., Midland, Michigan.
† Photoengravers Research Inst., Flossmoor, Ill. Laboratory at Park Forest, Ill.

and excessive color results. The same result is produced with the high connectors between halftone dots. These connectors are not present in powderless etched plates, and hence give no difficulties. In many cases, connectors have been found to be less than 0·001 in. below the printing surface. Such proximity to the printing surface is certain to result in color variation, and in the irregular printing at the junction between the connected and disconnected halftone dots of a halftone.

Similar problems result from vignetted edges, largely as a result of the " bear-off " phenomenon recognized by Carlsson and his co-workers* in their work on the influence of adjacent halftone dots on the pressures resulting from impression of printing plates against paper.

The wide application of multi-color wet printing has shown that uniformity in solid or heavy tonal areas requires that the ink distribution be controlled through use of limited total plate area in contact with the paper. The selection of a total plate area for the four printing plates, over any given part of the page, of 240% represents an arbitrary selection based on experience. Theoretically, this limitation need not be present, but to this date, trapping of inks is not sufficiently understood to permit or to obtain 100% trapping of four colors in wet printing. The limitation to 85% screen tends to improve the result by printing semi-gravure, and thus attaining a uniform layer of ink.

Careful study and comparison of the etching depth specifications with the average value of 120-line highlights, will show that etch depth is more nearly 0·0025 in. in practice, than the 0·003 in. shown in Table 1. The specifications have likely been adopted with the intent of emphasizing the need for depth, by asking for more than is attained readily. This technique is common for non scientists. However, it is usually impossible to attain an etch factor† which permits the specified etching depth, without resorting to powderless etching, or " powder bites " for deep etching when conventional iron chloride is used.

The improved engraving properties brought about through powderless etching by the Dow and PERI processes, have tended to eliminate the defects noted in the magazine publisher' specifications. Work carried out at the laboratory of Photoengravers Research Institute on powderless etching has made it possible to obtain copper relief images with no shoulders and with excellent molding surfaces, as shown in the illustrations. The line and halftone characters are obtained by etching in 30°Be iron chloride, using the additives.

* C. Carlsson, Swedish Graphic Arts Laboratory.

$$\dagger \text{ Etch factor} = \frac{\text{Depth of etch}}{\text{Lateral image loss}}$$

The undercut halftone has been mentioned, but not emphasized. This type of dot is not objectionable when the plate is to be printed direct, but when it is to be reproduced, then the overhang on the dot is either destroyed in molding, along with the color value represented by surface area, or the mold will not release, and the plate is lost. Frequently, when undercut dots are found after molding, it will be observed that the electrotype dot is smaller and has rough sidewalls.

ELECTROTYPE PLATES

Electrotype plates produced by duplicating the engravings, are among the most critical of the raw materials used by a printer. It is essential that the characters on the originals have tapered walls, and that every property lend itself to facilitating accuracy in molding and subsequent electro-forming.

The electrotype has for many years been the acknowledged high quality printing plate for letterpress printing. The capabilities of the electroforming process are amply demonstrated by the quality of the phonograph recordings which are produced by essentially the same process. The requirements of plates for rotary printing, however, are sufficiently more exacting on a schedule basis, and this offers a partial explanation of the failure of the electrotyping operations to meet all of the needs of the industry.

Some special requirements for the electrotype or other duplicate printing plate for rotary printing equipment include: conformance with the surface of the printing cylinder surface; uniformity in plate thickness; physical strength to withstand stress of press rotation and printing impression; and wear properties permitting the plate to make the required number of impressions. It seems superfluous to mention that the halftone dot sizes must be equal to those of the original, but printers consistently believe this is a common defect.

Conformance with the cylinder is necessary to prevent motion of the plate during impression, and to avoid failure of the printing surface or holding mechanism, through fatigue from flexing. Normally, the lead backed conventional electrotype appears to conform, but experience has always shown that higher failure rates take place with plates which do not conform fully to the cylinder. In this respect, the newly developed laminated plates may be prepared to greater accuracy.

Uniformity of plate thickness at first appears to be an obvious requirement, but it is complicated by the so-called " plate treatment " requirement. The operators of press equipment have been discussing (sometimes heatedly) for many years, the merits of " level impression " printing compared with that from " treated plate " printing. Common practice in the industry when using semi-rigid packing on the impression cylinder has been built up under the heavy tones, and drop packing under the highlight areas. In effect, the operator in doing this is adjusting the contact pressures so as to equalize them and produce a uniform appearance.

In an unpublished study by Malicki,* electrotype plates were supplied to a press room with no treatment, but they had been accurately measured to determine their thickness. When the plates had completed the run, they were removed from the presses, and again measured to determine the extent to which the operators had added impression through paper patches on the back of the plates. Malicki concluded that the degree of makeready applied by the operators was equivalent to a difference between highlights and shadows of 0·004 in. More than 75% of the plates had received some type of patch to improve their printing properties. It is likely that, in many cases of " level impression " printing, some of the added impression is obtained by build up under the packing, or harder surfaced packings are in use.

Historically, the electrotype has been an electroformed shell reinforced or " backed-up " with a lead-tin alloy containing about 6% tin. The electrotype, so constructed, has had several advantages:

1. It is readily curved or shaped to conform with the press bed, or the press cylinder.
2. Repairs are easily made, and inserts or corrections may be easily soldered into the plate.
3. There is a high recovery of the metals used in its construction.
4. The electroforming process provides an accurate replica of the original engraving.

Unfortunately, the insistence on higher production rates, and the inability for many years to develop interest in mechanization of the processes, have left the industry with little improvement in quality. Furthermore, the higher press rates have added stresses to the plates, and have placed a higher penalty on plate failure. There have been so many difficulties of a major nature that there has been a strong series of efforts to bring about improved plates. The following are the objectional features of electrotype plates for which solutions are being sought:

1. Lead backed plates do not have sufficient strength to be held to the press cylinders at high speeds now common. They tend to " breathe " or flex as they rotate with the cylinder.
2. Plates which are curved at room temperatures show significant stretch in the direction of curvature, to produce errors in register. They also reduce the amount of printed matter per page under some conditions.
3. Excessive cracking has resulted from higher speeds and poorly fitted plates. Damage to presses and lost time resulted, when the plates have fallen from their holders.

* MALICKI, R. R. Donnelley & Sons Co., Chicago, Ill.

4. The trend toward plates up to $\frac{1}{4}$ in. thickness have made finishing and removal of casting stresses so difficult that severe damage to highlight areas has resulted. Tones become heavier, and color matching of the original proofs has been impossible.

5. The newer " underlocking " clips to hold plates to the cylinder and reduce paper use at the same time, cannot be used with safety on lead backed plates.

There have been many attempts at improvement of the defects listed above. These have included new methods of casting, the application of plastics to plate backing, curving plates while heated, and the laminated plates. More recently, the introduction of etched metal and plastic plates has appeared to offer promise.

The rigid metal laminated plate* introduced by TIME Inc. has tended to reduce many of the strength defects of the standard electrotype plate. Its main feature has been the accuracy with which it may be prepared, and the low weight, and high strength-weight ratio. The plate is a laminate of aluminium and 0·090 in. electrotype bonded with an adhesive. Its principal disadvantage has been the inability to correct for irregularities in the printing surface through either normal hand finishing methods or through the use of paper patches under the plates at the low areas while on the presses.

One successful version of the laminated plate, using greater amounts of plastic filling material, is the Color Line† plate. Here no lead alloy is used, and plastic is used to fill in the shell of the plates. Reinforcement is provided by a pre-curved aluminium shell. This plate appears to have all of the advantages in running of the laminated plate, and few of the disadvantages related to the high casting temperatures of the lead electrotype.

It may be said of all newer press plates that their good properties eliminate the convenience of application of the expedients used at the press by press operators for so many years. In the case of the laminated plates, press runs of 1,000,000 or 2,000,000 impressions are common when the plates have been made to conform to the press cylinder while at the same time printing a good replica of the original engraving. Identical plates have failed at 100,000 impressions when the expedients of paper patches have been resorted to at the presses. These experiences are readily explained on mechanical and physical property bases, but their control in plate manufacture is not yet on a rigorous scientific base.

One cannot leave this discussion without mentioning the place likely to be occupied by the photopolymer‡ printing plate, and the etched originals on zinc, copper, or magnesium, which are finding their way into the industry.

* Time Inc., Springdale, Conn.
† Printing Plate Supply Co., 561 West Washington St., Chicago, Ill.
‡ E. I. duPont de Nemours Co., Parlin, N.J.

It is likely that with the increased control over area loss during etching of metals and plastics, provided by the newer processes, that the use of duplicated plates produced by molding methods may be substantially reduced in the future. There are many problems related to their production which cannot be mentioned in this paper.

It may be concluded that the press printing plates for high speed letterpress printing must be precision plates, produced under conditions of process control not heretofore considered necessary in the printing industry, and that the use of newer higher speed printing presses places mechanical requirements on the plates above those possible with the conventional lead-alloy types of plates so common in the industry for many years.

REFERENCE
1. Recommended specifications for advertising reproduction material in magazine letterpress wet printing. Report No. 4. American Association of Advertising Agencies. Magazine Publ. Assoc., New York.

THE INFLUENCE OF PRINTING CONDITIONS IN LABORATORY TESTS OF THE PRINTABILITY OF NEWSPRINT PAPER

by I. FABBRI and A. QUATTRUCCI

The Graphic Laboratory of Ente Nazionale per la Cellulosa e per la Carta,
Rome, Italy

Abstract—The influence of pressure and speed on printability test results has been studied; tests have been performed on Vandercook-Universal I and the Fogra laboratory tester.

This influence has been measured by determining the optical density and percentage transfer variation on the prints.

Furthermore compressibility and smoothness variation of newsprint samples has been measured as a function of pressure.

The values obtained have been compared with the results of the above study.

EXPERIMENTAL

Materials

Papers. Four groundwood high-grade papers were selected: two kinds of glazed papers and two of calendered ones, which are referred to in tables and figures as A, B, C, D. Table 1 shows the main physical and mechanical characteristics of newsprint samples.

Ink. A common black letterpress ink was used.

Methods and Testers

Printing tests by Fogra-tester. Prints were made on the felt side of paper at different pressures and speeds, e.g. for any pressure, prints were made at the different speeds.

Pressure values were 15, 30, 45, 60 kg (in tables P1, P2, P3, P4, respectively); speed values were 1, 2, 3, 4 m/sec (in tables, V1, V2, V3, V4, respectively).

An unscreened aluminium printing forme, 20 mm wide, and a rigid sample-holder, with a packing made by three strips of the papers to be printed, were used.

Prints were carried out with a fixed inking of the forme, 2·2 g/m².

148

TABLE 1. PHYSICAL AND MECHANICAL CHARACTERISTICS

| Sample | Caliper μ | Basis weight g/m² | Opacity % | Level of brightness | | Breaking length in m | | Elongation % | | Bursting strength | Porosity | Ash % |
				Felt-side	Wire-side	machine direction	cross direction	machine direction	cross direction			
Glazed A	80	50·0	90·6	53·1	50·1	3916	1634	0·95	1·47	0·55	1·62	1·01
Glazed B	75	55·6	87·8	61·5	59·4	3833	1629	1·09	1·86	0·60	1·16	5·09
Calendered C	75	57·9	94·3	62·0	58·6	2987	1275	1·16	1·89	0·57	1·12	12·18
Calendered D	70	55·0	93·3	51·6	50·6	2914	1289	1·14	1·55	0·46	1·06	4·97

L

The percentage transfer was calculated according to the formula:

$$T \% = \frac{x}{y}.100$$

where x is the weight of ink transferred to the paper and y the weight of ink distributed on the forme before printing. The weighings of the forme, before and after printing, were carried out on a Mettler semiautomatic balance having a sensibility of 0·1 mg.

For any pressure–speed combination 32 prints were made and the transfer results were averaged.

The optical density of the prints was evaluated with the aid of a " Photovolt " reflection densitometer, 24 hr after printing. The densitometer measurements were taken in the central area of every sample in five places, at a distance 1 cm each from the other. In this way, for any pressure–speed combination, the optical density is the average value of 160 readings.

The values of percentage transfer and printing density under the different testing conditions are given in Tables 2 and 3.

Printing tests by Vandercook Universal 1 proofpress. As for the Fogra-tester, prints were made on the felt side of paper at different pressures and speeds, e.g., at any pressure prints were made at the different speeds.

Pressures checked by the Huck-base, were 15, 30, 45, 60 kg (tables P1, P2, P3, P4 respectively); speeds were 0.27 and 0.54 m/sec (tables V1, V2 respectively), according to the highest and lowest speed values available on the tester.

Synthetic rollers, rigid packing, unscreened zinc printing forme, 7 × 14 cm sized, were used.

Prints were made with the forme inked with 2·8 g/m², in order to approach as nearly as possible to the results obtained with the Fogra-tester.

The percentage transfer value has been calculated, as for the Fogra-tester, by averaging 32 measurements for any pressure–speed combination.

The densitometer measurements were taken in the central area of every sample, in 15 places, at the distance 1 cm each from the other. In this way, for any pressure–speed combination, the optical density is the average value of 480 readings.

The values of percentage transfer and printing density, under the different testing conditions, are given in Tables 4 and 5.

Compressibility measurements. Compressibility curves as a function of pressure have been plotted for the newsprint samples, by measuring on the felt side of the paper, with the tester designed by the Graphic Laboratory of Ente Nazionale per la Cellulosa e per la Carta, at pressures increasing from 5 to 50 kg/cm², in 5 kg steps. The average values, given in Table 6 and Fig. 9,

TABLE 2. % TRANSFER (FOGRA)

Sample			P_1	P_2	P_3	P_4
Glazed	A	V_1	46·7	54·8	57·3	59·8
		V_2	45·0	49·4	52·9	54·8
		V_3	49·7	48·5	53·7	53·4
		V_4	52·5	52·5	53·7	56·8
Glazed	B	V_1	52·5	55·8	59·8	61·3
		V_2	50·4	53·4	55·8	57·6
		V_3	47·3	52·7	55·4	56·9
		V_4	50·5	56·4	59·7	59·7
Calendered C		V_1	58·3	61·0	65·6	65·0
		V_2	53·7	56·8	59·2	60·9
		V_3	53·8	57·9	58·7	61·0
		V_4	58·8	60·8	63·5	63·0
Calendered D		V_1	56·9	59·9	60·2	62·9
		V_2	52·6	55·6	55·5	59·5
		V_3	55·2	57·2	56·3	58·5
		V_4	61·9	61·0	59·2	60·4

TABLE 3. OPTICAL DENSITY (FOGRA)

Sample			P_1		P_2		P_3		P_4	
			Value	δ	Value	δ	Value	δ	Value	δ
Glazed	A	V_1	0·774	0·041	0·859	0·030	0·855	0·024	0·870	0·024
		V_2	0·723	0·050	0·787	0·037	0·833	0·033	0·840	0·024
		V_3	0·727	0·046	0·772	0·033	0·817	0·037	0·812	0·026
		V_4	0·773	0·051	0·786	0·032	0·803	0·028	0·829	0·030
Glazed	B	V_1	0·802	0·039	0·865	0·032	0·894	0·033	0·931	0·024
		V_2	0·774	0·032	0·831	0·024	0·881	0·026	0·922	0·024
		V_3	0·744	0·036	0·810	0·028	0·856	0·032	0·901	0·032
		V_4	0·780	0·043	0·830	0·039	0·890	0·036	0·883	0·035
Calendered C		V_1	0·881	0·031	0·912	0·017	0·957	0·020	0·974	0·017
		V_2	0·839	0·041	0·903	0·020	0·942	0·026	0·947	0·017
		V_3	0·835	0·033	0·886	0·028	0·901	0·017	0·918	0·017
		V_4	0·857	0·035	0·911	0·020	0·933	0·020	0·914	0·014
Calendered D		V_1	0·860	0·037	0·879	0·027	0·893	0·022	0·942	0·017
		V_2	0·818	0·041	0·850	0·033	0·910	0·030	0·916	0·032
		V_3	0·818	0·049	0·866	0·036	0·889	0·032	0·908	0·030
		V_4	0·838	0·022	0·872	0·024	0·901	0·024	0·919	0·024

were obtained, for any kind of paper to be printed, from 16 samples, each one having been subjected to 5 series of measurements.

Smoothness measurements. Smoothness as a function of pressure has been plotted for the newsprint samples from measurements on the felt side with the Chapman device at pressures increasing from 10 to 50 kg/cm^2, (in steps of 10 kg).

TABLE 4. % TRANSFER (VANDERCOOK)

Sample			P_1	P_2	P_3	P_4
Glazed	A	V_1	40·6	43·8	44·8	49·9
		V_2	31·4	39·1	43·4	49·4
Glazed	B	V_1	42·8	47·2	48·1	51·0
		V_2	31·1	37·8	46·4	48·6
Calendered C		V_1	48·4	53·2	55·0	55·8
		V_2	38·7	44·4	51·2	54·8
Calendered D		V_1	52·5	54·8	59·2	59·5
		V_2	44·2	49·7	55·4	58·2

The average values, given in Table 7 and in Fig. 10, were obtained, for any kind of paper to be tested, from 16 samples, each one having been subjected to 3 series of measurements.

The tests were carried out in a room conditioned at an r.h. of 65% and temperature of 20°C.

TABLE 5. OPTICAL DENSITY (VANDERCOOK)

Sample			P_1		P_2		P_3		P_4	
			Value	δ	Value	δ	Value	δ	Value	δ
Glazed	A	V_1	0·545	0·061	0·616	0·069	0·659	0·068	0·730	0·089
		V_2	0·392	0·046	0·511	0·068	0·612	0·065	0·700	0·068
Glazed	B	V_1	0·583	0·053	0·693	0·073	0·700	0·071	0·839	0·081
		V_2	0·373	0·052	0·472	0·042	0·630	0·083	0·689	0·074
Calendered C		V_1	0·675	0·056	0·742	0·056	0·800	0·069	0·833	0·086
		V_2	0·490	0·041	0·556	0·062	0·666	0·072	0·810	0·085
Calendered D		V_1	0·737	0·057	0·746	0·046	0·878	0·058	0·887	0·083
		V_2	0·529	0·064	0·620	0·075	0·760	0·073	0·855	0·084

TABLE 6. COMPRESSIBILITY (PENETRATION MICRONS)

Sample		5 kg/cm²		10 kg/cm²		15 kg/cm²		20 kg/cm²		25 kg/cm²		30 kg/cm²		35 kg/cm²		40 kg/cm²		45 kg/cm²		50 kg/cm²	
		μ	δ	μ	δ	μ	δ	μ	δ	μ	δ	μ	δ	μ	δ	μ	δ	μ	δ	μ	δ
Glazed	A	8·6	0·5	15·1	0·7	19·1	0·7	22·5	1·0	24·4	1·0	25·6	1·1	26·0	1·1	26·0	1·1	26·0	1·1	26·0	1·1
Glazed	B	9·0	0·0	13·6	0·5	16·4	0·6	18·6	1·0	19·7	1·1	20·6	1·1	21·0	1·5	21·0	1·5	21·0	1·5	21·0	1·5
Calendered C		7·6	0·5	13·0	1·0	16·1	0·9	18·5	1·0	19·6	1·0	20·5	0·9	20·7	0·9	20·7	0·9	20·7	0·9	20·7	0·9
Calendered D		6·0	0·0	9·5	0·6	12·1	0·9	14·2	1·0	14·9	0·9	15·2	1·2	15·5	1·4	15·5	1·4	15·5	1·4	15·5	1·4

TABLE 7. CHAPMAN

Sample	10 kg/cm²		20 kg/cm²		30 kg/cm²		40 kg/cm²		50 kg/cm²	
	Value	δ	Value	δ	Value	δ	Value	δ	Value	δ
Glazed A	9·4	0·5	13·0	0·7	16·0	0·8	18·8	0·8	21·0	0·7
Glazed B	7·8	0·6	11·2	0·8	13·7	0·8	15·9	0·9	17·6	1·0
Calendered C	9·8	0·5	12·5	0·6	15·1	0·5	17·9	0·7	19·8	0·6
Calendered D	8·3	0·5	11·0	0·8	13·7	0·7	16·1	0·9	16·9	0·9

CONSIDERATIONS

Figures 1, 2, 3, 4, 5, 6, 7 and 8 show the variation of percentage transfer and optical density values with printing pressure and speed increase.

Fogra tests

By examining Figs. 1 and 2, where transfer and optical density variations as functions of pressure respectively are given, for any single testing speed, the following conclusions can be drawn, that pressure increase causes a

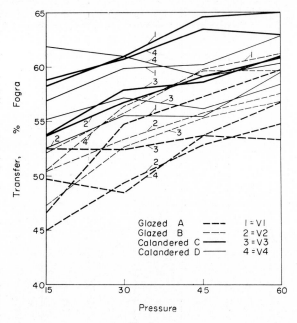

Fig. I

general increase of transfer and optical density, at any single testing speed; the dependence of the total variation of transfer and optical density with pressure is not clearly differentiated for different speeds. Total variation of transfer and optical density may be defined as the difference between the transfer and optical density values at the highest and the lowest testing pressure.

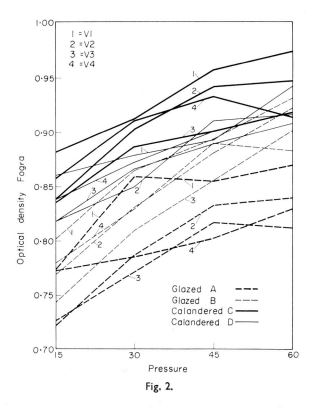

Fig. 2.

By examining Figs. 3 and 4, which show, respectively, the transfer and density variations as functions of speed at the different pressures, it follows that speed increase causes a general decrease of transfer and optical density, at the single testing pressures, up to the value 3 m/sec. In the range from 3 to 4 m/sec, a general increase of transfer and density is noticed for any sample and pressure tested. We were not successful in avoiding this unusual effect, which is very likely due to the noticeable vibrations occurring in the Fogra-tester in question. The presence of vibrations is also confirmed by the areas with different optical density resulting in the prints made at such a speed.

Vandercook tests

By examining Figs. 5 and 6, which show respectively transfer and density variations as functions of pressure, at any single testing speed, it will be seen that at any speed, transfer and density increase with increasing pressure;

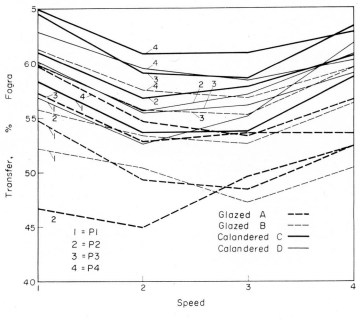

Fig. 3.

the two graphs, representative of any paper, converge with increasing pressure; total variation of transfer and density as function of pressure increases with increasing speed; e.g., at low pressure, speed influence upon transfer and density is very noticeable, while negligible at high pressure.

By examining Figs. 7 and 8, which respectively show transfer and density variations as functions of speed, for any tested pressure, it will be seen that at any pressure, transfers and densities decrease with increasing speed; the four graphs, representative of any paper, diverge with increasing speed; e.g. printing results are differentiated more at the highest speed; total variation of transfer and optical density as function of speed decreases with increasing pressure; this means, as previously mentioned, that speed influence becomes practically negligible at high pressure.

ANALYSIS OF VARIANCE

Though density values and their variations differ from paper to paper, an attempt was made to characterize the speed and pressure influence, which is common to any paper, by Snedecor's test. Calculations were made on density

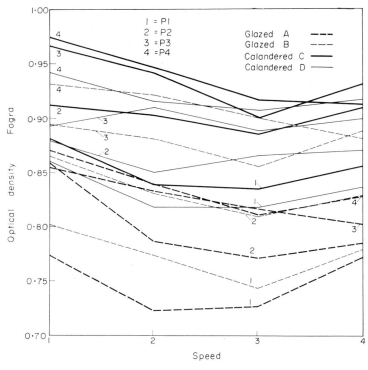

Fig. 4.

values (and not on transfer values), since density is more directly connected with the visual evaluation of printing quality.

In the application of the test, at the same time for any printing speed, density values of all the papers as functions of pressure were first considered, and secondly, for any testing pressure, density values of all the papers, as functions of speed, were also considered.

By examining the f values of the Snedecor test in relation with the results obtained with the Fogra-tester (Table 8), the following conclusions are reached.

For the papers as a whole, the influence of pressure upon optical density values is very significant at the 95% probability level for any speed. (For 3

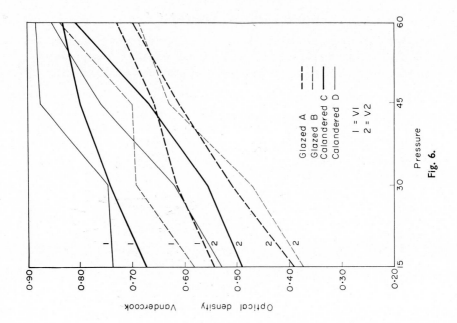

Fig. 6.

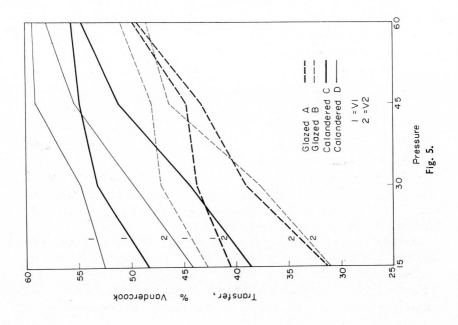

Fig. 5.

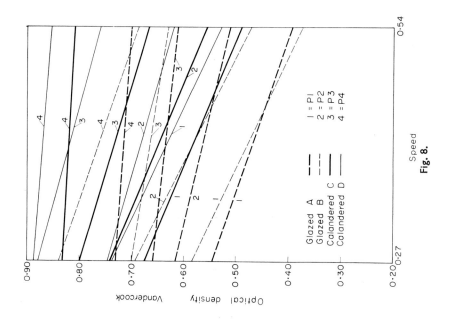

Fig. 8.

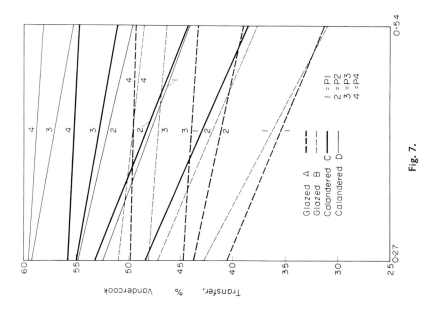

Fig. 7.

I. Fabbri and A. Quattrucci

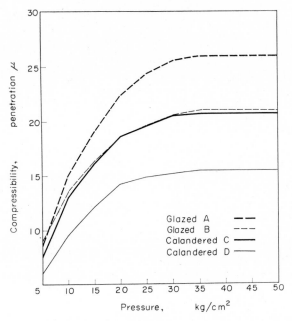

Fig. 9.

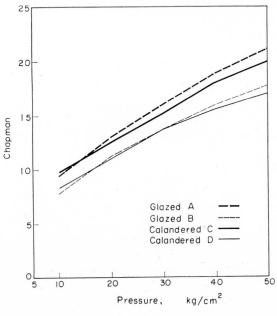

Fig. 10.

TABLE 8. f VALUE OF SNEDECOR FOR OPTICAL DENSITY (FOGRA)

Speed	f due to pressure	f due to paper
V_1	25·1	21·0
V_2	87·4	68·1
V_3	30·6	31·9
V_4	16·6	30·4

Pressure	f due to speed	f due to paper
P_1	21·7	106·3
P_2	5·0	25·9
P_3	4·7	41·3
P_4	13·0	59·0

The value of f obtained from Snedecor's table, to the probability level of 95% for 3 and 9 degrees of freedom is 3·86.

TABLE 9. VALUES OF f FOR OPTICAL DENSITY (VANDERCOOK)

Speed	f due to pressure	f due to paper
V_1	28·4	25·0
V_2	211·9	53·5

The value of f obtained from Snedecor's table, to the probability level of 95% for 3 and 9 degrees of freedom is 3·86.

Pressure	f due to speed	f due to paper
P_1	202·4	36·6
P_2	35·3	4·3
P_3	20·5	16·1
P_4	4·0	5·3

The value of f obtained from Snedecor's table, to the probability level of 95% for 1 and 3 to 3 and 3 degrees of freedom are 10·1 and 9·28 respectively.

and 9 degrees of freedom. Snedecor's table shows 3·86 and the calculated values are much higher.)

Speed influence at the single testing pressures, appears, for any paper, to be equally significant, at the same probability level.

Similarly, by examining f values of the test, which correspond to the results obtained on Vandercook proofpress (Table 9), the following holds.

For all the papers, the influence of pressure upon optical density is very significant at any speed.

Furthermore the significance increases appreciably with speed, in agreement with the conclusions of the graphical data. For any paper, the influence of speed upon optical density at the different tested pressures is also very significant.

Observations about compressibility and Chapman smoothness

The dependence of total variations in compressibility (expressed as penetration) and smoothness on pressure were studied.

It was noted that glazed A shows the greatest variations; glazed B and calendered C follow with the same order of magnitude and, finally, calendered D shows the lowest values.

This order is true also for the values corresponding to total variation of transfer obtained either on Fogra-tester or on Vandercook.

As to the optical density, the greatest variation was given by glazed B, followed by glazed A, calendered C and calendered D.

This change in order may be explained by the fact that glazed A, in spite of showing the greatest transfer variation, is the most porous one.

CONCLUSIONS

Concerning the instruments

Tests on Fogra-tester and Vandercook proof-press confirm that printing speed increase generally causes decreases in transfer and optical density at any single pressure, while pressure causes transfer and density to increase, at any single speed.

From the results, obtained with Vandercook, it appears that speed influence upon transfer and optical density total variation decreases with increasing pressure, while pressure influence upon transfer and density total variations increases with increasing speed.

The same considerations cannot be extended to the results obtained with Fogra-tester, which clearly shows unusual behaviour at high speed.

From the results obtained, the best Fogra conditions in order to differentiate the papers appear to be the lowest pressure and 2 m/sec speed.

For the Vandercook, the best conditions are the lowest pressure and the highest speed.

These results are referred of course, to the low inking (about 2·5 g/m²) utilized during the tests.

Concerning the evaluation of paper quality

If we refer to the density measurements, corresponding to the above told " optimum " conditions, as a criterion for a classification of quality of the four papers, the following order is found.

Fogra-tester   C, D, B, A
Vandercook Proof Press   D, C, B, A

while classifications based on Chapman and compressibility tests are as follows:

compressibility   A, B, C, D
Chapman smoothness   A, C, B, D

Neither of these last two tests can foretell the printing quality since they do not take into account the surface absorption characteristics of the paper.

However, the compressibility test explains the inversion in the classification order between papers C and D, inversion occurring when measuring on the printability testers; pressure influence is more marked in paper C, being more compressible than paper D. Since the effective pressure utilized on Vandercook is appreciably lower than the one on Fogra-tester, the optical density of prints agrees with this pressure effect.

DISCUSSION

GINMAN: If I understand you correctly you used different packings on the Fogra-tester. That means that even if the linear pressures were the same you could have different maximum pressures and different pressure distributions when printing the four papers.

FABBRI: We agree that the maximum pressure and the pressure distribution may be different for each paper used in these measurements but we preferred to back each paper that was printed with three sheets of the same paper in order to magnify the effect of the compressibility.

LARAIGNOU: I understand that you make a static measurement of the paper compressibility. During the printing operation we have to deal with a dynamic compressibility. Do you think, therefore, that you can draw any conclusion relating print quality and your measurements?

FABBRI: In our investigations we tried to find a correlation between the compressibility and transfer and density values but as we expected, the statistical evaluation of our measurements excluded any possibility of good correlation. This is due not only to the fact that our compressibility measurements have been made under static conditions but probably also because all compressibility measurements essentially ignore the surface properties of the paper, whereas printability is very much influenced by surface properties. In fact a search of the literature failed to reveal any indication of such a conclusion.

COMPARISON OF INK TRANSFER MEASUREMENTS ON FOUR LABORATORY PRINT MAKERS

by JACQUELINE M. FETSKO

National Printing Ink Research Institute, Lehigh University,
Bethlehem, Pa., U.S.A.

Abstract—The FAG Proof Press and the Fogra, I.G.T., and Leipzig Printability Testers were compared in a study of the transfer of one ink to two papers at two pressures and speeds. Despite their opposite cylinder–flat geometries, FAG and Fogra produced similar transfer in the practical ink film thickness range. The Fogra, however, picked the uncoated paper. The two cylindrical print makers, the I.G.T. and Leipzig, transferred less than the FAG and Fogra, and the film splitting factor was more sensitive to speed variations. Printing smoothness, as evidenced by low film thickness transfer parameters, generally increased with increasing packing smoothness, printing pressure, and dwell time. The influence of printing conditions on ink immobilization and film splitting depended on the paper and print maker. The position of the transfer curve peak correlated well with paper roughness; the height of the peak did not correlate with surface absorbency. Because of the complexity of the observed trends, it is suggested that further studies be conducted under comparable separation velocities and packings, and that research be directed toward clarifying the effects of speed on shear thinning, picking force, and position of final ink split.

INTRODUCTION

Many laboratory printing devices have been developed around the world, and, due to their different geometries and modes of operation, it is certainly of interest to compare the results from these small presses. The work described herein involves a comparison of transfer measurements made on four laboratory print makers. Three of these were European bench presses: the Fogra, the I.G.T. and the Leipzig Printability Testers. The FAG Proof Press was also included because it very closely resembles the Vandercook No. 4 Proof Press, which is the most commonly used laboratory press in the United States.

The experiments were conducted by the same person over a three month period at the respective Research Institutes where the printability testers were developed: Leipzig, Fogra, and I.G.T. in that order. The I.G.T. instrument used was the prototype of the new constant speed model, and the FAG Proof Press was the one available in the Fogra laboratories. The transfer measurements were taken with two papers and one ink at two speeds and pressures.

It was recognized at the outset that, although similar nominal conditions were used throughout, the actual conditions under which transfer occurred would differ considerably. For example, the properties of the ink would be influenced by the speed and composition of the distribution system, the properties of the paper would depend on the packing; the separation velocity and the pressure distribution would differ due to the different geometries and packings. For sake of expediency, however, each of the instruments was used under the conditions normally employed in the respective labora- iories at the time of the tests. As will become apparent, the results of this study have indeed proved most interesting, and it is hoped that they will encourage further comparative work.

EXPERIMENTAL TECHNIQUES
Description of the presses

The four laboratory presses differ widely in several respects. Figure 1, which is a diagram of the geometries, illustrates that the transfer of ink was accomplished in three ways: from flat to cylinder on the FAG, from

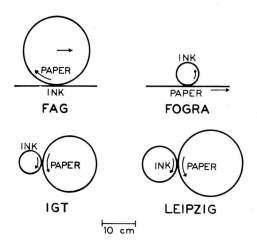

Fig. I. Geometries of the four laboratory print makers.

cylinder to flat on the Fogra, and from cylinder to cylinder on both the I.G.T. and the Leipzig Testers. Table 1 shows the differences in cylinder

M

diameters, drive mechanisms, packings, and print area. It was somewhat of a surprise to find that the diameters of the impression cylinders of the FAG, I.G.T. and Leipzig are of the same order of magnitude.

TABLE 1. BASIC FEATURES OF THE FOUR LABORATORY PRINT MAKERS

Print maker	Cylinder diameters Forme	Paper	Drive mechanisms Forme	Paper	Packing	Print area	Wt. of 1μ ink film
	cm	cm				cm²	ca.mg*
FAG	∞	20·1	Stationary	Hand	Tympan	200·	20±0·01
Fogra	6·5	∞	Electric	Friction	Rubber	41	4±0·01
I.G.T.	6·5	17·3	Friction	Electric	Paper	30·5	3±0·1
Leipzig	10·0	20·0	Electric	Electric	Rubber	21·5	2±0·1

* The ± values refer to the precision of the analytical balance used for weighing the forme before and after printing.

As is the case with the Vandercook No. 4, the FAG Proof Press is a hand-driven flat bed press. The large flat magnesium plate having an area of 200 cm² was held in place in the press bed by means of a vacuum base: the pressure was varied by changing the height of the movable press bed. The speed of the impression cylinder was measured with a microswitch-clock device, and only a little practice was required to obtain reasonable reproducibility. The slow speeds available on the proof press severely limited the range of speeds which could be studied.

The three bench presses resemble each other in that the printing disks are circular and of relatively small area; pressures are spring-controlled and automatically maintained; and speeds are also automatically controlled because either the disk or the impression cylinder or both are electrically driven. In the case of the Fogra,[1] the inked disk is driven, and the revolving disk in turn drives the paper, which is held by its leading edge in a flat rubber-packed sample holder. The I.G.T.[2] is the opposite case; here the paper cylinder is driven and it in turn causes the inked disk to rotate. In the Leipzig Tester,[3] both the inked disk and the paper cylinder are electrically driven. This tester is the only one in which the trailing edge of the paper is held in place as a matter of routine. The constant speed models of the instruments and aluminium disks were used throughout the study.

A major difficulty with circular inking disks is that it is virtually impossible to make exactly one revolution; consequently some overlap or underlap always occurs. With the Fogra, the printing line is controlled by the length of the sample holder; the resulting overlap was about 2 or 3 mm. With the I.G.T. an additional problem is created because the paper cylinder is brought into contact with the inked disk before the cylinder is activated, and some transfer obviously occurs during this time. To circumvent this difficulty, a small piece of Scotch Tape was placed on the disk during the inking process; the tape was removed, the disk weighed, and the cylinder brought into contact with the clean place on the disk. The Leipzig Tester, on the other hand, is mechanized to remove the disk from contact with the paper after 39·8 % of a revolution.

The distribution systems on the FAG, Fogra, and the I.G.T. Testers contained polyurethane rollers and operated at speeds of less than about 0·5 m/sec. The distribution system on the Leipzig Tester contained rubber rollers and operated at the considerably faster speed of 2 m/sec.

Papers and ink

The papers were an art (coated) paper and an illustration (uncoated) paper available in the Leipzig Research Institute, where the study was initiated. Their properties are summarized in Table 2.

TABLE 2. PAPER PROPERTIES ON THE FELT SIDE

Paper	Optical rough-ness (u)	Perth-ometer	Bekk smooth-ness (sec)	Bendtsen, mm/sec			Caliper (mm)
				Smoothness (1 kg) (5 kg)	Hardness	Porosity	
Coated	3·7	526	475	32·5 12·4	0·39	11·8	0·090
Uncoated	5·8	1097	290	38·5 16·1	0·36	64·3	0·075

The ink, also from Leipzig, was a black rotary letterpress ink containing 14% carbon black in a mineral oil–resin vehicle. Its specific gravity was 1·006. Rheological measurements taken at 25° with a Shirley–Ferranti Viscometer showed it to have a viscosity of 45 poise and yield value of 1600 dyn/cm². A film on glass failed to dry in a week's time.

Experimental conditions

The choice of speeds and pressures was based on experience and/or availability on the laboratory proof press. The speeds selected, therefore, were 0·6 and 1·2 m/sec.* These conditions were used for the Leipzig work;

*m/sec × 200 = ft/min.
 kg/cm × 5·6 = pli.

but changes had to be made later for the other work due to unforeseen circumstances. For example, the operator was not able to drive the FAG Press at a speed faster than 1·0 m/sec; the 0·6 m/sec speed was not available on the Fogra-tester; and 0·5 and 1·0 m/sec were more conveniently attainable on the I.G.T. Although the linear speeds varied somewhat from case to case, for sake of convenience they will be referred to nominally as 0·6 and 1·1 m/sec. (ca. 120 and 220 ft/min).

The pressures used were 20 and 40 kg/cm, which correspond to about 110 and 220 pli. The ambient room conditions were 23°C and 55% r.h. for the FAG and Fogra work and 20°C and 65% r.h. for the I.G.T. and Leipzig work. Since only one of the speeds selected was available on the Fogra-tester, additional experiments were carried out with the trailing edge of the paper held down as well as loose.

Transfer measurements

Transfer measurements were made by weighing the printing forme (plate or disk) before and after each printing. The ink film thickness on the forme ranged from ca. 0·5 to 18μ. The weighings for the FAG and Fogra work were carried out on an automatic five-place balance having a precision of ± 0·01 mg. Four-place balances with precisions of ± 0·1 mg were used for the I.G.T. and Leipzig experiments. Considering the weight of one micron of ink coupled with the precision of the balance (see the last column of Table 1), it is obvious that the FAG transfer data, particularly in the thin ink film region, had greater precision than the Fogra than in turn the I.G.T. and Leipzig data.

The results were plotted both as per cent transfer and as ink film thickness transferred to the paper vs. ink film thickness carried initially on the forme. This latter type of plot was used for applying the linear form of the NPIRI Transfer Equation (4); the slope of the straight line portion is f, the split of the free ink film; and the intercept divided by $(1 - f)$ is b, the ink instant-aneously immobilized during the time of impression. The values for these two transfer constants were then used to apply the thin ink film data to the calculation of the smoothness transfer coefficient k from the full equation

$$y = (1 - e^{-kx})\{b(1 - e^{-x/b}) + f[x - b(1 - e^{-x/b})]\}$$

These calculations were made on a Royal McBee LPG–30 computer available at Lehigh University.

RESULTS OF THE PRINTING EXPERIMENTS

Different trends with speed and pressure were noted from paper to paper and from tester to tester. The transfer results will therefore be discussed separately for each tester before they are compared. The bases of references

TABLE 3. RESULTS OF THE TRANSFER MEASUREMENTS

Print Maker	Speed	Pressure *	NPIRI transfer constants				Peak position		Total transferred at Ink on forme of		
			k smooth	1/k rough	b immob.	f split	Ink on forme	Transfer	5μ	10μ	15μ
	m/sec	kg/cm	μ^{-1}	μ	μ	%	μ	%	μ	μ	μ
A. Coated Paper											
FAG	1·0	20 A	1·02	0·98	0·64	45·0	2·2	55·0	2·6	4·9	7·1
		40 A	1·33	0·75	0·76	45·4	1·8	60·2	2·7	5·0	7·2
	0·6	20 B	1·08	0·92	0·87	45·2	2·2	59·0	2·7	5·0	7·3
		40 B	1·38	0·72	1·02	45·4	1·8	65·1	2·8	5·1	7·4
Fogra	1·2	20 NH	1·26	0·79	0·57	45·7	1·7	58·8	2·6	4·9	7·2
		20 H	1·49	0·67	0·57	45·7	1·7	59·5	2·6	4·9	7·2
		40 NH	1·45	0·69	0·59	46·0	1·2	60·5	2·6	4·9	7·3
		40 H	1·67	0·60	0·59	46·0	1·2	61·2	2·6	4·9	7·3
I.G.T.	1·0	20 A	1·10	0·91	0·66	39·4	—	—	2·4	4·3	6·3
		40 A	—	—	0·73	41·5	—	—	2·5	4·6	6·6
	0·5	20 B	1·12	0·89	0·82	43·0	—	—	2·7	4·8	7·0
		40 B	—	—	0·91	43·3	—	—	2·7	4·9	7·1
Leipzig	1·2	20 A	0·90	1·1	0·74	36·8	2·6	49·2	2·3	4·2	6·0
		40 A	1·36	0·73	0·73	38·8	1·7	56·1	2·4	4·3	6·2
	0·6	20 B	0·99	1·0	0·59	43·2	2·6	52·0	2·5	4·7	6·8
		40 B	1·47	0·68	0·61	42·7	1·7	57·0	2·5	4·7	6·8

B. Uncoated Paper

FAG	1·2	20 A	0·63	1·59	1·67	38·9	3·5	57·2	2·7	4·9	6·9
		40 A	0·77	1·30	1·84	38·8	2·7	62·1	2·9	5·0	7·0
	0·6	20 B	0·71	1·41	1·71	41·3	3·5	61·0	2·9	5·1	7·2
		40 B	0·90	1·11	1·95	41·8	2·5	65·8	3·1	5·3	7·3
Fogra	1·2	20 A	—	—	—	—	—	—	2·7	4·8	7·2
		40 B	—	—	—	—	—	—	2·7	4·8	7·3
I.G.T.	1·0	20 A	0·62	1·59	2·29	27·1	3·8	51·2	2·4	4·4	5·7
		40 A	0·75	1·33	2·31	27·3	3·5	53·5	2·6	4·4	5·8
	0·5	20 B	0·70	1·43	1·90	37·1	3·8	56·2	2·7	4·9	6·7
		40 B	0·90	1·11	1·74	36·7	3·0	58·8	2·9	4·8	6·7
Leipzig	1·2	20 A	0·63	1·59	1·56	29·3	2·8	51·6	2·5	4·0	5·5
		40 A	0·85	1·18	1·54	31·9	2·3	57·2	2·6	4·1	5·7
	0·6	20 B	0·58	1·72	1·36	37·3	3·8	51·8	2·7	4·6	6·4
		40 B	0·72	1·39	1·26	40·5	3·0	56·0	2·7	4·8	6·9

* The codes correspond to those on the graphs.

are the numerical values for various transfer parameters listed in Table 3 as well as per cent transfer graphs.

Included in Table 3 are the NPIRI transfer constants k, b, and f. In addition to the conventional smoothness constant k, which has reciprocal microns as units, also listed is the roughness factor $1/k$. The use of $1/k$ not only provides a roughness scale in the physically comprehensible units of microns,* but it is also thought to be the modulus of the distribution of roughnesses; as such, full contact should occur at four times its value.[5]

Other parameters listed are the position and height of the peak of the transfer curve and the total ink transferred at various film thicknesses on the forme. These latter quantities are presented to illustrate the practical significance of the various trends.

The numerous conditions under which transfer was measured provide an excellent opportunity to test theories concerned with the physical significances and interrelationships among the various transfer parameters. Also discussed are qualitative observations of print quality.

Effects of speed and pressure with each tester
FAG Proof Press

The eight transfer curves from the two papers printed on the FAG Proof Press at the two speeds and pressures are illustrated in Fig. 2. It can be noted therein that transfer was greatly influenced by pressure and speed at low ink film thicknesses. At 20 kg/cm on the coated paper, for example, a decrease in speed from 1·0 to 0·6 m/sec increased transfer at the peak from 55 to 59%. A pressure change to 40 kg/cm produced a further increase in peak transfer to 60 and 65% at the two speeds and furthermore caused the peaks to occur at lower ink film thicknesses. As ink film thickness increased, the influence of pressure and speed became less pronounced. On the uncoated paper, the influence of pressure and speed is noted throughout the ink film thickness range shown, but this influence is somewhat less at the higher than at the lower film thicknesses.

The transfer constants in Table 3 explain the reason for these trends. According to the physical picture on which the transfer equation is based, the smoothness constant k is operative mainly at low ink film thicknesses, with minor contributions from ink immobilization b and ink splitting f. As ink film thickness increases, the contribution from k disappears first; later the contribution from b diminishes until finally f is the controlling factor.

The increased transfer in the peak region is therefore accounted for on the basis that k as well as b both increased with decreasing speed and more so

* Walker and Fetsko realized after the publication of the equation that the exponential term for fraction contact might better have been x/k so that the units of k would be microns.

with increasing pressure. Both trends are logical. As pressure increases, an increase in contact of the plate with the paper should occur. Simultaneously, an increase in the instantaneous penetration of the ink should also occur. At the slower speed, the longer dwell time should serve to increase these two phenomena further.

Regarding the high film thickness trends, which are controlled by film splitting f, the values in Table 3 show that the f's for the coated paper were

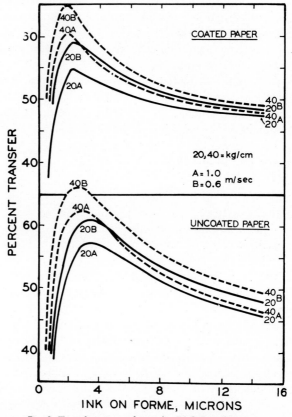

Fig. 2. Transfer curves from the FAG Proof Press.

not influenced by either pressure or speed, and consequently, the curves in Fig. 2 are expected to approach each other as they do with increasing film thickness. The f values for the uncoated paper were not influenced by pressure at either speed, but the decrease in speed increased the values about 2 or 3%. This trend is also logical on the basis that slower speeds permit more time for the ink to split toward the center of the separating film.

The values for the roughness factor $1/k$ and for ink immobilization b

show the uncoated paper to be above 1·5 times rougher and at least twice as absorbent as the coated paper at comparable printing conditions. These relative ratings would be expected from the physical test measurements listed in Table 2.

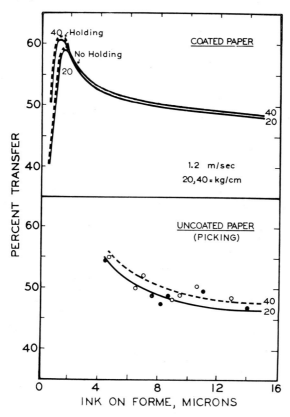

Fig. 3. Transfer curves from the Fogra Printability Tester.

Fogra Printability Tester

Experimentation with the Fogra-tester was limited first of all because, as mentioned previously, the 0·6 m/sec speed was not available. Secondly, the uncoated paper picked quite severely at the 1·2 m/sec speed. A few transfer measurements were made with this paper, but as seen in the bottom of Fig. 3, they were neither accurate nor precise because of the paper particles transferred to the inked disk. It is, however, rather significant that this paper picked only on the Fogra-tester.

The experiments on the coated paper at the one available speed were therefore conducted at the two pressures with the trailing edge of the paper loose as well as fastened down. The top of Fig. 3 illustrates that pressure and holding down hardly had any effect except at very low ink film thicknesses. That is, neither b nor f were affected, as the data in Table 3 show. The influence of pressure was not very great probably because of the smooth rubber packing used.

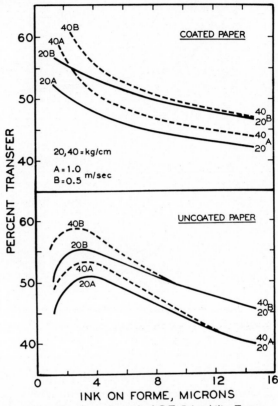

Fig. 4. Transfer curves from the I.G.T. Printability Tester.

At low ink film thicknesses, the steepness of the transfer curves at first prevented any noticeable observations of the influence of holding down, but subsequent calculations of k definitely showed the subtle difference in that k's for holding down were always higher than for not holding down. Slippage of the inked disk on the loose paper may account for this trend.

I.G.T. Printability Tester

Figure 4 illustrates the transfer results with the I.G.T. tester; unfortunately, insufficient data were taken in the thin ink film region to provide an accurate picture of the trends in the peak region. Nevertheless, it can be seen at a glance that speed had a much greater influence than was noted previously in the FAG results. The major reason is attributed to the sensitivity of the film split f to the change in speed on the I.G.T. For example, the increase in speed caused f's to drop an average of 3% on the coated paper and a full 10% on the uncoated paper (compared to 0 and 2 or 3% respectively on the FAG).

Although trends in k are not available for the coated paper, b followed the expected pattern in that it increased with increasing pressure and decreasing speed. The k's for the uncoated paper also increased as expected with increasing pressure and dwell time (decreasing speed). The uncoated paper b values, however, produced some unexpected reversals. Table 3 shows that the b's were higher at the faster speed than at the slower speed! Furthermore, increasing pressure caused no significant change at the faster speed and a decrease at the slower speed.

While the unusual trends with pressure may or may not be due to experimental error, the differences in b at the two speeds are large enough to be considered significant. If indeed b is mainly an ink absorption phenomenon, the greater absorption at the faster speed is difficult to comprehend. One possibility is shear thinning. That is, the higher shear in the nip zone at the faster speed may have reduced the viscosity of the ink, and hence penetration was increased. This hypothesis is only conjecture in lieu of a more logical explanation. The possibility that a higher maximum pressure at the faster speed forced more ink into the paper was ruled out because an increase in average pressure sometimes decreased b. Since increasing pressure increases shear, more credence is given to the shear thinning concept.

The transfer curves for the uncoated paper in the bottom of Fig. 4 show that, despite the higher b values, the peaks of the two curves 20A and 40A for the faster speed both were lower than those for the slower speed. The heights of the peaks are accounted for first of all by the increasing k with increasing pressure. Note in Table 3, however, that the 40A k value is larger than the 20B k value, yet the 40A peak is lower. The reason here is the markedly lower f value for 40A (27%) than for 20B (37%). These trends indicate that the peak height is not a measure of any single factor, and particularly not of surface absorption. This matter will be discussed in more detail later.

Leipzig Printability Tester

The Leipzig transfer curves in Fig. 5 immediately illustrate that, as was the case with the I.G.T. results, transfer was greatly sensitive to speed particularly at high film thicknesses, where ink splitting f is the controlling factor. It may be recalled that both instruments have cylinder–cylinder geometries. The increase in speed from 0·6 m/sec to 1·2 m/sec caused a reduction in f of about 4% on the coated papers and 8% on the uncoated papers. An increase of about 2% with increasing pressure was also found except in the high speed coated paper results.

The situations with k and b were even more unusual than the I.G.T. results. As seen in Table 3, only the coated paper k values followed the expected trends. The b values not only on the uncoated paper, but also on the coated paper, showed the same increase in b with increasing speed as

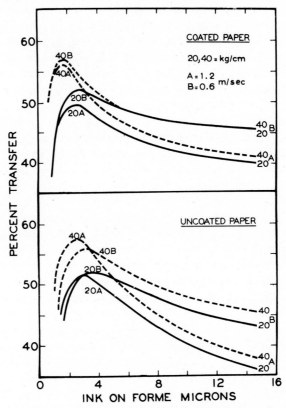

Fig. 5. Transfer curves from the Leipzig Printability Tester.

was found on the I.G.T.! There was also the same tendency for b to decrease, though very slightly, with increasing pressure. Whether these unusual effects are due to shear thinning is again a matter for conjecture.

The most unusual result with the Leipzig Tester was that the uncoated paper k values were lower at slower speed. This reversed trend is clearly apparent in Fig. 5. There the actual transfer curves for the slower speed are lower than for the faster speed in the thin ink film region, where the smoothness constant k is the controlling factor. Normally, smoothness increases at slower speeds supposedly because there is more time for the paper to flatten out or the ink to flow out beyond the actual points of contact with the paper surface. A possible explanation for the reversed trend in the Leipzig results is based on the fact that the rubber blanket used for the packing had a textile-like surface. It is quite likely that, at the slower speeds, the uncoated paper had more time to conform to the rough pattern on the blanket surface and actually became rougher. Evidently the hard coated paper was not affected. This hypothesis should certainly be checked, through a study wherein packing roughness and softness are varied.

Comparisons among the instruments

It has already been mentioned that the sensitivity of the ink splitting factor f to speed was greater with the I.G.T. and Leipzig Testers than with the FAG Proof Press. Furthermore, an increase in b with increasing speed was observed with the uncoated paper on the I.G.T. and with both papers on the Leipzig Tester. Although this phenomenon did not occur with either of the papers on the FAG Proof Press, it has been observed in several Vandercook No. 4 Proof Press studies at Lehigh[6,7] where more viscous inks were generally used than the one used for this study. The broad picture gathered from the various results indicates that b decreases at first with increasing speed, but, after some critical speed is reached, b increases with further increases in speed. This critical speed evidently depends on the press–ink–paper combination.

Figure 6 and close examination of the data in Table 3 reveal other interesting differences among the testers studied here. Figure 6 shows that, in the practical ink film thickness range, the Fogra and FAG transfer was quite similar, the I.G.T. lower, and the Leipzig the lowest. Although this ranking generally held at all pressure–speed combinations, the slower speed transfer curves were closer together than the faster speed curves illustrated in Fig. 6. On the coated paper, the ranking depended mostly on the ink splitting factor f, while on the uncoated paper the ranking was attributed to a combination of b and f. The ranking at low ink film thicknesses depended primarily on k.

It was rather surprising that, despite their opposite cylinder–flat geometries, different cylinder diameters, and different packings, the Fogra and the FAG produced almost the same values for the ink splitting constant f. It is, however, most significant that only the Fogra-tester picked the uncoated paper. Compared with the FAG, the Fogra's smaller disk gives it a greater separation velocity, which may explain the picking. On the other hand, the fact that the f's were similar indicates that within the sequence of nip actions, the forces involved in picking may reach a maximum prior to the determination of the ink splitting position.

The situation is more complex when all the testers are included in this analysis. Based on the geometries of the four print makers, the fastest separation velocity at the same linear speed should occur on the I.G.T., followed by the Leipzig, Fogra, and FAG, in that order. Yet the I.G.T. did not pick the uncoated paper and the Fogra did. Excluding the Fogra-tester,

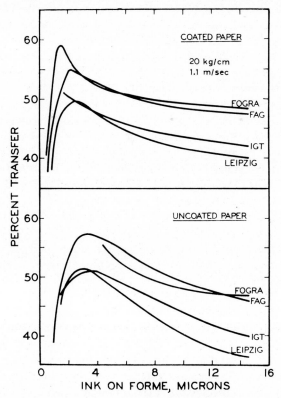

Fig. 6. Transfer curves from the four laboratory print makers.

the uncoated paper f's rated the testers in the proper order; that is, the fastest separating I.G.T. gave the lowest ink split. But on the coated paper, the Leipzig Tester generally gave slightly lower film splits than the I.G.T.

Another method for analyzing the splitting results is based on the distance between the paper and plate at the point of splitting. Assuming that splitting occurs at the same distance from the nip center, then in the two cylindrical systems, I.G.T. and Leipzig, less ink should split the paper because the distances between the plate and paper are greater than on the flat-bed systems, FAG and Fogra. This concept may not be fundamentally sound, and although it may explain the differences between the two types of geometric systems, it is not effective within a type of system. Packing characteristics are undoubtedly also important in determining geometry within the nip.

Regarding the smoothness constant k, the low pressure results generally show that the Fogra-tester provided the most contact between the plate and paper at low ink film thicknesses, the FAG and I.G.T. were alike in the middle, and the Leipzig Tester last. This ranking corresponds to the smoothness of the various packings: smooth rubber, tympan, paper, and rough rubber respectively. The b values on the coated paper were generally of the same order of magnitude. On the uncoated paper, I.G.T. had the highest b values, followed by the FAG, and in turn the Leipzig Tester. Shear thinning might explain the high I.G.T. values, but this concept breaks down with respect to the low Leipzig values.

Although the percent transfer and the mechanisms whereby the transfer was accomplished were different among the testers, the differences in total transfer were not significant from a routine control printing viewpoint. The last columns in Table 3 list the total amounts transferred to the papers at various ink film thicknesses carried initially on the forme. At 5μ there is no practical difference among the conditions, papers, and testers. At 10μ, the differences averaged about a half micron, and at 15μ, the spread among the testers increased to about 1μ.

INTERRELATIONSHIPS AMONG THE TRANSFER PARAMETERS

Smoothness and absorbency

In a previous study involving a series of widely different paperboards and coated papers,[8] it was noted that a decrease in the smoothness constant k, (or conversely, an increase in the roughness factor $1/k$) was accompanied by a simultaneous increase in the ink immobilization constant b. The question arose as to whether b measures a combination of porosity and roughness, or whether the relationship is coincidental because a rough surface is usually also a more porous surface (or vice versa due to coating, calendering, etc.). Subsequently, limited experiments on surfaces of equal porosity and greatly different roughness indicated that smoothness had little if any effect on the magnitude of b.[6]

The situation between the roughness values $1/k$ and ink immobilization b from the experiments described herein is illustrated in the top of Fig. 7. If the points had been plotted without reference to source, a general increase in both roughness and surface absorbency would be apparent. On the other hand, if the points are examined according to paper and print maker, various specific trends are noted. With the coated paper, the roughness factor $1/k$ increased with no increase or with a decrease in b. The uncoated paper results with the Leipzig Tester and the FAG Press also showed an inverse relationship between roughness and b. The FAG results, for example, were caused by the fact that $1/k$ decreased, while b increased, with increasing pressure and increasing dwell time (decreasing speed). The I.G.T. results did not follow this expected trend because, it may be recalled, b decreased instead of increasing with increasing dwell time.

It may be concluded from Fig. 7 that, broadly speaking, trends in surface absorbency and roughness generally parallel each other. Within a system,

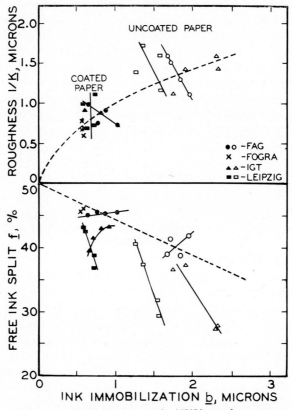

Fig. 7. Interrelationships among the NPIRI transfer constants

however, surface absorbency and roughness are separate entities. How closely the system must be confined is a matter for further research.

Surface absorbency and film splitting

In the previously mentioned study involving widely different stocks,[8] it was also noted that an increase in ink immobilization b was accompanied by a simultaneous decrease in film splitting f. It was certainly curious that the ink appeared to " know " to what it was splitting despite the fact that a layer of ink was already immobilized on the surface of the stock. The inverse relationship was explained on the basis of cavitation theory. It was assumed that the ink splits in the plane of least resistance, that is, where the " bubbles " exist in the largest number and size. Surface porosity would then be influential because the drainage of the vehicle produces pigment-enriched portions at the surface which act as nucleation catalysts. An alternative hypothesis of Taylor[9] suggested that the lower split to the paper involves zones of higher temperature and reduced viscosity on the paper side of the nip.

The large variety of b and f values from the present study provide another opportunity to examine the relationship. The results plotted in the bottom of Fig. 7 again show that, without reference to source, split decreased generally with increasing b. But, as was the case with the roughness–absorbency relationship, various specific trends due to paper and print maker are noted. The I.G.T. coated paper and the FAG coated and uncoated paper results show that b and f both increased with increasing pressure and dwell time. The other paper–tester combinations had shown a reversal in b with speed, and hence the b–f relationship reversed.

Again, it may be concluded from Fig. 7 that, broadly speaking, free film splitting decreases with increasing surface absorption, perhaps due to increasing cavitation near the paper surface. Within a system, however, splitting is not dependent on surface absorption.

Physical significance of the transfer peak

Various workers have attempted to rate paper properties from total transfer at some arbitrary ink film thickness and/or from the height of the peak. For example, Ginman[10] rated paper smoothness from E, the ink film thickness at which 50% transfer first occurs, and paper absorbency from H, a function related to the height of the peak. Similarily, Kozarovickij[11] used the ratio of transfer at an arbitrary low ink film thickness to that at the peak as his " coefficient of saturation," Kn, and transfer at an arbitrary high ink film thickness as his " coefficient of transfer," Km.

Since transfer data were not always taken at low enough film thicknesses to determine E, the ink film thicknesses on the forme at which the peaks occurred were listed in Table 3 as an alternative. The top of Fig. 8 illustrates the relationship of the position of the peak to the roughness factor $1/k$ and to ink immobilization b. An excellent correlation was found with roughness, irrespective of paper, print maker, or printing conditions. But the correlation with surface absorbency showed the same types of relationships noted previously between $1/k$ and b.

The bottom of Fig. 8 illustrates that the height of the peak also correlated with roughness, but here different correlations were found for the various

N

papers and print makers. Consequently, the height of the peak is felt to be related to smoothness plus some other properties. The height of the peak vs. *b* showed a variety of correlations including no trend, direct, and inverse. Functions related to the peak height must therefore be suspect as measures of absorbency.

It may be concluded from these observations that low ink film thickness parameters, such as position of the peak, Ginman's *E*, and Kozarovickij's coefficient of saturation *Kn* are good measures of paper roughness. The

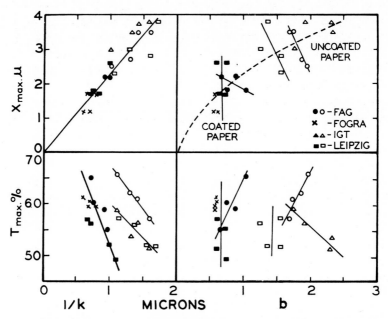

Fig. 8. Relationship of transfer peak characteristics to paper roughness and surface absorbency

height of the peak is related to a combination of factors, of which surface absorbency is not the most important.

Qualitative observations of print quality

Gloss Mottle. Although the non-drying characteristics of the ink make it amenable for transfer experiments from the press stability standpoint, other problems were created, particularly in the evaluation of print quality. For example, during the FAG Proof Press experiments, a gloss mottle was observed on the full coverage prints immediately after printing. This gloss mottle was so vivid at the higher of the two pressures that it would have to be noticeable even to the most casual observer. Unfortunately, the mottle disappeared a few minutes later; evidently, the regularly patterned ink filaments levelled out due to a flow-out of the ink over the surface of the paper or they may have been disturbed by the penetration process. [12]

It cannot be stated with confidence that the mottle patterns did not occur on the Leipzig prints, which had been made previous to the FAG prints, but they were definitely not noticeable on the Fogra prints made subsequently. Since both the Leipzig and the Fogra-testers had rubber packings, no mottle would have been expected on the basis of rubber plate results at NPIRI. [12] The mottle patterns were purposely looked for in the later experiments on the I.G.T. Tester. Although they appeared, they did not seem as noticeable as the memory of the FAG prints. If a drying ink had been used, it is likely that some of the gloss type of mottle pattern might have been preserved on the dried prints, and they could then be related qualitatively at least to speed, pressure, packing, and geometry.

Lower practical limits. Noteworthy in Table 3 and in the previous discussion is the absence of any reference to the lower practical limits, defined as the minimum ink film thickness required for full coverage. The major reason is that the LPL's were extremely difficult to select with any degree of precision by visual observation. At sufficiently low film thicknesses, discrete areas of covered and uncovered paper were discernible, and these areas clearly reflected the pattern of the respective packings. But as film thickness increased, there was no sharp demarcation between uncovered and adequately covered prints.

On the Fogra-tester, which had a very smooth rubber packing, the discrete uncovered areas gave way to a uniform gray tone at about $1 \cdot 5$ to 2μ ink on the forme (1μ or less on the paper) and merely increased in density with further increases in film thickness. On the Leipzig Tester, ridges on the print from the packing finally disappeared at about 4 to 6μ of ink carried on the forme (depending on the paper and pressure).

On the FAG and I.G.T. Testers, both of which had hard packings, the selection of the lower practical limit was particularly difficult because a " color " mottle set in between the region of uncovered and fully covered prints. It appeared that the cause of this color mottle was the fact that, although all of the paper surface might have been contacted during nip impression, upon release of the pressure the high spots on the surface recovered from the compression and did not accept the ink as well as the valleys did. The color mottle started at about 3 or 4μ ink on the forme and disappeared at 6 to 10μ. The mottle was more severe at the higher pressure and in fact lasted until higher film thicknesses than at the lower pressure.

An attempt was made to set up a comparison of the print densities based on reflectance measurements. The first attempt was not successful partly because of the vastly different ages of the prints at the time. Furthermore, even months later, the ink could easily be rubbed off the paper, and the prints could otherwise be damaged by simple handling. For these and other reasons, quantitative evaluation of the prints was abandoned.

CONCLUSIONS

(1) The geometry and packing of the print maker influence percent transfer of ink to paper, the mechanisms whereby the transfer is accomplished, and the sensitivity of transfer to variations in pressure and speed.

(2) A broad relationship exists between paper roughness, surface absorption, and ink splitting. Within a system, these factors are separate entities.

(3) Low film thickness transfer parameters, such as the position of the transfer curve peak, are good measures of paper roughness. The height of the peak is related to a combination of factors, of which surface absorption is not the most important.

RECOMMENDATIONS FOR FURTHER WORK

(1) Further comparisons of print makers should be carried out under the same conditions of separation velocity and packing. Faster speeds should be employed to magnify the differences due to geometry.

(2) Action in the nip zone of the press must be clarified. There is evidence that the forces involved in picking reach a maximum prior to the determination of the ink splitting position. It was also suggested that shear thinning of the ink with faster press speeds overcomes the effects of reduced dwell time in determining ink penetration during nip contact.

ACKNOWLEDGMENTS

The author is indebted to the Directors of the Leipzig, Fogra, I.G.T., and NPIRI Research Institutes for their cooperation in permitting the use of their staff and facilities. Staff members who were particularly helpful were K. Rieche, Leipzig; H. Dürner, K. Schirmer, and B. Schirmer, Fogra; G. Blokhuis, I.G.T.; and W. D. Schaeffer, A. B. Fisch, and C. E. Grund, NPIRI.

REFERENCES

1. J. ALBRECHT and K. H. SCHIRMER, A contribution to the determination of printing ink printability, Int. Bull. for the Printing and Allied Trades No. 73, 47 (1956).
2. G. BLOKHUIS, W. LENAARTS, L. J. LODEWIJKS and J. J. MONROY, The Printability of paper. Manual of the I.G.T. printability tester, I.G.T. Publication 12 (1955).

3. E. RUPP and K. RIECHE, Beitrage zur Bedruckbarkeit von Papier und Folien, Institut fur Graphische Technik, Leipzig (1959).
4. W. C. WALKER and J. M. FETSKO, A concept of ink transfer in printing, *Amer. Ink Maker* **33**, No. 12, 38 (1955).
5. W. D. SCHAEFFER, NPIRI, Lehigh University. Private Communication.
6. L. C. C. LIN, The effect of printing conditions on the ink transfer and print quality of non-porous stock, M. S. Dissertation, Lehigh University (1958).
7. Unpublished data from TAPPI Research Project 168, Transfer and penetration aspects of ink receptivity, Lehigh University.
8. J. M. FETSKO, Printability studies on a survey series of paperboards and coated papers, *Tappi* **41**, No. 2, 49 (1958).
9. J. H. TAYLOR and A. C. ZETTLEMOYER, Hypothesis on the mechanism of ink splitting during printing, *Tappi* **41**, No. 12, 749 (1958).
10. R. GINMAN, A. SVEDLIN and L. NORDMAN, Estimating the printability of paper by means of proof printing, *Norsk Skogindustrie* **11**, No. 1, 14 (1957).
11. L. A. KOZAROVICKIJ, Graphic Arts Research Institute, Moscow. Private Communication and Russian Literature,
12. J. M. FETSKO, Factors affecting print gloss and uniformity, NPIRI Project Report No. 45 (1960) esp. pp. 24–30.

DISCUSSION

LASSEUR: In order to explain the differences between flatbed and two-cylinder print makers you presume that ink splitting occurs at constant distance from the centre of the nip, and independently of the ratio of the cylinder diameters. What is the background for this assumption?

Assuming that your presumption holds, can you explain why, on a flat-bed print-maker, less ink will reach the paper than on a two-cylinder apparatus?

FETSKO: I do not think for a moment that the position of film split is independent of geometry. We do not know the horizontal distance (out from the nip centre) at which the film finally splits, nor can this be determined readily with available instrumentation. Lacking the necessary data, the assumption was made merely to explain the case in point.

Having therefore presumed the same horizontal distance of film split for all geometries, let us further presume that the vertical distance of split (determined by the transfer constant f) is largely dependent on the cavitation process. That is, the film ruptures where the cavities exist in the largest number and size. The preponderance of cavities is thought to be formed on the paper side of the nip. If the cavity growth rate is the same in all geometries, then the fraction of the distance travelled by the cavities from the paper to the plate would be less for the cylindrical systems than for the flat-bed systems.

It might be easier to visualize if we assign numbers to the various cases. Let us say hypothetically that the distance between the plate and paper at the position of final split is 1 cm for a cylindrical system and 0·5 cm for a flat-bed system. If the film split occurs at a distance of 0·2 cm from the paper in both cases, then the split to the paper would be 20 % for the cylindrical system and 40 % for the flat-bed system. This picture is, of course, oversimplified but I feel it does illustrate how geometry can influence film split.

ROGERS: Film splitting may be presumed to take place at the centre of the entire system (Printing surface–ink–paper). The use of two dispersions (1) a Newtonian one and (2) a highly visco-elastic one tested over a wide range of instrument speeds would be of great assistance in explaining both transfer proportional differences, and in some instances differences between instruments.

FETSKO: There is no doubt about it: a great deal more research is needed to ascertain what goes on at the moment of impression.

LARAIGNOU: We have obtained transfer curves on various non-porous stock like polyethylene, saran, p.v.c., Cellophane and metals like zinc and aluminium. These surfaces can be considered at the moment of impression as non-porous and having a very high degree of smoothness. In all these cases we find b values which are zero. But we have also done transfer curves on grained aluminium and zinc plates and find in this case finite values for b. If you consider that b is only related to penetration we should find in the above case a zero value for b.

FETSKO: At the time the transfer equation was derived, we believed that b was mostly a matter of instantaneous penetration, but we did not rule out other influences such as surface area of the sheet, adhesion, etc. So we purposely labelled b the ink immobilization constant rather than a penetration constant.

In subsequent studies on a wide variety of paperboards and coated papers, we found a good correlation between k and b. That is, as the smoothness of the papers increased, ink immobilization decreased. The question naturally arose: " Is smoothness a factor in determining the magnitude of b, or is a smooth sheet generally also a sheet of low surface porosity? " We then made a statistical study with two aluminium laminated surfaces, one very smooth, and the other very rough. We found large differences in k but no differences in b. This finding led us to believe that the correlation between k and b in commercial papers comes from the fact that a smooth sheet generally also has low surface porosity.

The finding that the aluminium surface has a b value at all, although it was quite small (*ca.* 0.3μ), leads us to think that a property such as surface adhesion has to be considered. We would like to extend this work to surfaces having varied roughnesses and porosities at controlled levels, for example, with specially-made halftone plates as the paper, and with Millipore filter paper. The expense of these materials is rather high, however.

In regard to the differences in k and b which you observed between smooth and roughened metals, if the differences are statistically significant, the results might be explained on the basis of differences in adhesion and/or wettability due to the various surface areas. Also, even metal surfaces are not completely non-porous.

RUPP: Arising from Miss Fetsko's comments, I think it would be useful to extend the work on a co-operative basis to non-absorbent plastic or even aluminium foils.

BANKS: Miss Fetsko is to be congratulated on a very illuminating study of the performance of various so-called printability testers. It should not surprise us that they do not all give the same results, for the simple reason that in general we do not know how comparable they are in regard to the hydrodynamic pressures generated during impression. A knowledge of the external loading so often referred to as printing pressure is not sufficient to establish the pressures in the ink film. It is probable that the situation is more easily known in platen type impression, but unfortunately this is unrealistic for most printing, though if one is interested in the relationship of transfer to pressure as a paper property it should not matter.

TONE RENDERING IN GRAVURE

by Dr. A. J. W. Sweerman, W. M. du Pont and H. ter Haar

I.G.T., Holland

INTRODUCTION

As is known in gravure printing, the ink rests in the recesses of the printing forme. During the printing process the higher as well as the lower parts of the printing forme are inked, after which the superfluous ink on the higher parts is removed by a doctor blade.

The bearing grid of the doctor blade must be made up from one or more continuous systems of lines, as separate dots may be damaged by the doctor blade.

However, the systems of lines crossing each other have one more function. They divide the printing surface in recessed cells that prevent the low viscosity inks necessary for gravure printing from running out.

PRINTING OF TONES IN CONVENTIONAL GRAVURE

The amount of ink in the cells determines the density on the paper. In conventional gravure the content variations of the cells are mainly obtained by variation in depth of etching. For this a photosensitive layer (carbon tissue or rotofilm) with soft gradation is used, possessing the property that the passage of the etch through it is dependent on the degree of exposure.

The photosensitive layer is successively exposed through a screen to obtain the doctor blade bearing grid and a continuous tone positive for the adjustment of the depth of etching.

The disadvantages of the conventional gravure are:

(1) The relatively great influence of only slight wear of the printing cylinder on the tone rendering of the highlights.

(2) The many variations in properties of the carbon tissue, this being a natural product in addition to which it is also sensitive to atmospheric conditions.

From researches made by I.G.T. it was found that the shapes of the curves relating the densities of the continuous tone positive and print show little variation (see Fig. 1).

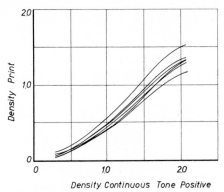

Fig. I.

A grayscale was copied, etched and printed a number of times together with a large run of a periodical. The grayscale was always entirely treated with the various etches and the etching was not done locally. It appears that the relation between density of continuous tone positive and print can be represented by $D_{\text{print}} = K.f(D_{\text{continuous tone positive}})$. The shape of the curve $f(D_{\text{continuous tone positive}})$ was practically identical for the etchings examined. $K.$ is a factor depending on the etching of the grayscale and the combination " paper and ink ".

Among others the factor $K.$ depends upon the opacity of the ink. From some examples compiled in Table 1 it appears that the difference in gradation, as given in Fig. 1 can be compensated for the greater part through adaptation of the opacity of the ink.

TABLE 1.

Density continuous tone positive	Density of the print during the process				
	Etching 1			Etching 2	
	150·000	500·000	700·000	100·000	700·000
0·29	0·10 (0·07)	0·08 (0·06)	0·12 (0·07)	0·08 (0·06)	0·04 (0·03)
0·34	0·12 (0·08)	0·11 (0·08)	0·15 (0·09)	0·11 (0·08)	0·06 (0·05)
0·44	0·17 (0·12)	0·15 (0·10)	0·21 (0·12)	0·15 (0·11)	0·08 (0·07)
0·58	0·25 (0·17)	0·22 (0·15)	0·31 (0·18)	0·20 (0·14)	0·13 (0·11)
0·76	0·38 (0·26)	0·33 (0·23)	0·43 (0·25)	0·33 (0·24)	0·23 (0·20)
0·96	0·53 (0·36)	0·50 (0·35)	0·60 (0·35)	0·44 (0·31)	0·37 (0·31)
1·30	0·81 (0·55)	0·75 (0·52)	0·89 (0·52)	0·70 (0·50)	0·60 (0·51)
1·62	1·20 (0·82)	1·12 (0·78)	1·37 (0·80)	1·05 (0·74)	0·86 (0·73)
1·89	1·39 (0·95)	1·30 (0·90)	1·57 (0·92)	1·33 (0·94)	1·08 (0·92)
2·08	1·46 (1·00)	1·44 (1·00)	1·71 (1·00)	1·41 (1·00)	1·18 (1·00)

The bracketed values show the densities, calculated on a reduced scale, with a final density of 1·00. After printing, the gravure shell with the gray-scale was stripped. From every section of the grayscale the product of the depth of etching and area of the cells was determined.

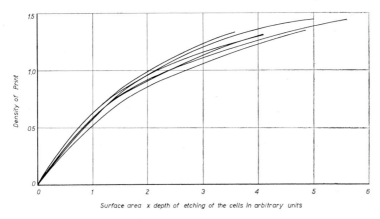

Fig. 2.

In Fig. 2 the relation between the density of the paper and the product of depth of etching and printing area is given for six separate etchings. The curves are well represented by the formula of Dr. Tollenaar:

$$D = D_{\infty}(1 - e^{-mx})$$

where D = density of the print,

D_{∞} = a constant representing the printing density for a very large quantity of transferred ink.

The constant D_{∞} is not directly measurable as the formula does not hold when large amounts of ink are transferred. Accordingly D_{∞} is a parameter and is an extrapolation of the properties under normal printing conditions when the formula does apply.

m = a constant, which takes account of the contact area between paper and printing surface during the printing process (printing smoothness).

x = the product of depth of etching and printing area of the cells and is approximately the amount of ink applied. For this the depth of etching only appeared to be less suitable.

> *Note:* The term approximation is used. It is clear that the cell content is not directly proportional to this product. Besides the transfer factor will not be the same for every depth of etching.

The outermost curves in Fig. 2 can be described by the above formula, with $m = 0.49$ and $D_\infty = 1.37$ and 1.59.

Physically D_∞ can be considered a measure of the covering power of the ink.

(3) A third difficulty in conventional gravure is the making of continuous tone positives with an initial density of 0.3 and a final density of 1.6–1.7. In principle this can be measured, but it is time consuming.

In Fig. 3 the average deviations in end-densities and density range as found in a number of gravure printing plants are given.

The standard deviations in end-densities and density ranges varied from 0.2–0.25 and showed little variation.

These standard deviations give an estimate of the accuracy with which an observer can estimate a density.

(4) Naturally the relation between density of original and continuous tone positive can be influenced by adaptation of the film characteristic, masks and multilayer films, etc., but it still remains difficult to attain a non-linear relation, which is reproducible.

PRINTING OF TONES IN AUTOTYPE GRAVURE

The advantages are well-known. The wear of the printing cylinder is less disturbing and the reproducibility of any phase between screen positive and printing is appreciably better.

In pure autotype gravure the cell content depends on the area of the screendots. If the copy and etching are reproducible the cell content depends on the screendot area only.

It seems there are two requirements which a pure autotype gravure process must have:

(a) The process from screen positive to printing forme must be reproducible.

(b) The screen positive must have exact tone rendering without correction. The exact tone rendering must be easy to attain and easy to check. We wish to confine ourselves to discussing item (b).

GRAVURE SCREEN POSITIVE WITH THE IDEAL TONE RENDERING

The difficulties experienced here are caused by the fact that insufficient control can be exercised on the tone rendering while screening.

We also come across these difficulties when making screen negatives or positives for letterpress and lithography. In gravure we have in addition the exact shape of the shadow dots. The result is that with most of the processes, methods are used in which during every exposure the corrections in the tone rendering must be carried out.

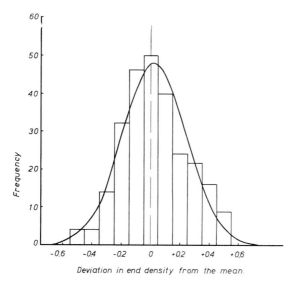

Fig. 3(a).

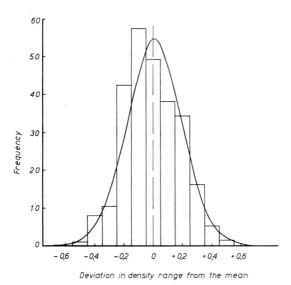

Fig. 3(b).

It is thus clear that only contact screens with an exact tone rendering can offer a solution here.

DETERMINATION OF THE EXACT TONE RENDERING OF THE CONTACT SCREEN

In order to achieve a reproducible copy and etching, every dot-size of the screen positive and printing process must correspond with a specific density of the print. Measuring the dot-size takes time and it appears that for a given screen ruling the dot-size corresponds with a certain apparent density of the screen positive.

Hence, for a reproducible process there exists a relation between apparent density of the screen positive and density of the print.

The same conclusion holds for the relation between apparent density of screen positive and density of original.

Given the simple case that the required tone rendering is determined by equality in density of original and reproduction, then it is clear that the relation between screen positive and print is identical with the relation between screen positive and original.

The relation between the density of the screen positive and the original when any other tone rendering is required is found by transforming the scales relating density of print and screen positive in the ratio of maximum density of print to maximum density of original. This applies not only to original–screen positive–print, but also, for instance, to: original–screen negative–print, provided the whole process is reproducible.

A NEW METHOD FOR MAKING GRAVURE SCREEN POSITIVES

It is possible to get a gravure–screen–positive by making two line–screen–negatives with a contact–line–screen from an original or diapositive. The line–screen–negatives only differ in the position of the screen (e.g. 90° with regard to one another).

The line–screen–negatives should be made up in such a way that in the shadows a small covered line appears, while a transparent line in the highlights may be missing.

Both line–screen–negatives are laid upon one another in register and contacted on a lith film with a point light source. It is not possible to carry out both exposures for the line–screen–negatives on the same lith film, as the two exposures together would result in a distribution of light of which the isophotes show roundings in the corners (see Fig. 4).

The doctor blade bearing grid appears automatically in the way described and therefore it is not necessary to take special steps with regard to the density distribution in the screen.

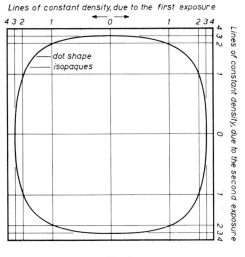

Fig. 4.

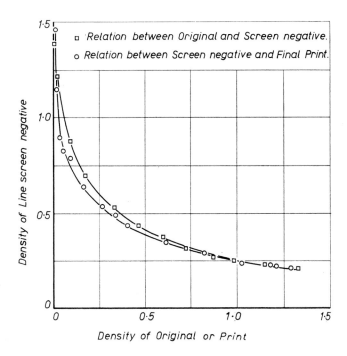

Fig. 5.

During the manufacture of gravure–crossline–contact–screens at I.G.T. it appeared impossible to achieve a density distribution in the screen so as to produce an acceptable bearing grid in the shadows with a correct tone-rendering. However, the I.G.T.-method of making the line–contact–screens is such that the tone rendering can be varied within wide limits.

For the chosen process the relation between the density of the line–screen–negative and density print was determined.

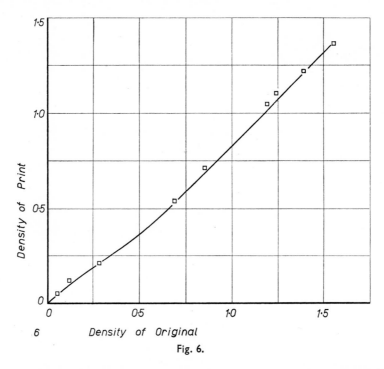

Fig. 6.

As the density of original and copy ought to become equal to one another, the relation between density original and density line–screen–negative is known.

From tentative tests this relation was found (see Fig. 5). The screen-positive was copied on carbon tissue and the etching took place in one phase with $FeCl_3$ of 36°BE. It is clear that, when using another copying and etching method the relation will be slightly altered. It is remarkable that the shape of the curve looks much like the ideal curve for screen-negatives suitable for lithography and letterpress. [1, 2]

In Fig. 5 the tone rendering of the lines–contact–screen used, is given.

In Fig. 6 the relation between the density of original and copy may be noticed.

CONCLUSIONS

(1) Halftone positives show less variation than continuous tone positives and in consequence less corrections are necessary in the etching process.

(2) Halftone photography makes it possible to influence the tone rendering with the screen in a simple and reproducible way.

(3) Halftone photography is easily inspected by using an " ideal " screen, as it is only necessary to measure the dot-size and width of lines at the extreme highlights and shadows.

(4) With the method described the tone rendering of the screen positive can be adapted to the process of etching.

REFERENCES

1. V. G. W. HARRISON, S. A. MITCHENER and L. E. LAWSON, *J. Photogr. Sci.* **3**, 97 (1955).
2. S. D. WINN, *J. Photogr. Sci.* **8**, 173 (1960).

DISCUSSION

LOVASZ: We are particularly interested in the work concerning autotype gravure printing since we are also dealing with this question.

In our opinion the use of two line-screen-negatives mentioned in your paper causes technological difficulties. We should like to know what advantage the use of two line-screen-negatives presents.

We too have developed an autotype gravure contact screen, by which we get a screen diapositive directly from a continuous tone negative. These screen diapositives are used for making printing cylinders.

SWEERMAN: With the method described the density distribution in the screen has no influence on the correct shape of the shadow dots.

This independence of density distribution in the screen and dot shape gives the designer of the screen more freedom regarding the tone rendering of the screen.

ROGERS: You have shown good agreement between copy, halftone negative and print densities. What etching depth was required for these results?

How did you control the area loss during etching?

SWEERMAN: If the area loss during etching is reproducible, it is possible to take this into account with regard to the density distribution in the screen.

Therefore we do not control this.

PROGRESS REPORT ON THE INK DRYING PROCESS OF ROTOGRAVURE PRESSES

by WOLFRAM ESCHENBACH

Institut für Druckmaschinen und Druckverfahren der Technischen
Hochschule Darmstadt

INTRODUCTION

The drying problem has become especially important because of the increasing use of high speed printing presses, in particular in multicolour rotogravure. Printing quality and hourly output depend strongly on the behaviour of the drying process and especially so in the case of rotogravure with its particular inks. In the following we shall outline some methods developed by the Darmstadt Institute which make possible measuring techniques for the continuous observation of drying behaviour in the rotogravure press under actual working conditions.

To begin with let us review a few points about the process of rotogravure ink drying.

Rotogravure ink, a relatively fluid liquid consists of pigments, binding agents, fillers and solvents. Pigments and fillers stay carefully distributed in suspension within the solvent; in addition to these there are binding resins which fix the ink particles to the printing surface after evaporation of the solvent. Once the solvents have, during the actual printing process, transferred the ink particles to the printing surface it is desired that the solvent evaporate as rapidly as possible. The demands of the process and considerations of health make it practicable to use solvents of good volatility of the aromatic series (toluene, xylene) and of aliphatic hydrocarbons (benzines). For special inks, esters, glycoles and simple alcohol may be used. The study of the drying process in rotogravure raises questions of a physical and chemical nature.

It may be assumed that the solvent in rotogravure inks is bound by adsorption to the fixed ink components. As has been stated already, drying of rotogravure ink occurs through evaporation of the solvent, therefore through transfer of solvent molecules from the ink layer to the surrounding air. It is known that the speed of evaporation depends, among other factors, upon solvent vapour pressure and the "substance transfer factor." The latter depends, among other factors, on the speed with which the drying air flows over the printing paper surface (slope of the concentration curve). The following equation can be established for evaporation intensity:

$$J = (\alpha/r)(t_2 - t_{fe})$$

where α = Heat transfer coefficient kcal/m² hr°C

$\quad t_2$ = Air temperature °C

$\quad t_{fe}$ = Surface temperature of evaporating liquid °C

$\quad r$ = Latent heat of evaporation of solvent kcal/kg.

In practice the increase necessary in vapour pressure is attained through heat transfer by convection, radiation or contact drying methods. It is customary in a rotogravure press to heat either the drying air or the printing material from below by means of a drying drum or to use both methods simultaneously.* In the example of an air heating system which we shall use in our discussion, the ink layer is drying from above and, as a rule, is forming a so-called skin quite rapidly.

In the heat drum system the ink layer is heated from below, a more advantageous solution; however, the heat necessary must be conducted through the paper web. Paper is a bad heat conductor and loses humidity during the drying process; this can cause undesirable fluctuations in paper tension and register trouble.[1] It must be emphasized that, as a rule, completion of the drying process within the machine itself is not possible because some solvents will remain adsorbed within the paper capillaries and in the ink film as it skins over. The goal aimed at is primarily the achievement of a stick free surface drying process corresponding to the ink smear limit at a given ink consistency.

Immediately after transfer of ink to the paper in rotogravure the solvent and binding agents penetrate the depressions and capillaries of the paper followed by ink filtration. Pigments fix themselves at the paper surface and are in turn retained in their binding agent, that is bonded in the solvent as well as in the main part of the highly fluid solvents. Here the skin formation already referred to occurs more or less rapidly, thus making the diffusion process more difficult. Penetration depends on thickness of ink layer, viscosity, printing pressure, contact time and naturally on the pore structure of the paper.

The duration of the evaporating process depends on the characteristics and quantity of available printing ink (a function of etching depth and printing

* Some big German printing works use a mixture of benzine and toluene using dry air at room-temperature to effect short drying processes and a good dimensional stability of paper.

structure), on the printing material, on temperature, on speed and direction of hot air flow and on the substance transfer factor.

In 1954, Beloserskij[2] attempted to express, in mathematical terms, the drying process during the evaporation of rotogravure solvents. He began by defining the evaporation process of pure solvents without assuming an auxiliary air flow. This author noticed that benzole evaporates from saturated picture areas within about 40–50 sec, a period several dozen times greater than that of the paper web travelling through the drying system of the machine. If air, circulated at room temperature, is being used, evaporation can be speeded up four to six times. Because the paper web remains in the drying system of the machine only fractions of seconds, it is necessary to apply additional heat to the air used in the drying process. For safety reasons, at this increased drying temperature, the volume of benzole vapours in the waste air removed from the drying system may not exceed 20–25 g/m³ (explosion limit is 48·7 g/m³ at 20°C).

Beloserskij established the following basic equation for the evaporation processes:

$$\mathrm{d}B/\mathrm{d}t = -j(B + a)$$

$\mathrm{d}B/\mathrm{d}t$ = Evaporating speed of the solvent at the moment

B = Quantity of non-evaporated solvent at a given time

a, j = Constants which take into account all parameters influencing the drying process.

From this follows the equation for evaporation time:

$$T_0 = \frac{1}{j} \ln \left[\frac{B_A}{a} + 1 \right] \sec$$

where B_A = Original solvent volume.

Determination of constants j and a is naturally important for the practical usefulness of this formula. Evaporation speed of the solvent and, also, the characteristic values for " a " and " j " depend on the following:

1. Vapour pressure of the solvent.
2. Room temperature and heat supply to the ink layer.
3. Heat conductivity of the ink layer.
4. Specific heat of the solvent.
5. Entropy of vaporization of the solvent.
6. Surface tension of the ink.
7. Molecular associations within the ink.
8. Molecular weight of the solvent.
9. Resin and pigment concentrations.
10. Air humidity.

11. Aerodynamic state above drying layer of ink.
12. Thickness of ink film.
13. Viscosity of ink film.
14. Chemical and physical properties of pigments and bonding agents.

The drying of rotogravure ink on the " printing material " is thus dependent on many factors. Quantitative prediction of drying time is therefore difficult.

APPROACH TO THE PROBLEM

As already mentioned, the performance of a rotogravure press depends essentially on the pattern assumed by the drying process. Practically, this process is determined by type and design of drying system on the one hand, and by evaporating capacity of the solvent on the other. Quantitative measurement of solvent evaporation following the printing process is, therefore, of considerable interest not only for the manufacturer of printing machines but also for the ink manufacturers (this paper will not deal with the mathematical treatment of aerodynamic effects on evaporation).

In practice several methods have been developed for measuring the evaporation rates of different solvents. To mention but a few: the apparatus of MAN, those of Waldschmidt and of Warburg.

At the present time, the Darmstadt Institute has used the method of gas chromatography and was successful in measuring the first phase of the drying process directly on the paper web of the printing press. This was done by sucking the air solvent mixture from above the inked paper web and passing it into a system of alternating accumulators and thence to a Perkin–Elmer Gas Chromatograph. It was thus possible to establish a series of evaporation curves.

In the second phase of this research program we used an apparatus for detecting the presence of hydrocarbons, most of the commonly used inks belonging to this group; this apparatus was the Hydrocarbon Detector 213 (Perkin–Elmer) which works on the principle of flame ionisation. It was used to check solvent concentration for compliance with MAK values in printing establishments. This will be discussed later in section A.

Methods of measurement based on the realization that the solvent content in drying chamber air is reciprocally related to the solvent content of the printed paper ($K \simeq 1/L_m$; K = concentration in the drying air; L_m = residual solvent), were developed in order to establish the solvent concentration in the drying chamber at a given instant under differing drying conditions on one hand and, on the other to evaluate the drying process by determining the quantity of residual solvent in the ink layer on the running paper web. Measurements of the first kind were made with the hydrocarbon detector:

a report on this is found in section B. The investigations of the latter type were conducted by using a method for isolating solvents from printing ink layers through distillation of a boiling liquid containing the solvent. This is discussed in section C.

For a materials balance the following relationship applies for the solvent. Input = solvent content of the drying air + residual solvent content + solvent loss. The latter is caused mainly because of leakage from the drying chamber and losses during transportation of paper.

$$G_E = G_T + G_R + G_V$$

The drying chamber tests, it should be pointed out, were merely preliminary tests conducted for orientation purposes on the Rotogravure press of the Institute. (Drying air by heating rods; electrically heated drying drum; cylinder with full tone surface. Web width 670 mm, printing cylinder circumference 594 mm, maximum printing speed 12,000 rev/hr.)

TESTS CONDUCTED

A. Solvent concentration in room air

In rotogravure printing the solvent evaporation process during physical drying begins in the ink fountain because of the solvent's high vapour pressure and continues across the freshly printed paper web before the web reaches the drying chamber, and, is not finished completely even after passing through the chamber. Through this process which takes place in every single printing unit, the room atmosphere of a printing establishment is more or less permeated by solvent vapours. This creates an explosion hazard; it is possible that, apart from unpleasant odours, health hazards for the workers may appear through toxic effects. To establish effective room ventilation and air evacuation, especially at the source of the vapour, it is necessary to determine the degree of saturation for the room atmosphere and the areas of highest concentration in particular. For this experience has shown the usefulness of the Hydrocarbon Detector 213; which at the same time (see sections B and C) serves also for determining the solvent concentration of the " drying air " and for registering the residual solvent content of the printed paper. The Hydrocarbon Detector 213 apparatus serves for the determination of hydrocarbons and organic matter found in the air in vapourized or gaseous condition. Flame ionization is made use of in this apparatus. It depends on the production of an ion current when a voltage is applied to a heated gas.

This phenomenon is utilized in the detector, which is an ionization chamber consisting of a cylindrical aluminium block with a jet flame nozzle, a wire type lighter and a thermoelement. An aluminium electrode insulated against the housing with Teflon is introduced through the axial bore of the ionization chamber (Fig. 1). The housing is connected directly by way of an amplifier with an ammeter.

Ionization is caused by a hydrogen flame. If we now inject a sample into the hydrogen stream, the magnitude of the energy freed by the flame, through the burning of the introduced hydrocarbons, changes and with it the degree of ionization as well as the current. A one-tube arrangement serves as amplifier for the electrometer.

At this point, the Fractometer 116 which was used for the determination of residual solvent contents should be described briefly.

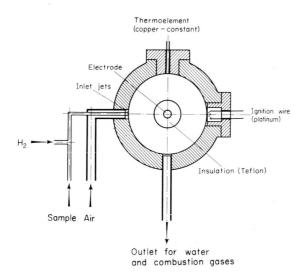

Fig. 1. Design of the ionization chamber.

It is used for the separation of chemical mixtures which can be transformed into a gaseous condition by heating up to 250°C. The sample is injected into a heated sample injection block, vapourized and flushed into the fractioning column by means of a carrier gas (in this case helium). The fractioning columns have the characteristic of adsorbing the components for different retention times. After a time span, characteristic for the individual phases, the components are freed and carried to the detector block. This is how the separation effect of the components occurs.

It should be emphasized that the latest tests have shown a high correlation between the results of the detector and those of the fractometer.

The problem of protection against explosions in printing plants may be mentioned briefly. For instance, in Germany, on rotogravure presses, explosion-protected electrical installations only may be used within a safety range of 1 m. Lower and upper explosion limits for the mixture of air and an inflammable material are expressed in volume per cent and in g/m³ at 760 mm Hg. and 20°C. The lower explosion limit for pure toluene is 1 vol% and the upper about 8 vol%, corresponding to 38·2 g/m³ and 305·6 g/m³ at 20°C. respectively. A few comments will now be made about the physiological effect of the solvent which, in industrial medicine, has evolved into the concept of " maximum concentration at working place ", MAK, for short.

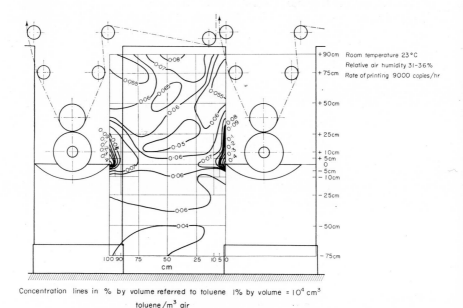

Concentration lines in % by volume referred to toluene 1% by volume = 10^4 cm³
toluene/m³ air

Fig. 2. Distribution of concentration between two printing units.

It must be emphasized that benzole has been prohibited as a solvent in Germany because of its damaging effect on blood formation. Based on experience, the MAK figure indicates that there should be no ill effects for a daily working time of about eight hours even though exposure at this rate may go on for years. The MAK value for benzole has been fixed at 35 p.p.m. (1 p.p.m. = 1 part per million = 0·0001 %) and at 200 p.p.m. for toluene and xylene; therefore, permissible maximum concentration for benzole is six times lower than for the latter. Benzine has a value of 500 cm³/m³ and alcohol one of 1000 cm³/m³. Because suitable measuring methods for determining allowable solvent concentrations have not been available until now, the Hydrocarbon Detector 213 was used for this purpose for the first time by the Darmstadt Institute. During these measurements the following has to be considered:

(a) The printing machine (type of solvent, air exhaust system, aerodynamic conditions, machine speed, etc.).

(b) Air pressure, air humidity and temperature relative to the concentration ratios of the mixture.

(c) The climatic conditions (weather).

(d) Reproducibility of results (this has not yet been solved).

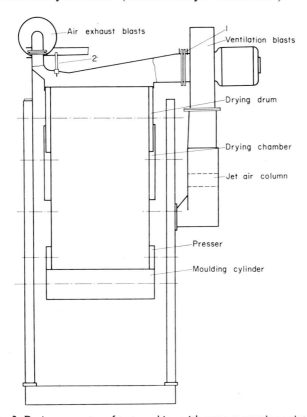

Fig. 3. Drying apparatus of test machine with some measuring points.

In connection with protection against explosions it was of particular interest to learn more about the concentration distribution between printing units and solvent vapours escaping sidewise. Measurements were carried out on a large production machine installed at a printing establishment (a suction tube was used). The concentration was strongest vertically above the ink fountain. Figure 2 illustrates distribution of concentration between two printing units.

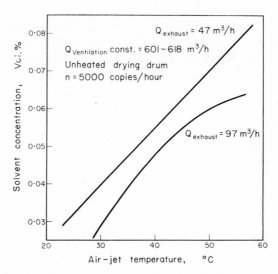

Fig. 4(a). Concentration as a function of jet air temperature.

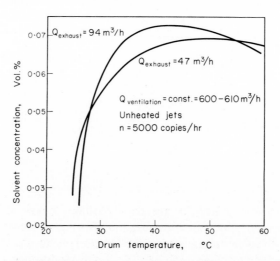

Fig. 4(b). Concentration as a function of drum temperature.

B. Solvent concentration in the drying chamber

Further uses of hydrocarbon detector may be reported on as follows. As stated already, it is possible to accelerate the drying process in rotogravure in two ways, namely by choosing suitable printing inks and by erecting drying systems which allow for an optimum drying process. In Germany, rotogravure ink pigments and their binding agents are frequently dissolved in volatile toluene (evaporation coefficient 6) or in benzines of different fractions. The drying process, it is known, can be accelerated by lowering the pressure in the drying chamber and by suitable heating. At constant machine speed the degree of drying is therefore inversely proportional to the solvent

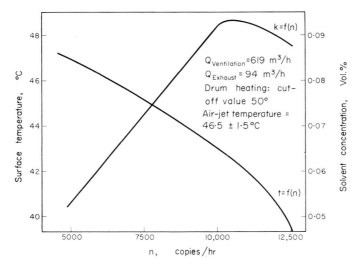

Fig. 5. Concentration of solvents and surface temperature as a function of printing speed.

concentration. By now measuring the solvent concentration in the drying chamber, it is possible to study how this concentration behaves under differing drying conditions. The Hydrocarbon Detector was used for such an investigation on the Rotogravure press of the Institute. Figure 3 shows the layout of the drying installation. The drying installation with electrical jet-air-heater, circulation and exhaust blower and heatable drying drum is enclosed. Solvent concentrations, flow volumes through both blower systems, as well as drum and circulating air temperatures were measured. One test series was conducted which revealed the influence of the jet heater, the influence of drum heater and indicated the influence of machine speed on the drying process under constant drying conditions. Some results are shown graphically. Figure 4(a) shows the dependence of solvent concentration on the jet-air temperature under conditions of varying exhaust air volumes with unheated drying drum, Figure 4(b) the dependence of solvent concentration as a function of drum temperature. Figure 5 shows solvent concentration and surface temperature as a function of printing speed. Drying conditions were kept constant as far as practicable. Change in concentration is therefore proportional to change in speed (up to a critical point). Loss of moisture by the paper and the melting of the ink binding agent set limits to the temperatures which can be used.

C. Detection of residual solvent

The usual methods of extracting and isolating residual solvents from the ink layer having proved inadequate, it was necessary to develop a method based on heating with a solvent and subsequent distillation of the solution (liquor) in order to isolate the solvent from the ink layer. This method was carried out in three individual processes:

(a) The printed paper was refluxed for half an hour in order to transfer the residual solvent quantity from the ink layer into the refluxing liquid.

(b) There after followed a distillation of the refluxing liquid containing the solvent.

(c) Finally, the separation of the residual solvent from the distillate (toluene from xylene) followed.

In order to avoid losses we developed an apparatus in which all the three processes immediately follow one another. This analytical method is characterized by the fact that the solvent contained in the ink layer is absorbed by a known quantity of " extraction-solvent " and that the concentration of the solvent in the " extraction liquor " is determined gas-chromatographically.

This method, in our opinion, should permit clarification of a series of relationships existing between drying speed and thickness of ink layer, dependence on ink viscosity, smear limits, etc.; it is further possible to investigate the inter-dependence of drying process and paper character by determination of residual solvents.

The method just outlined may offer alternate ways toward exact control of the drying process and therefore give the designer valuable aid in laying out a drying system of optimum drying performance.

Let us sketch briefly the method for determining residual solvents. Residual solvent content is defined as the quantity of solvent remaining in the ink layer on one square meter of paper after printing. In the apparatus mentioned the ink is then removed from the paper through cooking (natron base as cooking liquor) and by adding a certain amount of carrier solvent (0–Xylol) the residual solvent is separated from the ink and absorbed. The mixture ratio is then determined in the gas chromatograph and from it the quantity of residual solvent is derived, which can be called " residual solvent content per square meter of paper ".

Figure 6 shows the machine drawing. A full tone surface is etched on to the forme cylinder. Etching depth measured by means of the interference microscope amounted to 27μ with a screen of 70 lines–cm. Figure 7 illustrates the distillation apparatus consisting of cooking and distillation components. The gas chromatograph which is comparable to an apparatus for fraction distillation is shown in Fig. 8. Figure 9 illustrates the Hydrocarbon Detector with accessories.

The studies were made under conditions of constant air temperature and humidity, the same paper (70 g/m^2) was used and the inking speed was kept constant for any given test. The following variable quantities were measured, temperature of the drying air (using 2 thermometers), the heating drum temperature at the surface (by thermocouple), the flow rate of drying air (2 measuring shutters) and the solvent concentration in the drying air as well as machine speed.

As soon as the drying conditions reached a steady state, test samples were taken from the paper web, either through paper punch sampling (about 20 circular disks were removed from the rewound roll by means of a punching device or through removal of strips immediately after printing). In view of the capacity of the available distillation apparatus the samples were restricted to 0.15 m^2 of paper surface. Brown flasks of 10 ml volume were used to store the distillates. The distillation process with paper (after numerous painstaking tests) yielded residual solvent quantities which by their very nature were smaller than their theoretical values. Measured values fluctuated up to 11%. Sample injections into the fractometer were accomplished by means of syringes of 10 μl. capacity. Test mixtures of known concentrations were used for calibration. The calibration curves obtained were practically straight lines.

In this way a series of tests were run which aimed at determining the influence of the jet heater, the drum heating and of machine speed at different exhaust air conditions. Figure 10 shows the effect of machine speed upon residual solvent content and upon solvent concentration in the air of the drying chamber.

Critical observation of these tentative measurements revealed as yet sizeable scattering in the measured values, caused in particular by the sample removal method as well as a significant discrepancy between residual solvent content data and saturation data of the drying air.

It should be pointed out further that the " fresh air supply " for the drying room during these tests was imperfect because essential air already enriched with solvents could be sucked in through the inlet opening of the drying cabinet and through the sides thereof. This distorts the relationship between

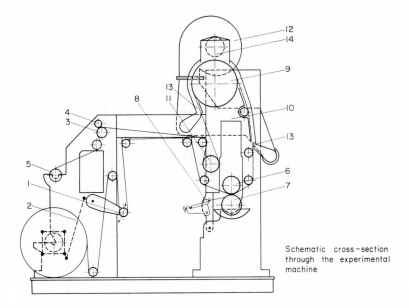

Schematic cross-section through the experimental machine

Fig. 6. Test machine—schematical drawing.

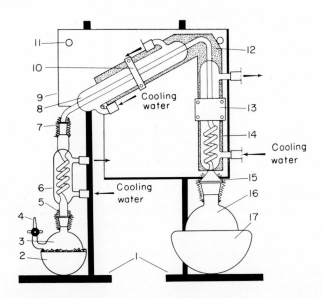

Fig. 7. Apparatus for isolating of solvents from rotogravure ink layers.

the volume of exhaust air and the total volume of air flow. (It is self-evident that the humidity content of the printing paper influences the drying process.) These shortcomings will be corrected in later tests.

Fig. 8. Illustration of Vapor Fractometer Perkin Elmer.

Fig. 9. Illustration of Hydrocarbon Detector 213.

It is possible to calculate the printing ink consumption per square meter by weighing a printed sheet after one week f.inst. establishing thereby its dry content in %. (A dry ink content of 42% (3·8 g/m²) thus corresponds to a solvent input of 4·8 g/m² into the printing process.) Drying time is expressed as the quotient of web length and web speed.

Figure 11 shows approximately the curve of the drying process. By the way, this may be mentioned also, concerning the speed of evaporation in general, the curve of Krischer[3] (Fig. 12) can be sensibly applied. (First

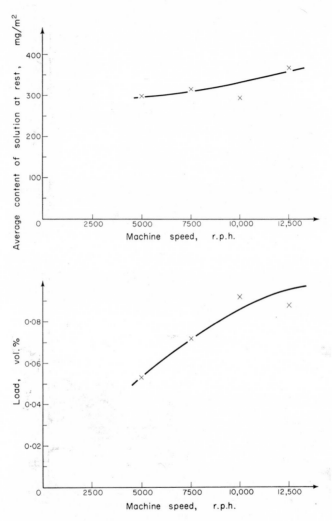

Fig. 10. Influence of machine speed.

section = evaporation phase, free surface; second section = drying phase, diffused, with surface skin existing; third section = phase of capillary effect. Simplified, wet-humid and hygroscopic range.) The evaporation curve shifts with changing temperature.

In printing practice it is necessary that the drying process takes place under conditions of constant inking and unchanged operating conditions in all printing units, for changes in the rate of solvent evaporation lead to changes in ink viscosity and thereby to tonal shifts.

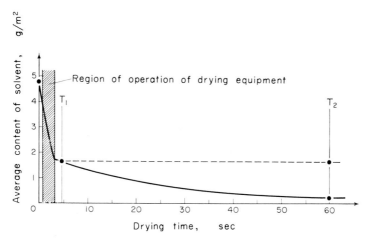

Fig. 11. Drying curve (solvent content in paper).

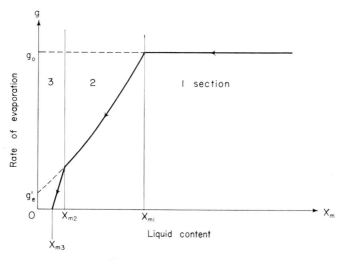

Rate of evaporation

Fig. 12. Vaporization speed.
(Analog Krischer[3])

SUMMARY

The tests conducted at the Darmstadt Institute by means of gas chromatography and a hydrocarbon detector aimed firstly at determining the concentration of solvents in the air of printing plants under actual operating conditions and secondly at studying the drying process in running rotogravure presses under differing working conditions.

The methods outlined for the determination of solvent concentration and especially those methods dealing with the experimental determination of solvent content of the air of the drying installation and of the printed paper are still subject to certain shortcomings and disturbing influences because of the relatively short testing time. Therefore the hitherto existing studies— except the tests " Solvent concentration in room air "—are only tests for orientation. However, the curves clearly show certain tendencies. Further investigation remains to be undertaken therefore. The new avenues chosen appear to promise success.

Our working team, including Dr. Wagenbauer, Messrs. Primavesi, Keppler, Antonoff, Fink, Tejidor and Richter, contributed primarily to these tests.

REFERENCES

1. W. ESCHENBACH, *Archiv für Drück und Papier*, **2**, 275 (1960).
2. A. A. TJURIN, *Die Rotationsmaschine* Bd. IV S.330/337, Moskau 1954 (Isskusstwo).
3. O. KRISCHER, *Trocknungstechnik*. (Drying technique.) p. 246 Springer (1956).

DISCUSSION

LARAIGNOU: When you measured chromatographically the residual solvent did you use inks containing the same type of resin or high polymer, and do you know what type of resin was used? Ink-makers pay much attention to what they call the solvent retention and this is very different from one resin to another.

ESCHENBACH: The results quoted in my paper refer to one special ink containing dammar resin. Naturally the method is applicable to other kinds of gravure inks.

ALBRECHT: Following the comment of Mr, Laraignou I should like to point out that with water based gravure ink very quick drying is obtained although water evaporates 80 times slower than many solvents. This illustrates the influence of the resin and its capacity to retain the solvent.

ESCHENBACH: Yes I agree, but because of the poor printing quality the water gravure ink is not often used in Germany in spite of quick drying.

TOLLENAAR: In the determination of the residual solvent content, refluxing the printed paper seems to me a rather severe treatment. I wonder whether normal high vacuum distillation with liquid air traps would not be a safer way.

ESCHENBACH: I thank you for your suggestion. We have chosen our method because the paper itself is broken up but the treatment does not influence the solvent.

ROGERS: Your listing of factors on page 198 appears to omit one important factor in the mass transfer of solvent during drying. It is the thin film of immobilized (still) air adjacent to the paper surface. Solvent transfer through this film is a function of the driving forces and the film thickness (which is usually unknown). Thus if the film coefficient of mass transfer is K, film thickness d, concentration of solvent C_m, C_i in air and ink film respectively, then the transfer through the film T_s in time t is given by

$$T_s = \frac{K}{d}(C_i - C_m)t$$

REID: Although Dr. Eschenbach has mentioned briefly the "aerodynamic state above the layer of drying ink," he has not yet included measurements of it. It is suggested, in line with Dr. Rogers' comments, that the velocity of the drying air in the boundary layer over the printed surface is a most important factor. Not only does this velocity influence the mass transfer of solvent from the ink film to the air stream, it also controls the rate of heat transfer by convection from the air to the ink. Hence, consideration of this velocity gradient should be placed high on his list of future problems. As a suggestion, the rate of drying of the ink film should be related to the Reynolds Number of the air over the paper. This dimensionless parameter, which is the ratio between the dynamic forces and the viscous forces in a fluid during flow, has been found most useful in such studies.

ESCHENBACH: It is true that aerodynamic considerations are very important, but it is a difficult problem to define the aerodynamic state in our installation.

BANKS: I would not have expected molecular effects (items 7, 8, 9) to have any significant effect on evaporation rate because, while in principle they exist, the effects must be small on account of the high molecular weight of the dissolved polymer (resin). Put another way, such high molecular weight materials will not reduce the vapour pressures to any important extent. I agree with Mr. Reid that the problems are essentially ones connected with transport—such as diffusion of mass and heat.

ESCHENBACH: I agree with your opinion; I mentioned these points for the sake of completion.

HUNDERUP JENSEN: In your paper you refer to the MAK figures for solvents. In practical rotogravure printing you are not dealing with pure solvents. The solvent will be a mixture of a whole family of chemically related solvents, the composition of which depends on the quality used. Now and then you get some solvents in which there are small amounts of toxic impurities, for example chlorinated ethylens. Are you in possession of MAK figures for other solvents than those mentioned and do you know how to determine whether there is a dangerous concentration of toxic materials in the atmosphere?

ESCHENBACH: By means of gas chromatography we are able to measure all the separate components in an exact quantitative and qualitative way.

OPTICAL DENSITY AND INK LAYER THICKNESS

by Dr. D. Tollenaar and P. A. H. Ernst

Stichting Instituut voor grafische Techniek TNO,
Amsterdam, The Netherlands

REFLECTANCE OF THE PRINTED SURFACE

The optical densities of a printed surface determine to a large extent the quality of an impression. The sequence of technical operations, necessary to obtain a print of the desired tonal range, includes photographic and etching procedures in order to make a printing forme, and actual printing from which the impression results. All these procedures involve numerous steps which may influence the tone rendering.

In this paper the influence of ink and paper on the optical density of the print will be discussed.

The relationship between the reflectance of a solid print and the film thickness of the ink has been studied by Zettlemoyer, Eckhart and Walker[1] who also reviewed the older literature. Their theoretical treatment was based on a simplified Kubelka–Munk equation.

This equation:

$$\ln \frac{R_p - R_\infty}{R - R_\infty} = \frac{SX}{R_\infty}$$

relates the reflectance R of the print to the reflectance R_p of the paper, the scattering power or absorbing power S of the pigment and the average film thickness X. The quantity R_∞ represents the reflectance of a very thick film of ink on the paper. It is of interest to note that R_∞ is not only a property of the ink but is influenced also by the paper stock. Thus it is possible to obtain different values of R_∞ with the same ink on different papers.

The equation can represent the measurements in the region of ink film thicknesses as used in practice; however, it fails if the ink layers become very thin. The authors explain this by pointing out that under these circumstances the assumption of a continuous ink film is not allowed.

Gambioli *et al.*[2] have measured the tristimulus coefficients X, Y and Z of coloured inks, printed with increasing thickness on coloured glossy papers. They report inflexion points in the curves—log X (or Y or Z) vs. ink layer thickness for all combinations of paper and ink. If we take the tristimulus values proportional to the reflections (for instance for a black ink) then the increase in density with ink layer thickness would be higher in the region of thick ink layers than in the region of medium thickness. Such a behaviour could be explained by the interference of gloss with density measurements. Density measurements on printed surfaces with different amounts of ink are, strictly, only comparable if the structures of the printed surfaces are similar. Especially on glossy papers the influence of ink layer thickness on the gloss of the print is quite remarkable. This is confirmed by the conclusion of Gross who measured the relation between gloss and in kfilm thickness.[3]

DENSITY CURVE

The optical density D of a print, made at a constant pressure and speed, increases monotonously from zero to a saturation value D_∞ if the ink layer thickness y on the paper is increased. The general shape of the curve suggests an exponential relationship which may be derived in the following way:

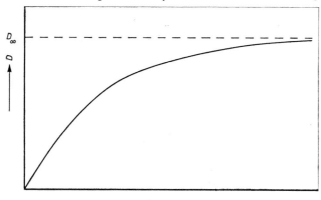

Fig. I. Density D vs. ink film thickness y on the paper.

A slight increase in density from D to $D + dD$ cannot be proportional to an increase in layer thickness from y to $y + dy$ since this would lead to a proportionality between D and y. This is clearly in contradiction with common experience which shows that optical densities cannot be increased indefinitely. Therefore a relationship

$$dD = m\,(D_\infty - D)\,dy \tag{1}$$

may be postulated which takes account of the fact that the increase in density dD is becoming less and less if the saturation density D is approached.

By integrating equation (1) we obtain:

$$D = D_\infty(1 - e^{-my}) \qquad (2)$$

For low values of y becomes

$$D = D_\infty my \qquad (3)$$

or

$$m = \left(\frac{dD/D_\infty}{dy}\right)_{y=0} \qquad (4)$$

The factor m represents the increase of relative density D/D_∞ per unit increase of ink layer thickness at low values of y. It determines the steepness of the density curve in the region of very thin ink films. In practice, formula (2) may also be applied if the density is plotted against the ink layer thickness x on the forme. Poinçon used this method, which is very practical in printing shop experiments. [4] Of course in this case the constant in the exponent takes a different value because it now includes the transfer function proposed by Walker and Fetsko. [5] The general shape of the density curve, however, is not appreciably altered and deviates only in the low ink layer thicknesses.

EXPERIMENTAL

Three inks of equal flow properties but of different optical densities were prepared by mixing opaque white letterpress ink with coloured inks: mixture M_1 contained 8% by weight of a black ink, mixture M_2 15% of a red ink and mixture M_3 17% of a blue ink. The flow properties were measured in a bar viscometer at 20·5°C (Table 1).

TABLE 1.

Shearing stress in 10^3 dyn/cm²	Rate of shear in sec^{-1}		
	M_1	M_2	M_3
60	46	48	47
100	86	90	90
200	210	211	211
300	352	356	348
400	500	503	500

It could be expected that the amount of ink transferred to the same paper surface under identical circumstances would be the same for the three mixtures. By means of the I.G.T. Printability Tester prints were made on three papers. *A*, an art paper, *B* a wood-free writing paper and *C* an offset paper. Each impression was made at low speed with a force of 70 kg on a forme width of 2 cm. The ink transfer was measured by weighing the printing forme before and after the impression was made and from the weight of ink the ink layer thickness was derived.

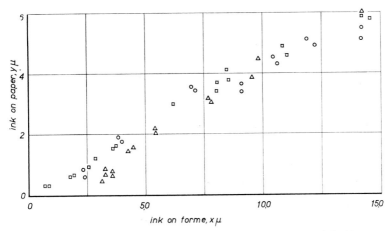

Fig. 2. Transfer of three inks with identical flow curves on art paper. Inks $M_1 - \triangle$, $M_2 - \square$, $M_3 - \bigcirc$.

From the Figs. 2, 3 and 4 it can be concluded that the three ink mixtures did not show any appreciable difference in transfer behaviour.

The optical densities of the dried prints were measured with reference to the density of the unprinted paper by means of a Baldwin Reflection Densitometer.

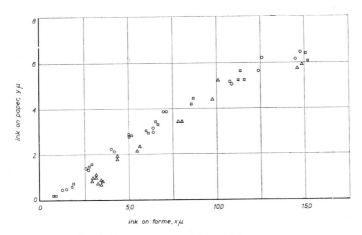

Fig. 3. Transfer on wood-free writing paper.

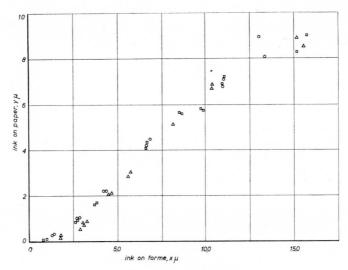

Fig. 4. Transfer on offset paper.

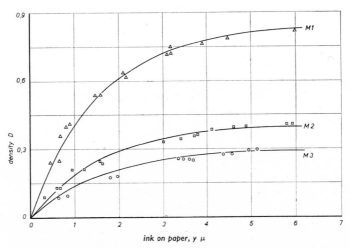

Fig. 5. Density D vs. ink film thickness y on the paper. The inks M_1, M_2 and M_3 have identical flow curves. $m = 0.62\,\mu^{-1}$. Art paper.

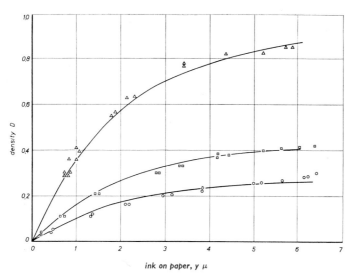

ink on paper, y μ

Fig. 6. Density curves for wood-free writing-paper, $m = 0\cdot48\ \mu^{-1}$.

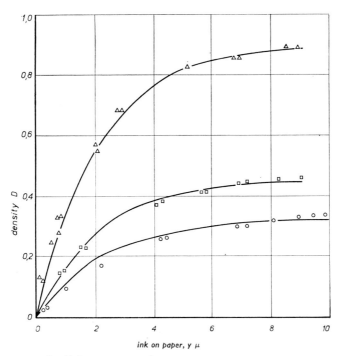

ink on paper, y μ

Fig. 7. Density curves for offset paper, $m = 0\cdot045\ \mu^{-1}$.

Figures 5, 6 and 7 show the densities plotted against ink layer thickness on the three papers. The drawn curves have been calculated from the values of D_∞ and m given in Table 2.

TABLE 2. SATURATION DENSITIES D_∞

Ink	Paper A, $m = 0.62\mu^{-1}$	Paper B, $m = 0.48\mu^{-1}$	Paper C, $m = 0.45\mu^{-1}$
M_1	0·85	0·92	0·91
M_2	0·41	0·43	0·46
M_3	0·30	0·275	0·325

The agreement between calculated and measured values is quite satisfactory.

OPTICAL DENSITY AND CONTACT AREA

The formula of Murray-Davies[6] relates the density D of a halftone print with a fractional area a to the density D_s of the dots:

$$a = \frac{1 - 10^{-D}}{1 - 10^{-D_s}} \tag{5}$$

Yule and Neilsen[7] have introduced a correction factor n taking account of the changes in optical density due to internal reflections in the paper layers

$$a = \frac{1 - 10^{-D/n}}{1 - 10^{-D_s/n}} \tag{6}$$

From observed densities D and measured areas a the factor n can be calculated. On coated stock it varies between 1·3 for coarse screens to 3 for fine screens.

Although a theoretical derivation of n seems to be far-off, Yule's formula is very well suited for the purpose of deducing a from the density of solid prints,

Pollak[8] has made the important observation: ". . . when $n = \infty$. the density is proportional to the dot area and to the quantity of ink per unit area; we then have the effect of continuous tone. It can be said that real halftone is intermediate between theoretical halftone ($n = 1$) and continuous tone ($n = \infty$)." If we calculate the dot area a from equation (6) substituting $n = \infty$ we get:

$$a = \operatorname*{Lim}_{n \to \infty} \frac{1 - 10^{-D/n}}{1 - 10^{-D_s/n}} = \operatorname*{Lim}_{n \to \infty} \frac{\dfrac{d}{dn}(1 - 10^{-D/n})}{\dfrac{d}{dn}(1 - 10^{-D_s/n})} = \frac{D}{D_s} \tag{7}$$

or
$$D = aD_s \tag{8}$$

REDUCED CONTACT AREA

The contact area F of a solid print has been used by Walker and Fetsko[5] to explain the ink layer transfer in the region of low coverage. They assume a power function $F = 1 - e^{-kx}$ and the value of k is determined by rather elaborate calculations from ink transfer data.

Ichikawa, Sato and Ito[9] measured the contact area planimetrically and proposed an integrated lognormal distribution function $F(x)$ which differs from the power function at low values of x, especially on rough papers. This would mean that the value of k is not a constant but increases with increasing ink layer thickness on the plate.

If a solid print is looked upon as a halftone print made with a very fine screen F becomes identical with the dot area a and equation (8) may be applied. For reasons which will be discussed later another contact area O is introduced by the equation:

$$D = aD_s = OD_\infty \qquad (9)$$

O is the contact area which in a homogeneous solid print yields the overall density D if it is covered to the saturation density D_∞. This quantity O will further be called reduced contact area. It follows from (4) that $O/a < 1$. Prints with entirely different contact areas a, may give equal reduced contact areas O. This can be illustrated by the density distributions represented in Fig. 8 I, II and III.

Figure 8 I shows the density distribution in a solid print with area A where minute surface points have been in contact with a dense ink. The density variations are very high but if the black specks are closely packed together they behave as the dots of a very fine halftone and in accordance with equation (9) the overall density D is proportional to the saturation density D_∞. In Fig. 8 II the contact area of the print is larger but the printed spots have a lower density and the overall density is the same as in case I. This overall density also may be reached by covering the entire printed area (case III). If in the three prints the saturation densities D_∞ and the overall densities D are equal the reduced contact areas are also equal.

Generally a solid print properly made shows only small variations in density. The mottled appearance which often can be observed in the microscope reveals area elements of the types shown in Fig. 9.

If the densities of these area elements do not differ too much, the overall density approximately equals the mean value of the densities of the separate elements, notwithstanding the fact that within one element the density may vary greatly.

Dr. D. Tollenaar and P. A. H. Ernst

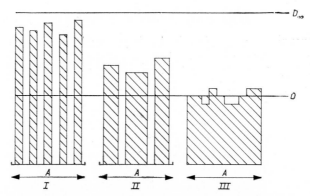

Fig. 8. Density distributions with identical overall density.

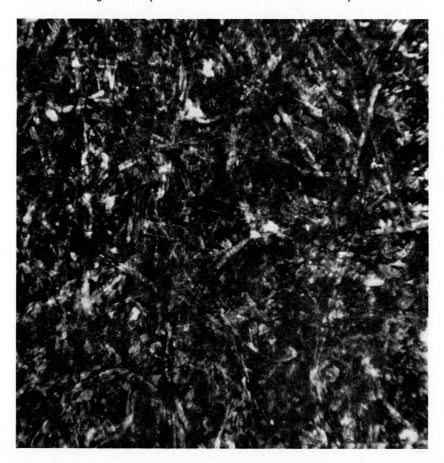

Fig. 9. Density variations in a solid impression.

This means that for each element, i equation (9) can be applied:

$$D_i = O_i D_\infty \qquad (10)$$

and

$$D = \overline{D_i} = \overline{O_i} \, D_\infty = O D_\infty, \text{ or } O = \frac{D}{D_\infty} \qquad (11)$$

In each of the Figs. 5, 6 and 7 the three curves should coincide if the relative densities D/D_∞ are plotted against the ink film thickness. This follows already from the constant m–value in Table 2. Values of $O = D/D_\infty$

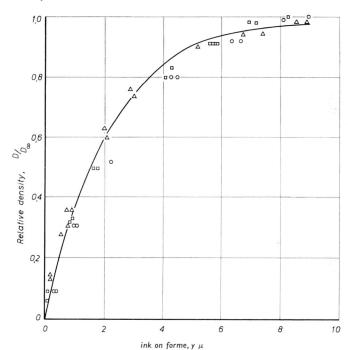

Fig. 10. Reduced contact areas for art paper and three inks with identical flow curves.

for the three ink mixtures M_1, M_2 and M_3 on the papers A, B and C are shown in Figs. 10, 11 and 12.

From equation (2) it follows that the reduced contact area

$$O = \frac{D}{D_\infty} = 1 - e^{-my} \qquad (12)$$

The concept of reduced contact area as it is defined by equations (9) and (12) might be useful in bridging the gap between two fields of graphic research: the investigations on ink transfer and the studies on optical densities of prints.

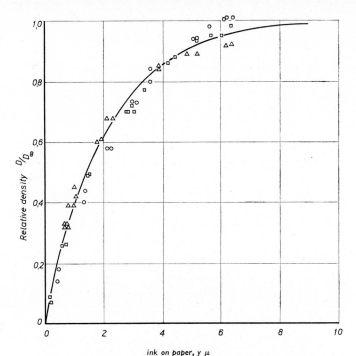

Fig. 11. Reduced contact area for wood-free writing paper.

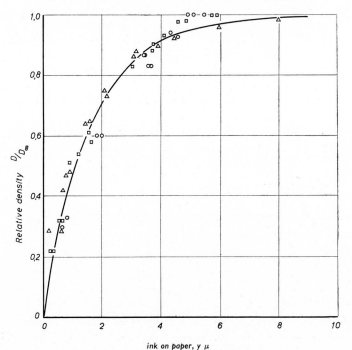

Fig. 12. Reduced contact area for offset paper.

Since the reduced contact area is determined completely by the exponential constant m it may be useful to express printing results in relation to m. Preliminary investigations seem to indicate for instance that m is proportional to the screen fineness that can be used in a certain combination of ink and paper.

In order to elucidate the physical meaning of m a comparison of the " printing smoothness " k introduced by Walker and Fetsko[5] and the " density smoothness " m may be helpful. Whereas k determines how fast the real contact area approaches unity, the factor m determines how fast the relative density D/D_∞ approaches unity, or (which is the same thing) how fast the overall density D approaches its saturation value D_∞. Since the density of the real contact area is always smaller than the saturation density, m is smaller than k.

CALCULATION OF m AND D_∞

The two constants m and D_∞ may be calculated algebraically from two equations

$$D_1 = D_\infty(1 - e^{-my_1}) \tag{13a}$$

and

$$D_2 = D_\infty(1 - e^{-my_2}) \tag{13b}$$

where D_1 and D_2 are the measured densities of two prints with known ink layer thickness y_1 and y_2.

The assessment of y_1 and y_2 is too troublesome for quick measurements and it is far more practical to use another variable instead of y, for instance the ink layer thickness x on the forme or the ink volume on the ink distribution apparatus. It is even conceivable that in rotogravure printing the etching depth of the cylinder might be used.

We have selected the two inklayer thicknesses on the forme x_1 and x_2 at 2·3 and 4·6μ. If we take x-values instead of y-values we derive from (13a) and (13b):

$$D_1 = \frac{1 - e^{-mx_1}}{1 - e^{-mx_2}} \cdot D_2 \tag{14}$$

If D_1 and D_2 are assessed, the value of the constant m may be taken from a nomogram (Fig. 13).

It consists of two logarithmic outer scales for D_1 and D_2 and a middle scale for the values of log

$$\frac{1 - e^{-mx_1}}{1 - e^{-mx_2}}$$

on which directly the m-values have been indicated.

A straight line, connecting the two measured values for D_1 and D_2 will intersect the middle scale at the required m-value.

The construction of a nomogram for the solution of D_∞ is somewhat more involved. From equation (13a) we derive

$$m = \frac{1}{x_1} \ln \left(1 - \frac{D}{D_\infty} \right) \tag{14}$$

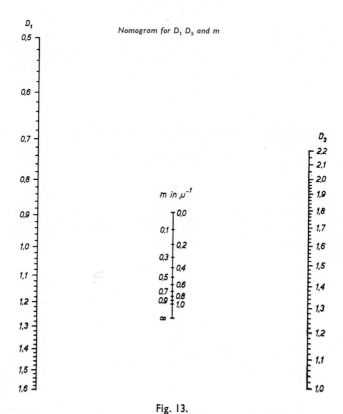

Fig. 13.

By substituting this value in equation (13b) m is eliminated:

$$1 - \frac{D_2}{D_\infty} = \left(1 - \frac{D_1}{D_\infty} \right) \frac{x_2}{x_1} \tag{15}$$

In our case $\qquad x_2 = 2x_1$

so we obtain a quadratic equation:

$$D_2 + PD_1^2 = 2D_1 \tag{16}$$

where $\qquad P = 1/D_\infty.$

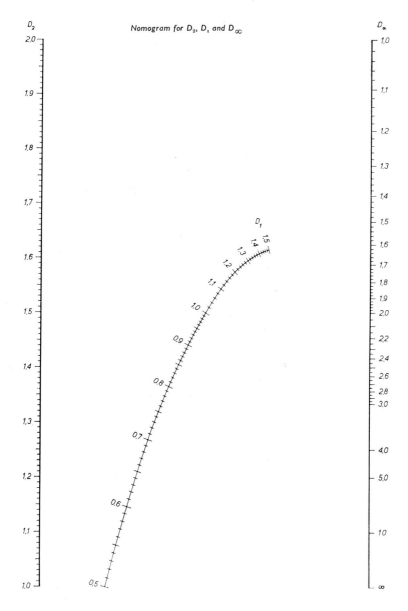

Fig. 14.

This equation can be written as follows:

$$f_1(u) + f_2(v) \cdot f_3(w) = f_4(w) \tag{17}$$

if:

$$f_1(u) = D_2$$

$$f_2(v) = P = 1/D$$

$$f_3(w) = D_1{}^2$$

$$f_4(w) = 2D_1$$

Equation (17) is one of the types normally found in handbooks of nomography.[10] The nomogram for D_2, D_1 and D_∞ consists of a linear left scale for D_2, a reciprocal right scale for D_∞ (which is linear for P) and an elliptic middle scale for D_1 (Fig. 14).

It should be remarked that the numerals in the nomogram for the solution of m are only valid for ink layer thicknesses $x_1 = 2 \cdot 3\mu$ and $x_2 = 4 \cdot 6\mu$, whereas the numerals in the nomogram for the solution of D_∞ are valid for any pair of ink layer thicknesses x_1 and $x_2 = 2x_1$.

The ink layer thickness $x_1 = 2 \cdot 3\mu$ and $x_2 = 4 \cdot 6\mu$ correspond to ink dosages of $0 \cdot 3$ and $0 \cdot 6$ cm³ on the inking apparatus of the I.G.T. Printability Tester. Although theoretically any combination of x_1 and x_2 would suffice to calculate m and D_∞ the thickness mentioned above generally gives values of m and D_∞ from which the best agreement is obtained between experimental and calculated densities. However, when using rough papers it seems advisable to select thicker ink films, e.g. $x_1 = 4 \cdot 6\mu$ and $x_2 = 9 \cdot 2\mu$. In this case the nomogram for D_∞ also applies, the numerals on the m-scale should be recalculated from equation (14).

INFLUENCE OF PRINTING PRESSURE AND PRINTING SPEED

Common experience shows that the increase of printing pressure leads to higher optical densities, whereas the optical density is lowered with an increase of printing speed.

If we try to express these effects in terms of m and D_∞ we find that a variation in density may result from a variation in D_∞, or from a variation of m or from a variation of both.

Our experiments lead to the conclusion that the m-value of the paper-ink interaction is very little affected by speed whereas D_∞ is strongly influenced by the two variables. Eight papers, ranging from art paper to wood-free offset paper, have been printed with illustration black. On each paper two impressions were made with ink layer thickness on the forme of $2 \cdot 3\mu$ and $4 \cdot 6\mu$ respectively. With the aid of the nomograms mentioned on p. 225 the

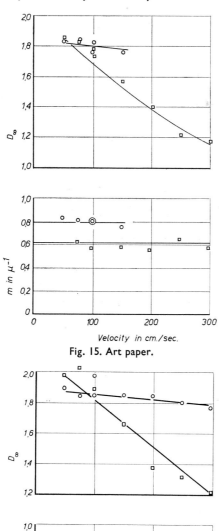

Fig. 15. Art paper.

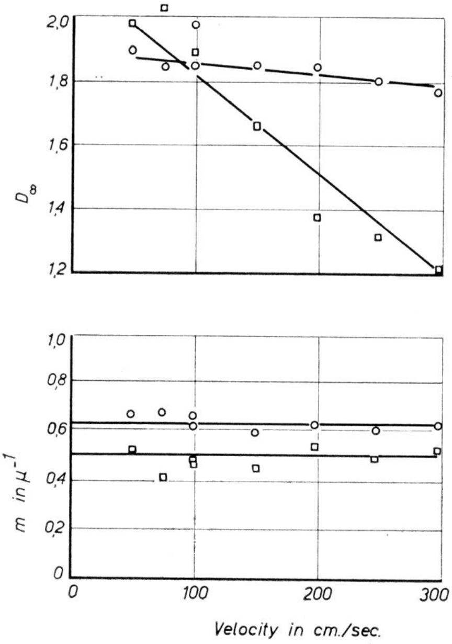

Fig. 16. Wood-free chromo.

Q

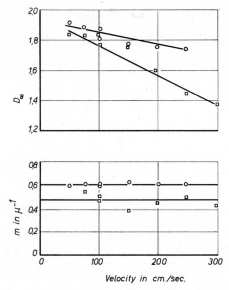

Fig. 17. Casein machine-coated.

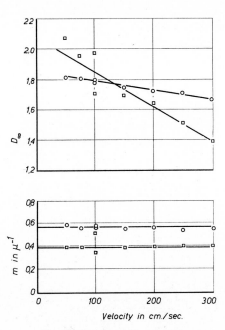

Fig. 18. Starch machine-coated.

of m and D_∞ could be assessed. The impressions were made at two printing pressures, viz. 20 kg and 70 kg per strip width of 2 cm and at seven printing speeds varying from 75 cm/sec–300 cm/sec.

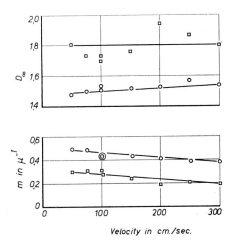

Fig. 19. Wood-free writing paper.

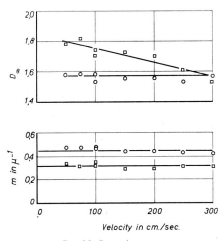

Fig. 20. Bristol carton.

In Figs. 15–22 the values of m and D have been plotted against printing speed for the two pressures.

Variations in m and D_∞ due to printing velocity at two pressure levels.

☐ 20 kg/2 cm.

○ 70 kg/2 cm.

It becomes clear at once that the *m*-values show very little variations with speed. At higher pressures the *m*-values reach a higher level, as could be expected. The values of D_∞ generally decrease markedly with increasing speed, especially if the pressure is low.

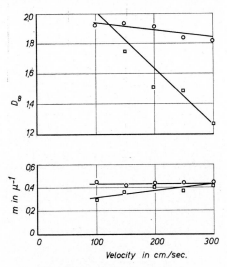

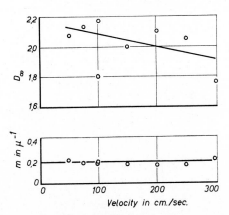

Fig. 21. Starch machine-coated.

Fig. 22. Wood-free offset paper.

It should be emphasized that *m* and D_∞ do not represent parameters of a paper–ink combination as such, but that they require a specification of printing conditions. D_∞ is sensitive to pressure and speed variation, *m* is scarcely affected by speed and more by pressure variations.

CONCLUSIONS

A general formula for the relation between optical density D of a solid impression and the ink layer thickness y on the paper is proposed:

$$D = D_\infty(1 - e^{-my})$$

The formula contains two parameters D_∞ and m. D_∞ represents the optical density of the solid at infinite ink layer thickness under specified printing conditions. m represents a contact factor for corrected uniform density D_∞ of the contacted area, equally under specified printing conditions. The two parameters can be assessed from two density measurements D_1 at ink layer thickness y_1 and D_2 at ink layer thickness y_2.

Assuming that under practical printing conditions the ink layer y on the paper is approximately proportional to the ink layer thickness x on the forme, it is possible to use x instead of y. The two parameters seem to offer an easy method to express printing results under varying conditions of speed and pressure.

REFERENCES

1. A. C. ZETTLEMOYER, C. G. ECKHART and W. C. WALKER, *Amer. Ink Maker*, 23 (August 1949).
2. M. GAMBIOLI, G. CALABRÓ and A. D'ASPRANO, *Indicatore Grafico Suppl.* 1101 (January 1960).
3. K. GROSS, Rep. 3rd Symp. 375 Eu Ce Pa Paris (1959).
4. G. POINÇON, Rep. 3rd Symp. 67 Eu Ce Pa Paris (1959).
5. W. C. WALKER and J. M. FETSKO, *TAGA Proceedings* 139 (1955).
6. A. MURRAY, *J. Franklin Inst.* **221**, 721 (1936).
7. J. A. C. YULE and W. J. NEILSEN, *TAGA Proceedings* 65 (1951).
8. F. POLLAK, *J. Photogr. Sci.* 3, 112 (1955).
9. I. ICHIKAWA, K. SATO and Y. ITO, *Res. Bull. Gov. Printing Bur. Japan*, No. 2 29 (1959).
10. A. S. LEVENS, *Nomography* p. 99, Chapman and Hall, London. Wiley, New York (1948).

DISCUSSION

BANKS: Would Dr. Tollenaar care to say how far his treatment and conclusions depend on the assumption that a solid print is the limiting case of screen dots of increasing fineness? I would like to be convinced about the logic of this argument?

TOLLENAAR: I think that in Yule's publication it was stated that the value of n increases when finer screens are used, that it, when the dots were closer together. Now it makes very little difference whether n has the values of 5 or 6 or ∞. That means that on solid prints where contacting spots are very close together and n can be presumed to take a relatively high value, the effect approximates the continuous tone case.

LASSEUR: In comparing three rheologically identical inks to find a value for the reduced contact area you plot the relative density D/D_∞. I understand that in the case D_∞ is the actual measured density at high ink layer thickness, while normally there is a considerable difference between this density and the D_∞ you calculate from your equation. Can you explain why in this case it is justifiable to use the measured density value?

TOLLENAAR: The three measured curves have been normalized by plotting D/D_∞ against x for each curve. For each curve the value of D_∞ has been calculated separately from the measured points. The normalization could have been carried out in another way, for instance by multiplying each density with a suitable density factor.

SCHIRMER: Can you explain the influence of gloss on the factor m? Gloss changes are dependent on ink film thickness.

TOLLENAAR: In some inks the surface tends to level out if they are printed in very thick layers. Because of this the reflection caused by the irregularities of the surface decreases and the measured density is higher than would be obtained if the surface had kept its unevenness.

CALABRO: The increase in density of coloured inks at very high ink layer thicknesses may also be caused by a shift in the spectral distribution curve of the transmitted light.

THEORETICAL PRINCIPLES OF THE APPLICATION OF ALUMINIUM OXIDE LAYERS —PREPARED BY THE ANOFSAL PROCESS— IN THE PRINTING INDUSTRY

by VILMOS SALGÓ

V., Reáltanoda u.5. Budapest, Hungary

ONE OF the basic conditions of increasing printing speed and of reducing printing force is the availability of adequate printing formes.

Increased printing speeds are detrimental to printing formes from any point of view. Stresses on the printing formes increase and the life of formes is reduced proportionally with increasing speed.

Investigation of the printing force—necessary from the viewpoint of print quality—proves that the requirements which printing formes must satisfy are even more exacting in the latter case.

The printing force must be reduced as far as possible in order to prevent point deformation. This, however, is limited in the majority of cases by the surface structure and also by the manner of preparation of the printing forme.

This paper deals primarily with the basic properties of offset plates prepared by the Anofsal process developed at the Experimental Plant and Laboratory of the Printing Industry in Budapest.

The requirements mentioned in the foregoing can only be satisfied by offset printing plates which possess the following properties:

(1) Both printing and non-printing areas must possess a high degree of resistance against mechanical and chemical actions.

(2) Ink-receptive areas must strongly adhere to the base, must readily receive and give off the ink in order to reduce loads on these parts during printing.

(3) Maximum selectivity of the printing and non-printing areas must be ensured.

(4) The surface of the plates must be smooth as possible, their specific surface must be large as possible at the same time.

Point reproduction is true on smooth plates, the points not being deformed as on grained plates. Increasing the specific surface is essential for mono-metal plates in order to achieve adequate bonding—by adsorption in some cases—of the various substances applied to the plates. A smooth surface is essential for reducing the printing force. It is a well known fact that coarse-grained plates require a higher printing force than fine-grained plates.

Only bimetal plates were able to satisfy all of the above requirements thus far. It is known, however, that bimetal plates cannot be employed economically in all fields.

Research work has been conducted at our Institute on the utilization of plates with aluminium oxide surface for offset printing.

The suitability of aluminium oxide for offset printing is proved by the hardness of the properly developed layer, its resistance to abrasion, to the chemicals used in printing and even to a number of acids.

The thickness of layers produced by chemical and electro-chemical treatment ranges from $4-5\mu$ to $30-40\mu$. The structure of these oxide layers is almost the same as that of lithostone, that is, they incorporate almost identical capillaries as limestone does.

Before dealing with the properties of the oxide layer of Anofsal plates, a short survey of oxide-surfaced aluminium plates, used at present in printing, will be given.

Oxide surfaced aluminium plates employed in offset printing can be classified into two groups.

Oxide layers of the first group are characterized by a soft oxide surface produced by chemical or electrochemical methods, while oxide layers belonging to the second group may be characterized by relatively high surface hardness and durability. Oleophilic substances, however, do not adhere well to these surfaces.

The natural oxide on the surface of aluminium plates consists of chemically pure aluminium oxide hydrate. The bound moisture content depends upon the circumstances under which the layers were formed.

Since the oxide layer is bound very strongly to the base metal, a macro-molecular linkage between the two substances can be assumed. It has been proved by practical measurements that the composition of the oxide layers obtained by chemical or electrochemical treatment conforms to the formula Al_2O_3. X-ray studies disclosed a so-called γ Al_2O_3 crystal structure, but neither corundum nor an aluminium hydroxide structure could be discovered. Recent X-ray measurements and electron microscopical studies showed that the portion of the oxide layer directly in contact with the metal consisted of solid $Al_2O_3 \cdot H_2O$, while the top portion of the layer consists of very fine γ Al_2O_3 crystal grains.

Summarizing the above, it can be stated that the structure of the oxide layer formed on aluminium either naturally or by artificial means is a hydrogel consisting of macromolecules whose H_2O content depends upon the circumstances under which the layer has been prepared.

A part of the aluminium oxide molecular structure is shown in Fig. 1.

Besides the chemical, molecular structure of the oxide layers, morphological properties also play a decisive role from the viewpoint of utilization in printing.

A glimpse into the microstructure of aluminium oxide may be obtained by examining the formation of a layer prepared by electrochemical treatment.

Two kinds of oxide layers can be distinguished also in respect to microstructure. One is the barrier or blocking type, the other being aluminium oxide of a cellular-porous structure. The mechanism of formation is simple for the first type. Heavy current flows at first, and oxide is formed

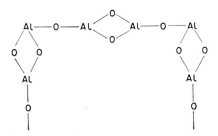

Fig. 1. Macromolecule of aluminium oxide.

rapidly, the current falls, however, in a short period of time to a steady low value and layer formation ceases therewith. Layer thickness is a function of the applied voltage, approximately 14 Å/V, and can be increased only by increasing the voltage. The process of layer information is more complicated in the second case. At first, the oxide boundary layer forms in the usual way but, after the formation of a certain quantity of oxide, the solvent action of the electrolyte makes itself felt, tending to reduce the thickness of the boundary layer. Finally, a porous cellular structure is formed as a consequence of the simultaneous dissolution and re-formation of the oxide layer.

The properties of an anodic layer of such type depend upon the following four variables: the pore dimensions, the cell wall thickness, thickness of the boundary layer at the cell bottom, and the character of the oxide formed.

An idealized oxide cell and pore are illustrated in Fig. 2.

The importance of these variables is decisive for printing applications as well. Pore volume or, conversely, the quantity of solid oxide are of the highest significance from the viewpoints of hardness and of resistance to wear and abrasion. The number and size of pores must be reduced to obtain an increase in hardness and resistance to wear since the solid oxide carries the load and constitutes the layer resistant to wear. This can be achieved by the choice of an appropriate electrolyte and the application of low voltage.

A wear-resisting and hard, i.e. microporous, layer can be employed for offset printing only if the oxide layer is used as a non-printing element and the oxide is etched off beneath the printing elements, that is, the ink carrier actually adheres to the base metal. An explanation of this is as follows.

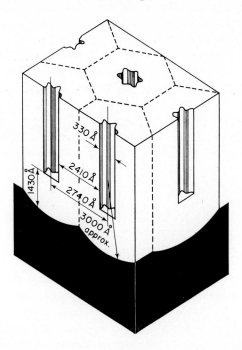

Fig. 2. An idealized cell and pore constructed from the image of the basic structure of the cell, magnified 65,000 ×, according to Keller and others.

Adsorption plays a decisive role in all phases of the preparation of plates with an anodic oxide layer and in printing using such plates. In the process of adsorption, aluminium oxide figures as an adsorbent applied to a carrier, i.e. the base metal. Not only are the absolute dimensions of the surface significant from the viewpoint of adsorptive activity, but also its other geometrical features such as radius of curvature, roughness, protruding and receding parts, etc. The effect of the geometrical features attains a high degree of significance mainly with adsorbents of a type rich in internal surfaces, voids and capillaries. Aluminium oxide is one of this type.

The surfaces of internal-surface adsorbents can be differentiated into three types.

Surfaces of the first order: external surfaces, the rough macroscopic and microscopic surfaces of internal cavities, voids and channels.

Surfaces of the second order: the surfaces of submicroscopic voids and channels.

Surfaces of the third order: the surfaces of amicroscopic voids, channels and capillaries.

This classification is justified by the different adsorptive behaviour of the surfaces belonging to the various orders. This phenomenon is due to the fact that the adsorption layers are polymolecular, that is, their thickness exceeds the average size of molecules.

Polymolecular adsorption layers can develop freely on surfaces of the first order because the internal voids are sufficiently spacious. On surfaces of the second and third order, however, only correspondingly thinner adsorption layers can form. The volume adsorbed on them will be smaller, as thicker adsorption layers are formed on the surfaces of the first order under conditions otherwise identical. Only monomolecular layers are adsorbed, in any case, upon surfaces at the third order because only molecules of small size can penetrate into the amicroscopic thin channels.

The surfaces of various order may cause considerable differences in the phenomenon of capillary condensation. Active from this point of view are primarily spots of the second order. This is due to the fact that the radii of curvature of the surfaces of the liquids contained in coarse voids are not small enough to produce a sufficient difference between the tensions of the liquid and the vapour. Surfaces of the first order, therefore, play a subordinate role in capillary condensation. Capillary condensation cannot occur at all in amicroscopic voids since they offer sufficient space only for the formation of monomolecular adsorption layers.

Consequently, excessive reduction of the diameters of capillaries offers no advantage from the viewpoint of capillary condensation.

If an adsorbent is rich in surfaces of the first order, its adsorptive capacity can hardly be increased by raising the degree of dispersity, for it will possess extended adsorptive surfaces already in its coarser state due to its mesh structure.

If, however, the adsorbent mainly contains surfaces of the second and third order, its adsorptive capacity will increase on raising its degree of dispersity because the surfaces of the second and third order are converted partially into surfaces of the first order.

This classification of aluminium oxide adsorbents is of the utmost importance for their utilization in printing.

As has been mentioned above, the aluminium plates provided with an oxide layer and commercially available at present can be classified into two groups. The oxide layers of the first group show a coarse macroscopic and microscopic structure, i.e. surfaces primarily of the first order. This character is enhanced by the fact that the pore channels of amicroscopical size—the diameter of which is about maximum 1000Å in the hard oxide layers—are here much larger. Therefore the resistance to wear and the hardness of the layers is relatively low on account of reduced wall thickness. Consequently these plates are suitable for the printing of small editions.

Plates belonging to the other type are provided with relatively hard, wear-resisting oxide layers. Contrary to the former, the oxide layers on these plates are smooth, with surfaces predominantly of the third order which ensures very strong adsorption of water and of other micromolecular substances, their adsorptivity for macromolecules, however, is insignificant or even nil.

Good hydrophilic properties of the oxide layers on these plates can be exploited only by etching off the oxide at the location of the printing elements and by fixing the oleophilic lacquer layer, consisting of relatively large molecules, on the cleaned metal surface in the same manner as with mechanically grained plates.

The idea of linking the favourable properties of both types—without their disadvantages—suggests itself.

The theoretical solution of the problem seems to be obvious on the basis of the foregoing. The disperse character of the oxide layers possessing surfaces overwhelmingly of the third order must be increased in such a manner as to have surfaces of the first and of the second order as well. Thus, the oxide layer would retain its hardness, while increasing its adsorptivity for macromolecular substances.

THE SURFACE STRUCTURE OF ANOFSAL PLATES

The foregoing considerations were used for preparing the surfaces of Anofsal plates.

Practical realization is effected in two stages. The soft oxide layer possessing surfaces of the first, second and third orders is formed in the first stage. It can be assumed that this layer is of the barrier type and that the surfaces of the third order are insignificant. A hard surface, mainly of the third order is developed during the second stage, this layer, however, becoming dispersed in conformity with the morphology of the coarser grained surface formed in the first stage. Though not proved by measurements so far, it may be inferred from preliminary electron-photomicrographs that the dimensions of the surfaces of the first and second orders formed during the first stage of the process are reduced in the second one while the dimensions of the pores constituting the surface of the third order are slightly increased by the intensified oxide-dissolving action.

The character of the oxide layers formed during the various stages is presented in the attached series of photos.

Figure 3 illustrates the surfaces of a mechanically grained zinc plate, of an Eggen micral plate and of a completely prepared Anofsal plate, magnified 200 ×.

Figure 4(a) shows the surface of an Anofsal plate subsequent to the first stage of surface treatment. It is clearly visible that surfaces of the first and of the second order are larger than after the last stage. Figure 4(b) presents a final surface. Magnification in both photographs is 200 ×.

Figure 5 illustrates the surface of a finished Anofsal plate at a magnification of 1150 ×. The primary and secondary disperse character of the surfaces is clearly observable.

Figure 6 shows the development of surfaces of the third order in various stages of preparation.

The electron-photomicrographs have a magnification of 50,000 ×.

Figure 6(a) shows a surface obtained in the first stage of preparation. The subordinate character of the porosities constituting the surface of third order can be observed.

Figure 6(b) separately illustrates the action of the second stage upon formation of the surface of the third order.

Figure 6(c) presents the surface developed by linking the first and second stages of preparation. Amicroscopic porosities are clearly observable at certain spots.

THE CHOICE OF TECHNOLOGICAL PROCESSES FOR ANOFSAL PLATES

A conclusion of the foregoing is that technological processes in printing must be viewed in a different manner, when talking of aluminium plates provided with an oxide layer, than is usual for monometal or polymetal plates.

The first characteristic feature is that although a typically hydrophilic adsorbent, aluminium oxide will bind molecules consisting of lyophilic and lyophobouic particles—inks, lacquers—with great force by means of polar or apolar adsorption when the surface has been prepared in the above manner.

This permits the fixation of these substances directly to the oxide layer with a far higher binding force as compared with their adhesion to the metal surface. The presence of adsorptive forces appears to be proved by the fact that the oxide layer is given an irreversibly hydrophilic or oleophilic character by the substances first contacting the oxide. If the oxide comes first into contact with an acid hydrophilic colloid, the plate cannot be toned with an oleophilic substance even if the latter is dried on it. Conversely, an oleophilic substance having come first into contact with the oxide layer, cannot be removed by any kind of etching agent. That is why it is not practicable to use on Anofsal plate photo resists developed by acids. Adsorption is the reason why traces of such a substance cannot be removed from the pores.

Vilmos Salgó

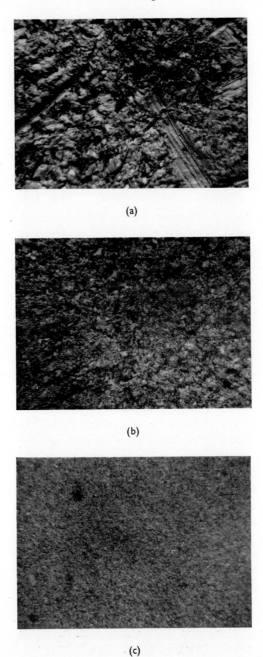

(a)

(b)

(c)

Fig. 3. (a) Mechanically grained zinc plate. (b) Mechanically grained Eggen micral plate.
(c) Completely prepared Anofsal plate.

(a)

(b)

Fig. 4. (a) Surface of an Anofsal plate after completion of the first stage. (b) Surface of a completely prepared Anofsal plate.

Fig. 5. Surface of a completely prepared Anofsal plate, magnified 1150 ×, Collodion copy.

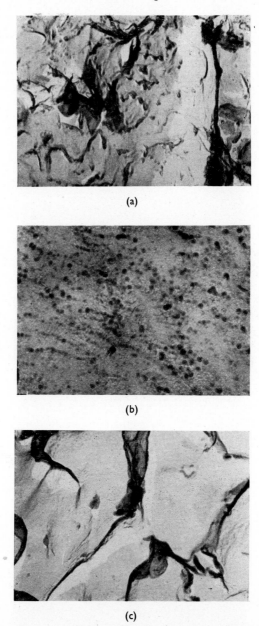

(a)

(b)

(c)

Fig. 6. (a) Electron microphotography of the surface of an Anofsal plate after the first stage of the process. (b) Electron microphotography of a plate surface formed by the action of the second stage. (c) Electron microphotography of a plate surface formed by the joint action of the two stages. Collodion-carbon copies, magnified 50,000 ×.

If lacquer is subsequently applied to such spots, it will adhere much more weakly to the oxide. Water and hydrophilic, mainly inorganic, substances dissociating into ions and consisting of small molecules are bound to the non-printing areas by means of capillary condensation. Only some slight wetting is required to increase the hydrophilic character of such areas during printing.

Oleophilic, lacquer-like substances applied to the surface cannot be removed by means of the conventional combination of solvent and etching agent, without removal of the oxide layer, if the applied solvent ensures physical dissolution only. An additional layer of solvent will adhere to the adsorbed layer of lacquer in such cases and will only increase the greasy character of the surface. Such substances can be removed only by means of chemical solvents. The removal of the lacquer and the hydrophilization of the oxide subsequent to the application of lacquer will be successful only if the solvent possesses an adsorption affinity to the oxide as well. Alkalinely hydrolyzing salts can be used to good advantage for the purpose.

The theoretical considerations in respect of the surfaces of Anofsal plates have been extensively proved in practice. The surface of an Anofsal plate is entirely smooth from the practical viewpoint, it is hard, binds an adequately chosen offset lacquer well, and shows minimum wetting water requirements during actual printing. The technological processes can be readily performed if the foregoing is taken into consideration.

The microphotographs and electron-microphotographs were made at the Research Institute for Technical Physics of the Hungarian Academy of Sciences. Thanks are due to scientific research fellows Dr. Béla Lovas and Dr. Klára Arkosi.

SUMMARY

Anofsal plate surfaces must be prepared in two stages. A relatively compact layer possessing surfaces of the first, second and third orders is formed in the first stage. This results in mainly macroscopic graining, while the oxide layer formed is soft. The second stage mainly involves the development of a layer incorporating surfaces primarily of the third order, dispersed in conformity with the structure obtained during the first stage. The layer developed in this manner is of sufficient hardness and resistance and also exhibits the grain necessary for the adsorption of the various substances.

REFERENCES

1. F. KELLER, M. S. HUNTER and D. L. ROBINSON, Structural features of oxide coating on aluminium, *Electrochem. Soc.* **100**, 411 (1953).
2. A. BUZÁGH, *Kolloidika* (Colloidics), Akadémiai Kiadó, Budapest (1951).

3. B. Bártfai, *Fémek felületi kezelése* (Surface treatment of metals), Müszaki Kiadó, Budapest (1955).
4. R. W. Franklin, Structure of non-porous anodic films on aluminium, *Nature* **180**, 1470 (1957).
5. D. Altenpohl, *Convention Record of I.R.E.*, 1954. National Convention, Part 3, p. 35.
6. Hungarian patent No. 147, 404.

DISCUSSION

Schaeffer: The adsorptive properties of the two types of oxide, soft and hard, as well as the various orders of surfaces are differentiated even though the same crystal structure is postulated. This is of importance for water adsorption. Is the oxide structure also important for the adsorption of polymeric electrolytes?

Tollenaar: In regard to Dr. Schaeffer's question I believe in 1936 the Russian investigators measured contact angles on oxide layers of zinc and aluminium. They found angles very close to 90°. In this region actual printing conditions may be so different from the equilibrium condition implied by contact angle measurements that the interpretation of the latter is obscured.

Schaeffer: Regarding the effect of surface roughness of metal, or more properly metal oxide surface, the recent work of Trenay and Johnson quoted in our paper has shown that anodized metal surfaces with mirror type finishes can provide quite uniform hydrophilic surfaces. Characterizing rough surfaces as hydrophobic or hydrophilic seems much more difficult.

MONOMOLECULAR FILM TRANSFER
AS APPLIED TO LITHOGRAPHIC SCUMMING

by W. D. Schaeffer, C. Y. Kuo and A. C. Zettlemoyer

National Printing Ink Research Institute,

Lehigh University, Bethlehem, Pa., U.S.A.

Abstract—A Mechanism for scumming of the desensitized area of a lithographic printing plate is proposed and tested. The hypothesis is presented that printing ink components will spread over the surface of a fountain solution. The transfer of monolayers of oleic acid and ink varnish to non-desensitized or poorly desensitized areas of the plate is demonstrated by withdrawing zinc and aluminium plates from the fountain solution through the monolayer and measuring the increase in surface tension of the solution or the increase in the contact angle of water on the monolayer covered plate.

An alternate mechanism for scumming is proposed involving migration of slightly water soluble ink components through the fountain solution and their reaction at plate surfaces.

INTRODUCTION

The success of the lithographic or planographic reproduction process depends more on the successful technological application of surface chemistry than any of the other graphic arts processes. The separation of ink receptive printing areas from the water receptive non-printing areas on the plate provides one of the keys to the successful operation of the process, and technological success in this step has provided some of the impetus for the continued expansion of the lithographic offset process.

An approach has been sought to investigate those problems in lithography in which behavior of the ink may limit the length of the run. One prominent problem is scumming. Confusion exists concerning the definition of scumming in relation to greasing and tinting. The following definitions are included to avoid misunderstanding.

Lithographic scumming is the process in which the non-image areas of the plate become ink receptive and begin to print. Etching or a combination of abrasion and etching of the offending areas is required to correct the condition.[1]

Greasing is synonymous with scumming.

Tinting is the mixing or emulsification of ink into the dampening solution on the plate. The non-image area is readily cleaned by wiping with extra dampening solution.[1]

Bleeding is dissolving of dye or pigment from the ink into the lithographic dampening solution.

While some disagreement in the definition of scumming has existed in the past, the foregoing definition is now generally accepted[1,2] and is the basis for the present investigation of scumming mechanisms.

This report is concerned with the physical chemical processes which can lead to lithographic scumming. The fact that abrasion of the plate surface, specifically the non-printing area, can also lead to scumming is recognized; however, good press room practice should normally preclude abrasive materials from the system. Poor press adjustments, excessive squeeze between plate and blanket cylinders and paper lint, powder and dust are common sources of abrasive wear of the lithographic plate. Abrasion of the non-printing area of the plate serves to remove the hydrophilic or water loving coating, usually gum arabic or sodium carboxymethylcellulose, and in many cases can also remove the oxide coating from the metal plate. The problem is to determine the nature of processes which are chemically capable of converting or supplanting the hydrophilic coatings in the non-printing areas of the plate and making the areas ink receptive.

Spreading of an oil at a metal–water interface can be determined with contact angle measurements, and this was one approach taken by Adams.[3] He found that all metals or metal oxides are wet to a sufficient degree by oils to preclude their direct use in the non-printing area of the lithographic plate without depending on an acid etch or desensitizing polymer. The hypothesis in this work was that all water films on the non-printing areas of the plate carry a film of ink vehicle, drier, or compound and transfer of the film to the metal substrate can cause scumming. This report describes the test of the hypothesis including studies of monolayers of ink vehicles and fatty acids on water and aqueous fountain solutions, and the transfer of these monolayers to metal or metal oxide surfaces.

MONOLAYER FORMATION

Polar chemical compounds have a pronounced tendency to spread over a water surface to form first a monolayer or single layer of molecules on the water surface and then a thicker film if sufficient material is present. Ultimately, an equilibrium state should be attained in which a monolayer is in equilibrium with a lense or droplet.*

---

* Nonpolar materials of sufficient molecular weight will generally remain in bulk or in droplets without spreading on water[4].

The criterion of whether a liquid b will spread or not on another liquid a is obtained from the spreading coefficient S. Harkins and Feldman[5] described the spreading coefficient as

$$S = \gamma_a - (\gamma_b + \gamma_{ab}) \tag{1}$$

where γ_a is the surface tension of the liquid a already present in bulk, γ_b is the surface tension of liquid b which is to be spread and γ_{ab} is the interfacial tension between the two bulk liquids. When S is positive, liquid b will spread on liquid a, and when S is negative, spreading will not occur. Banks[6] and Anderson[7] have obtained measurements of the surface and interfacial tensions of various ink varnishes and fatty acids with water and have demonstrated that varnishes will spread on the water because of this positive spreading coefficient. In fact, Anderson concludes that S will determine how easily the ink will cause scumming.

Since there is common agreement that most ink vehicles and driers will spread on a clean water surface, one of the first objectives was to determine the behavior of films of common lithographic ink vehicles on acid fountain solutions. Pressure-area curves were determined with a Cenco Hydrophil Balance similar to the traditional Langmuir balance.[8] The surface pressure, π_b, is defined as

$$\pi_b = \gamma_a - \gamma_m \tag{2}$$

where γ_a is the surface tension of the original clean substrate solution, a, and γ_m is the surface tension of the monomolecular, b, film covered surface.

Both the spreading coefficient of an insoluble film and the surface pressure depend on the surface tension of the water, γ_a. If a solution of an inorganic acid, base, or salt is used as a substrate, γ_a refers to the surface tension of that solution rather than the surface tension of pure water. In most of the experimental work solutions of ortho-phosphoric acid at a pH of 4·5 have been used. The surface tension of this solution approximates that of pure water. This solution is used because it is representative of the level of acidity used in lithographic fountain solutions, and under these conditions most weak acids which form films are present either in the nonionized form or as salts of metals.

When salts of metals are introduced into the solution some marked changes can occur in the monolayer. Some salts can cause a significant increase in the surface tension of water, but more important, extensive studies of stearic[9] and myristic[10] acid films on aqueous solutions, 0·0002 molar with respect to copper, magnesium, calcium, zinc, aluminium and iron, indicate that the salts of the metals are formed in the film, and their force–area curves can be quite different from that of the acid.

Studies of monolayers of a #4 regular litho varnish on 0·0002 molar magnesium and zinc nitrate solutions of pH 4·5, 5·5, 6·5 and 8·5 demonstrated no significant differences among the pressure–area curves. Presumably the free acid concentration (acid number 15) was sufficiently low that salt formation did not influence the behavior of the varnish monolayer.

MONOLAYERS ON GUM ARABIC AND CMC SOLUTIONS

Practically essential to the preservation of the desensitized areas of the lithographic plate is a water soluble polymeric acid. The role of the acid seems to be, though comparatively little study has been given to the

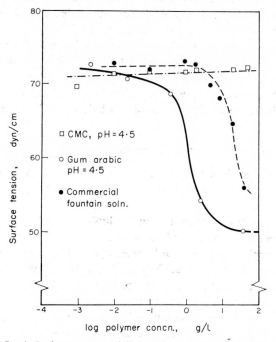

Fig. 1. Surface tensions of desensitizing polymer solutions.

subject, [11,12,13] the formation of an adsorbed hydrophilic film which will hold enough water to prevent the transfer of the ink to that section of the plate. Another possible use of the " desensitizer " is to be adsorbed at the water–air interface. The resultant lowering of surface tension may be sufficient to impede if not stop an insoluble film from spreading.

The two most popular " desensitizing " polymers are gum arabic and sodium carboxymethylcellulose. Figure 1 illustrates the effect of various concentrations of CMC 70 LL* and gum arabic† on the surface tension of water. The CMC has no effect on the surface tension of the water in agreement with other studies in the literature.[14] The molecule is evidently so hydrophilic that no adsorption occurs at the air–water interface. The present study was restricted to the lowest molecular weight CMC available; however, there is no indication in the literature than any increase in molecular weight induces surface activity.

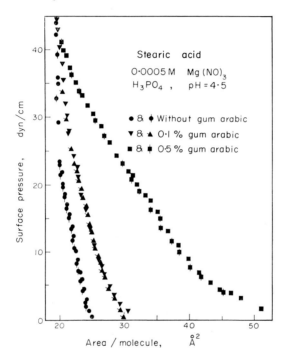

Fig. 2. Gum arabic penetration of stearic acid monolayers.

Gum arabic does show some surface activity at relatively high concentrations. A problem is encountered in the low concentration gum arabic solutions by the length of time required for the high molecular weight molecules to diffuse to the water surface. The diffusion time can be of the order of hours during which a great deal of foreign contamination of the water surface can occur. Certainly, gum arabic molecules will not have time on the press to diffuse to the surface of the fountain solution on desensitized

* The CMC 70 LL was the lowest viscosity grade manufactured by Hercules Powder Company. The number designation has been recently changed to CMC 70 AP.

†The gum arabic used was " selected sorts " obtained from Stein, Holland Company Inc., 285 Madison Avenue, New York.

areas of the plate; consequently, the data in Fig. 1 obtained on surfaces approximately 5 min old are at best approximations to the surface tension of fountain solution on the plate.

The absence of surface activity of CMC was confirmed from the determination of force-area curves for stearic acid on dilute solutions of CMC. The curves were essentially identical to that on water at the same pH. Monolayers of stearic acid on gum arabic, however, show a pronounced penetration of the gum which increases with concentration. In Fig. 2,

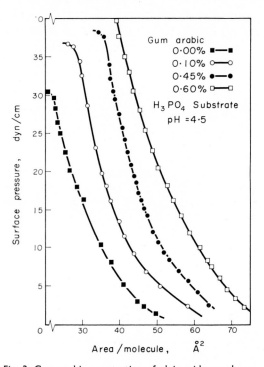

Fig. 3. Gum arabic penetration of oleic acid monolayers.

penetration of the film is detected by the increase in surface pressure observed at a given area per molecule of stearic acid. The change in pressure is rather drastic. Figures 3 and 4 illustrate the changes in the force-area isotherms of oleic acid and #4 regular litho varnish respectively, as the concentration of gum arabic is increased. The ease of compression of the liquid-like monolayers makes the effect of the gum arabic penetration less striking than with solid stearic acid films. It now remains to be demonstrated whether this penetration of the monolayer either influences the ease of transfer to the metal plate or entirely inhibits the transfer.

MONOMOLECULAR FILM TRANSFER

Figure 5 is a schematic diagram of the process hypothesized for scumming next to an image area. The process depicted on the top of the page is an extension of the image area by hydrophobic components in the ink replacing the hydrophilic coating. The lower portion of Fig. 5 is a pictorial representation of the system devised by Blodgett[15] and used to determine whether a monolayer on the fountain solution will transfer to the metal plate. The question is whether an oleic acid or litho varnish monolayer on a fountain solution will transfer to the metal plate during the time the plate is drawn through the air–liquid interface. Presumably the monolayer will have to replace the absorbed film of gum at the metal surface or at least find metal

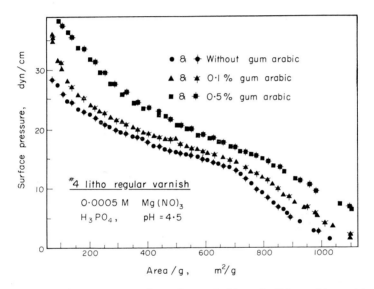

Fig. 4. Gum arabic penetration of monolayers of #4 regular lithographic varnish.

areas where gum is not absorbed if the monolayer is to adhere to the plate surface. If the monolayer does not adhere it will recede along with the water film as the slide is pulled slowly through the interface.

Transfer of the monolayer can be detected in two ways. During the withdrawal of the slide the surface tension of the solution will increase if surface active molecules are withdrawn with the slide, provided that a monolayer or less of the insoluble film is present at the water–air interface. This method will not work if a drop of excess acid is present since the additional material will spread over the surface to replace any of the film removed by the plate. The surface tension of the solution will therefore remain at its original level. In this event transfer of the insoluble monolayer is detected by measurement of the contact angle of water with the plate.

The contact angles of water plotted in Fig. 6 indicate some marked differences between zinc and aluminium surfaces alone and with adsorbed

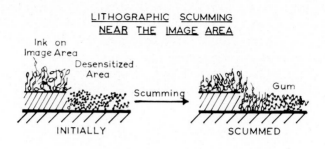

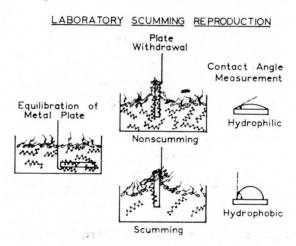

Fig. 5. Relationship of scumming to monolayer transfer.

films of gum arabic and CMC. Aluminium seems intrinsically more hydrophilic than zinc in view of the 50 odd degrees lower contact angles of water on the former. The values for both metals, however, are surprisingly large, and do not agree with the recently published measurements of the order of 10° on clean, smooth, anodized zinc and aluminium surfaces. [16] The higher contact angle values obtained in the present work are due to a number of causes. The metal surfaces in the present work were deliberately roughened or grained as is standard practice in lithography, even though the fact is recognized that rough surfaces have higher contact angles than smooth surfaces when other conditions are equal. The objective of the metal preparation in the present work was to employ a single rigorous mechanical and chemical cleaning which could provide reproducible surfaces without necessarily producing intrinsically hydrophilic surfaces. Duplicate contact angle measurements indicated satisfactory reproducibility on the original plates; however, large differences between duplicate measurements sometimes

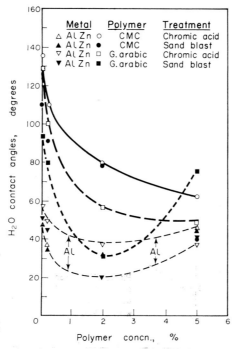

Fig. 6. Contact angles of water on carboxymethylcellulose and gum arabic on zinc and aluminium.

occurred after adsorption on the metal or transfer of the monolayer. One of the other possible causes for the large contact angles measured on some of the systems studied is illustrated in Fig. 7. Originally, little attention was paid to the length of time which passed between preparation of the slide and the measurement of the contact angle. The effects of possible contamination and/or corrosion of the slide during this interval are certainly significant as evidenced by two fold increases in the contact angle within 40 hr of preparation. Certainly contact angles should be measured as soon as possible after preparation of the slide.

The behavior of water on zinc and aluminium is surprisingly different. If the measured contact angles on each metal are extrapolated back to the time zero, the value on aluminium is 18° and on zinc 42°. Presumably, the values should be the same.[16] The initial difference may be due to variations in the solubilities of the acetates and phosphates of the two metals and the relative contamination of the metal oxide surfaces by these salts. The fact that the difference is sustained and even increases during storage suggests that systematic differences in hydrophobicity of corrosion products are responsible, since random contamination of both aluminium and zinc surfaces would be expected to yield similar contact angles.

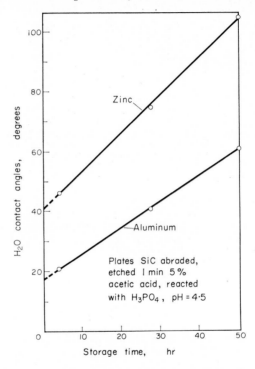

Fig. 7. Increase of water contact angles on aluminium and zinc plates after aging.

In spite of the marked influence of storage time on contact angle values, several significant comparisons in addition to that between metals can be obtained from the data illustrated in Fig. 6. The most important influence beside the metal on the contact angle is the addition of the desensitizing, water-soluble, polymer. The addition of 0·2% polymer invariably lowers the contact angle and 2% polymer lowers the angle somewhat more. Somewhat greater decreases might have been obtained had the equilibrium times been increased beyond half an hour; however, this period seemed sufficient for present purposes since during actual press runs considerably less time is available for the polymer to equilibrate with the metal. The method of surface preparation and the desensitizing polymer used affect the contact angles on zinc significantly. Gum arabic adsorbed on a sand blasted plate provides the lowest contact angle for any treatment combination of zinc. The differences on the aluminium surfaces are not nearly as pronounced.

The most important question of whether the transfer of a monolayer to a metal plate offers a mechanism of scumming can be answered positively.

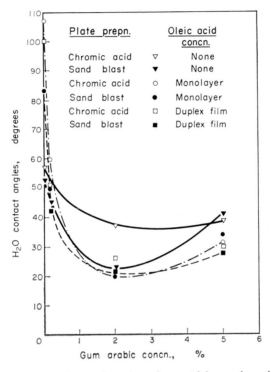

Plate prepn.		Oleic acid concn.
Chromic acid	▽	None
Sand blast	▼	None
Chromic acid	○	Monolayer
Sand blast	●	Monolayer
Chromic acid	□	Duplex film
Sand blast	■	Duplex film

Fig. 8. Water contact angles on aluminium plates withdrawn through oleic acid films on gum arabic solutions.

In Figs. 8 and 9 the contact angles of water on the aluminium plates withdrawn through the monolayer are considerably greater than the contact angles for the untreated plates, that is, in the absence of polymer in the aqueous substrate or fountain solution. Addition of as little as 0·2% gum arabic in the fountain solution causes the contact angles of water on the plates dragged through the monolayer to decrease to values equal to or less than those which have only been equilibrated with the fountain solution. The gum arabic clearly prevented transfer of the monolayer. The situation is similar with CMC as depicted in Fig. 9; however, the addition of CMC to the aqueous solution does not lower the contact angle as much as did the gum arabic. It seems clear that in these experiments that at low concentrations of CMC, that is 0·2 to 2·0% polymer, a part of a monolayer of fatty acid transferred to the desensitized plate.

The question as to whether monolayers have transferred to zinc under similar circumstances cannot be answered decisively from contact angle measurements. The increase in hydrophobicity of the plates after preparation (see Fig. 7) was responsible. In the case of monolayer covered solutions the

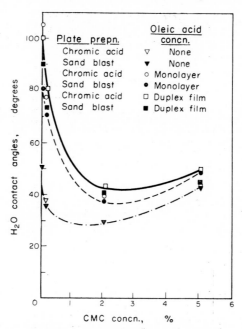

Fig. 9. Water contact angles on aluminium plates withdrawn through oleic acid films on carboxymethylcellulose solutions.

observed changes of surface tension have to be used to indicate whether or not the monolayer transferred. Listed in Table 1 are the observed γ's after withdrawing the two plates from the solutions. In this as in the previous work, the chromic acid treated plate was always withdrawn first through the monolayer followed by the sandblasted sample.

There seems to be little question from the data in Table 1 that the oleic acid monolayers transferred in whole or in part to the desensitized zinc at the lower gum arabic and CMC concentrations. Transfer is indicated by a plus sign in Table 1, and the question mark indicates a smaller than anticipated surface tension change for complete monolayer transfer to occur.

In the majority of cases the withdrawal of the plates caused an increase in the surface tension regardless of whether the chromic acid or the sand blasted plate was withdrawn. The variation in the surface tensions of the monolayer covered surfaces, γ_{m_0}, is due to variations in the amount of oleic acid solution added to a given area of water solution and to the contribution of the water soluble polymer to the surface tension.

TABLE 1. TRANSFER OF OLEIC ACID MONOLAYERS TO ZINC PLATES AS EVALUATED
FROM SURFACE TENSION CHANGES

Gum Arabic Concentration	None	Tr.	0·2%	Tr.	2%	Tr.	20%	Tr.
Surface tension, γ_a	73·1₃		73·1		48·8		49·3	
Monolayer covered, γ_{m_0}	46·0		43·4		42		40	
γ_{m_1} after chromic acid treated plate withdrawn	53·4	+	47·8	(?)	42	—	41·4	—
γ_{m_2} after sand blasted plate withdrawn	66·2	+	57·0	+	46·3	(?)	42·4	—
CMC Concentration	None	Tr.	0·2%	Tr.	2%	Tr.	5%	Tr.
Surface tension, γ_0	73·1		73·7		72·5		72·7	
Monolayer covered, γ_{m_0}	46·0		42·3		39·6		45·2	
γ_{m_1} after chromic acid treated plate withdrawn	53·4	+	49	+	47·1	+	48	(?)
γ_{m_2} after sand blasted plate withdrawn	66·2	+	57·7	+	54	+	51·5	(?)

An additional series of monolayer transfer measurements were made to circumvent some of the difficulties encountered in the first experiments. The system was modified so that transfer of the monolayer was made slowly. The slide was withdrawn at a rate of 0·6 cm/min, and the surface pressure was maintained at a constant value independent of the amount of the film transferred to the slide. Most important of all, the contact angles were measured within minutes after the slide was withdrawn from the solution. The resulting contact angles are plotted on Fig. 10 as a function of time. The time in hours is that allowed for the plate to equilibrate with the desensitizing polymer in the aqueous substrate. Heretofore, the slides were equilibrated with all solutions for 20 min prior to withdrawal.

Aluminium is uniformly desensitized by either gum arabic or CMC when present at 2% concentration according to the data in Fig. 11 since there is no evidence of different degrees of oleic acid monolayer transfer at either of the two film pressures, 10 or 20 dyn/cm. At 1% CMC, however the contact angles are somewhat greater than at the higher polymer concentration due presumably to partial transfer of the monolayer. This view is supported by the greater contact angle obtained after transfer of the oleic acid monolayer at 20 dyn/cm than at 10 dyn/cm.

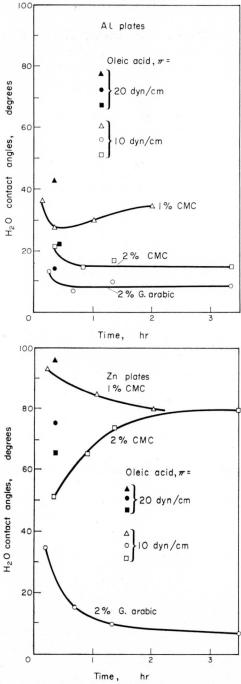

Fig. 10. Contact angles of water on zinc and aluminium plates withdrawn through oleic acid monolayers at constant film pressure.

The contact angles changed much more drastically on zinc plates than on aluminium with experimental conditions. Gum arabic of 2% desensitized zinc only after equilibration times of 40 min or longer. CMC did not desensitize zinc at all. The variation in the dependence of contact angle on equilibration time with changing CMC concentration is unusual. The

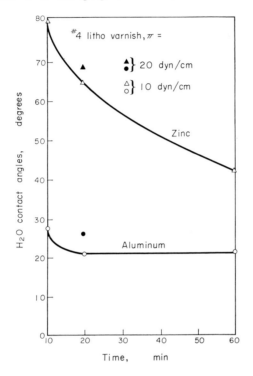

Fig. 11. Water contact angles on zinc and aluminium plates withdrawn through #4 regular litho varnish monolayers on 2% gum arabic solutions.

higher CMC concentration provided some desensitization on brief exposure to the zinc, however, prolonged corrosion destroyed the hydrophilic film. To summarize, zinc appears to be somewhat more difficult to desensitize than aluminium with gum arabic, and impossible to desensitize with CMC using the present techniques.

Oleic acid monolayers were used as the prototype of ink spreading components in most of this study. A limited amount of work was done with varnishes, and illustrated in Fig. 11 are the contact angles measured for water on aluminium and zinc plates withdrawn through films of #4 litho varnish spread on aqueous solutions of gum arabic. The contact angles on aluminium are sufficiently low to indicate that little if any transfer of varnish

s

occurred to the slide. The contact angles on zinc plates show a marked dependence on the time of equilibration between zinc and gum prior to withdrawing the slide. Comparison of these contact angles with those in Fig. 10 for zinc plates withdrawn through oleic acid films under comparable conditions indicates that varnish transfers to the zinc plates even at the low surface pressure of 10 dyn/cm. No work was done with CMC on zinc plates in the transfer of varnish monolayers.

DISCUSSION

The present work confirms the hypothesis that one potential mechanism of scumming involves the spreading and transfer of an insoluble monolayer from the aqueous surface of desensitized areas of the plate to sites at which the adsorbed hydrophilic polymer film is incomplete or has been disturbed, e.g. abraded. The work is, of course, incomplete in many respects. Perhaps the most important factor neglected on a practical basis is the demonstration that more ink components will and must spread. Previous work in the field, [7,17] however, illustrates very clearly that spreading will occur with most types of varnishes and driers. One other practical question to be answered is whether monolayer spreading occurs sufficiently rapidly on the offset press so that surface sites are reached by the monolayer before it is washed away in a new passage of the dampening rollers. The kinetics of spreading of insoluble monolayers has been treated theoretically and experimentally as a diffusion process. Crisp[18] found that the flow constant for the monolayer decreases with decreasing depth and increasing viscosity of the substrate solution. These observations provide further justification for lithographing with a minimum practical flow of fountain solution. Competing kinetically with the monolayer diffusion is the rate of diffusion of the gum arabic polymer molecule to the affected sites. This is a slow process, and it is entirely possible that in most of the present studies that the fifteen minute time allowed for equilibration between metal and polymer in bulk solution was not adequate. The other studies using different metal treatments provide longer equilibration times and slower withdrawal rates from solution; nevertheless, the results are very much the same as the first series.

One of the objectives of the study was to assess the importance of monolayer penetration in inhibiting monolayer transfer to the metal plates. The penetration of oleic acid films by gum arabic does not stop the transfer; consequently, monolayer penetration can only have minor if any effect in inhibiting transfer. The rate of diffusion of gum arabic molecules to the surface of a film of fountain solution on the non-image area of the plate is a slow process compared to the rate at which the fountain solution film is transferred to the blanket and the paper. In other words, penetration of the surface is believed to be a much slower process than spreading of an insoluble film. Therefore, in the practical case, penetration can be expected to be of minor influence.

The formation of a hydrophobic monolayer, i.e. scumming on a lithographic plate, may also proceed by another mechanism. In the present case, the molecules causing scumming were water insoluble because of the overwhelming size of the hydrocarbon portion of the molecule. Other polar molecules having smaller hydrocarbon chains, C_4–C_{10}, and active functional groups, acids, amines, etc. are water soluble, and when adsorbed from water solution can form hydrophobic films. Shafren and Zisman[19] have demonstrated the formation of hydrophobic films by n–alkyl monoacids when adsorbed on platinum from solution. A similar phenomenon might be expected when an acid or amine can be transferred from the ink to the fountain solution and then adsorb on a chemically active metal. This mechanism of scumming is the subject of an independent current investigation.

CONCLUSIONS

1. Most lithographic printing ink vehicles and driers will spread on the surface of a fountain solution to form a single layer of molecules or a monolayer.

2. The insoluble monolayer can transfer to an inadequately desensitized aluminium or zinc plate to make the area hydrophobic and ink receptive.

3. Contact angles of water on zinc and aluminium equilibrated with gum arabic and sodium carboxymethylcellulose are larger on the former metal indicating that the zinc is less hydrophilic than the aluminium.

REFERENCES

1. Discussion, *Intern. Bull. Printing and Allied Trades*, **73**, 29, January (1956).
2. *Printing Ink Handbook*, pp. 24, 25, Nat. Assoc. Printing Ink Makers, New York (1958).
3. R. A. C. ADAMS, Contact angles and their significance in lithographic research, *Intern. Bull. Printing and Allied Trades* **73**, 20, January (1956).
4. W. D. HARKINS, *Physical Chemistry of Surface Films*, p. 99, Reinhold, New York (1952).
5. W. D. HARKINS and A. FELDMAN, Films, the spreading of liquids and the spreading coefficient, *J. Am. Chem. Soc.* **44**, 2665 (1922).
6. W. H. BANKS, Some physico-chemical aspects of lithography, *Intern. Bull. Printing and Allied Trades* **73**, 17, January (1956).
7. P. W. ANDERSON, The influence of fountain solution on the printing quality in offset, *Intern. Bull. Printing and Allied Trades* **80**, 110, June (1958).
8. N. K. ADAM, *The Physics and Chemistry of Surfaces*, pp. 29–71. Oxford Clarendon (1930).
9. J. A. SPINK and J. V. SANDERS, Soap formation in monomolecular films on aqueous solutions, *Trans. Far. Soc.* **51**, 1154 (1955).

10. G. A. WOLSTENHOLME and J. H. SCHULMAN, Metal-monolayer interactions, *J.O.C.C.A.* **34**, 378, 571 (1951).
11. F. J. TRITTON, A study of the theory of lithographic printing I and II, *J. Soc. Chem. Ind.* **51**, 299–313, September (1932).
12. E. OLSEN and C. W. CHRISTENSEN, Some experiments to ascertain the applicability of the anthrone method for measuring quantities of gum arabic-adsorbed on zinc lithographic plates, etc., *Intern. Bull. Printing and Allied Trades* **73**, 39, January (1956).
13. J. E. HEALE, A method for measuring the amount of gum adsorbed on zinc lithographic plates, *TAGA Proceedings* **8**, pp. 189–195, May (1956).
14. J. STAWITZ, H. KRAMER and W. KLAUS, Oberflächenspannung und Membranbilding von Zelluloseathern in wässriger Lösung, *Kolloid-Z* **133**, 69 (1953).
15. K. B. BLODGETT, Monomolecular films of fatty acids on glass, *J. Am. Chem. Soc.* **56**, 495 (1934).
16. D. J. TRENAY and H. JOHNSON, Jr., The water wettability of metal surfaces, *J. Phys. Chem.* **62**, No. 7, 833 (1958).
17. J. A. LONG, C. WHITEMARSH and W. L. YUAN, Adhesion and Adhesives, pp. 1231–1240. *Official Digest*, December (1956).
18. D. J. CRISP, Two-dimensional transport at fluid interfaces, *Trans. Far. Soc.* **42**, 619 (1946).
19. E. G. SHAFREN and W. A. ZISMAN, Hydrophobic Monolayers and their Adsorption from Aqueous Solution, *Monomolecular Layers*, p. 150. Ed. by H. Sobotka, Am. Assoc. for the Advancement of Science, Washington, D.C. (1954).

DISCUSSION

TOLLENAAR: Is it feasible to determine the mean molecular weight of a polymer by spreading methods?

SCHAEFFER: The mean molecular weights of polymers have been determined by spreading methods, but the studies should be carried out at far lower spreading pressures, e.g. 1 dyn/cm, than were employed in the present work. Here the pressure area relationships of the two dimensional films correspond to the three dimensional cases of ideal gases.

BANKS: In the constant pressure deposition experiments did you measure the decrease in area of spread film because you could then get an estimate of the amount of surface active material deposited.

SCHAEFFER: We did not measure the decrease in area of the residual film because the plate area, 12.5 cm^2, was small in comparison with the area of the spread film, 200 cm^2.

BANKS: We have detected the presence of surface active material on the desensitized areas of a plate by sampling the water layer with clean filter paper used as an absorbent wick and later transferring this to a clean water surface which then showed a surface pressure corresponding to a spread layer. This would support Dr. Schaeffer's suggestion.

CHRISTENSEN: Mr. Olsen and I some years ago concluded that CMC desensitizes zinc better than gum arabic, and this is because the former is more strongly adsorbed and in larger amounts, when used in a fountain solution.

Your work differs from ours in that we were only interested in the adsorbed layer on the plate while you are concerned with the surface of the water, where you find that the surface tension is independent of the CMC concentration. Applying Gibb's law, doesn't this mean that no adsorption has taken place at the water surface? This does not, however, say anything about adsorption on the plate which of course for practical purposes is the important question. In practice CMC has proved to be a better desensitizer than gum arabic. We believe that any corrosion taking place on the plate is rendered ineffective as to tinting, provided the gumming agent is adsorbed sufficiently strongly and in sufficient quantity.

SCHAEFFER: Your work on the adsorption of CMC and gum arabic on zinc should certainly have a bearing on our results, but at the present stage the relationship is not obvious. Normally the extent of polyelectrolyte adsorption might be expected to determine how well the surface is desensitized and resists monolayer transfer. Our work with zinc provides, however, no evidence that CMC is a better desensitizing agent than gum arabic; in fact, the exact opposite conclusion can be reached. Moreover, commercial practice in United States evidently does not correspond to the experience in Denmark since the use of CMC in fountain solutions is not as popular as gum arabic.

The fact that the CMC does not lower the surface tension of acqueous solutions under the conditions investigated is in itself good evidence that CMC is not adsorbed at the air-water interface. Your conclusion based on the application of the Gibbs equation is identical; however, this equation must be used with caution since it must be applied to the system as a whole rather than to single components.

Our results do have a bearing on tinting in so far as this problem can arise from the spreading of duplex (multimolecular) ink films on the surface of the fountain solution on the plate. Passage of the duplex film through a nip can result in the dispersion of the film to form an ink in water emulsion. This process has not been investigated adequately to date.

Finally, I cannot agree that the corrosion products on the metal surface are of no consequence. Our present opinion is that the corrosion process in the desensitized areas proceeds as described by Banks (1956) until irreversible reaction of the polyelectrolyte in the anodic areas induces more or less complete polarization. The effectiveness of one desensitizing agent vs. another may very well depend on the configuration of the adsorbed phase. If the molecule is strongly solvated, as in the case of CMC, only a few points of contact between polymer and metal may exist, and the polymer will not inhibit corrosion effectively. On the other hand, if the molecule is not strongly solvated, it may prefer the metal surface not only at the spots where irreversible reaction occurs but also other sites which are only physically shielded.

THE PRESENT POSITION AND THE TREND OF FUTURE DEVELOPMENTS IN THE GRAPHIC ARTS

by V. G. W. HARRISON

PATRA

I HAVE been asked to introduce this general discussion on the present position of the graphic arts and the likely trend of future developments, with particular reference to reproduction processes. This, however, is no easy task, for, in my view, the printing industry is in process of transition: it is changing slowly and rather painfully from a craft industry, having its roots directly in the medieval craft guilds, to a branch of applied engineering. From a recent investigation into letterpress bookprinting made by PATRA in a number of British plants, it has become apparent that the greatest progress is likely to be found, not in the adoption of new and revolutionary methods of printing or scientific gadgets, but in reorganization within printing works and, above all, in the training of operators as engineers. This is not being done to anything like the extent that it should, and the key to the whole problem lies in the word " education."

By this, I do not mean that research into new aids to production and increased knowledge of the printing processes will not bear fruit—I am sure that they will; nevertheless, I am convinced that the impact they are likely to make on the industry within the next twenty years is small compared with what can be done by way of educating those entering the industry to use the knowledge which is already available and to adopt modern precision engineering methods.

I think the thing that impressed me more than anything else during a recent visit to Japan was the quality of the young men entering the printing and allied industries as heads of departments and under-managers. These men were not trained as craftsmen through the traditional channels of apprenticeship; they were trained in the Tokyo Institute of Technology or a similar technical university as engineers or scientists, and it became apparent

266

after a few moments' conversation with them that they had a firm general grip of scientific principles. I understand that they are trained and selected very carefully by a process of competitive examination at every stage in their career, and that promotion is made on the results of these examinations coupled with good reports from their superiors. In Great Britain one can still go round the camera department of a large printing works and find no one who understands what a densitometer is or how it should be used. In a corresponding Japanese works I found densitometers in general use and the operators anxious to talk about their limitations and the possible uses of scanners and information theory. We in Great Britain are certainly lagging far behind the Japanese in this respect and have much to learn from them.

The old system of apprenticeship still adopted in our country, whereby the pupil learns his craft by the side of the master at the bench, is hopelessly out-dated. In many cases, the master does not know his subject properly and, even if he does, he may not be willing or able to impart his knowledge to his pupil. In any case, modern science and technology are more readily taught in the lecture theatre of a large school than in a works under the rush of production conditions. At the present time, the only examinations of any standing applicable to printing students are the City and Guilds examinations. It is a great disappointment to teachers in printing schools that only a minority of their students ever bother to sit for these examinations, on the grounds that even if they pass, they will not earn any more when they go into industry—so why bother? This attitude is deplorable but pretty general. Moreover, the City and Guilds examinations, though rightly respected throughout the country, are nevertheless framed on a craft basis rather than on science. They therefore do not encourage the sort of training that modern conditions are making essential.

During a four years' course on psychology which I attended a few years back, we dealt with the very important problem of the employment of people of sub-normal intelligence. The problem is, of course, important since there must be in any community a proportion of sub-normal people who must, if possible, be found suitable employment so that they can be self-supporting. It was, nevertheless, rather a shock to find in the psychology textbooks that printing was seriously recommended as an employment for sub-normal people—not indeed for idiots and imbeciles, but certainly for the higher moronic and feeble-minded groups. This view must be combated vigorously. There are already numerous mechanical and electronic devices which can aid production very considerably provided that we have the trained personnel to operate them intelligently. We have already automatic controls for registration and strength of colour, colour scanners, powderless etching and other devices, and the future opens up wide possibilities. These tools are, however, useless unless they are operated by trained men who know their value and also their limitations.

Happily there are now distinct signs of a change of attitude in Great Britain. I am able to look back over twenty-five years of service in PATRA and there is an astonishing difference in the curricula of the large printing schools between then and now. Twenty-five years ago science was not taught at all and the scientist and technologist were regarded with the greatest suspicion. I well remember my first contact with one of the large printing schools at the beginning of my career when I timidly entered, in order to have some practical work done on a machine. I was regarded with the greatest hostility and, on walking through the corridors, uncomplimentary epithets were hurled at me which at that tender age I did not fully understand. No science was taught; the foundry of the same school did not even boast a thermometer and an assay of its metals had never been made. Nowadays, science forms an important part of the school examinations and a high standard is expected; and the standard tends to rise year by year. PATRA's research reports are awaited with interest, and the results when applicable are incorporated into the instruction. Many of our staff teach at evening classes at printing schools within a convenient radius of Leatherhead, and they are also much in demand as part-time lecturers at special courses throughout the country. This is a remarkable change, not noticeable over a year or two, but very substantial over a quarter century. It can be said, therefore, that scientific and technical knowledge is becoming available to students who wish to avail themselves of it. Unfortunately, as I have already mentioned, incentive to pass examinations is lacking, and the standard reached by some of the students is astonishingly low. As an external assessor, I have the opportunity of seeing some of the papers submitted and, in all too many cases, it is apparent that even when the candidate has had some idea of the answer to a question, he is quite incapable of expressing it in simple and clear English. It is a paradox of our times that this occurs at an age when free education is available on a scale never before experienced in Britain's history.

It is because of this situation that it has gradually become apparent that there is a great need for an independent professional body capable of granting diplomas or qualifications in printing science and engineering; and I am glad to be able to report that plans for the formation of an Institute of Printing in Great Britain are now in an advanced state and the Institute will probably be launched in the autumn of this year. Part of the functions of the new Institute will be to set examinations in printing science and technology of a high standard, for which the printing schools throughout the country will be encouraged to prepare candidates. These examinations will require a training in general science, plus theoretical and practical instruction in several branches of the graphic arts processes, from several options left to the choice of the candidate. The instruction will always be given from the viewpoint of the scientist or engineer rather than from the craftsman; and it is intended that those candidates who successfully pass a three or four years' course shall be awarded a diploma in technology of about degree standard. There is a great deal of work still to be done in getting the Institute going and the examinations generally accepted by the industry, but at least a good start has been made.

I do not apologize for dwelling so long on this vital problem of education, for I believe that it is the most important task facing us in the printing industries during the next ten years and, as this Conference has been organized by the Graphic College of Denmark, this seems an appropriate place and time to air these matters. There are all sorts of exciting tools already accessible to the printer if he knows how to use them; their use should enable better quality work to be produced more cheaply and rapidly than before, but it is no use placing them in the hands of people who do not understand their capabilities and, above all, their limitations. Moreover, once we have in industry a body of men, sympathetic to the scientist and engineer and anxious to use the results of their work, this will provide a tremendous impetus to further scientific research in these fields.

ROTARY LETTERPRESS PRINTING
IN GERMANY

by WOLFRAM ESCHENBACH

THE MINIMIZING of unproductive time and the establishment of continuous working processes are sought in all fields of technology as a result of rationalization. In printing technology this means greater use of the rotary principle as far as possible. Compared to the progress made in gravure and offset processes, letterpress has lagged behind during the past years. Intensive rationalization efforts in the letterpress field promise a rapid improvement of this situation. The problem is primarily the obtaining of qualities on (sheet fed) rotary letterpresses, which so far seemed to be the exclusive prerogative of high speed presses, and without undue cost. Specially qualified printing formes on correspondingly designed (sheet-fed) rotary letterpresses have already brought this goal much nearer. New type printing plates have already given excellent results.

On (sheet-fed) rotary letterpresses it is possible to use about 4/5ths of the machine time for the actual printing process. This means an increase in productivity of more than double that or ordinary two revolution presses at the same press speed. (It should be said that we have a rotary letterpress process also in a two-colour high speed press in which a curved printing forme works in conjunction with a printing cylinder. This means merely the simultaneous printing of a second colour. The working speed of this machine remains that of a letterpress. However, performance is doubled because a second printing cycle is eliminated.) The advantages of rotary letterpress (sheet-fed) are noticeable especially for higher print runs of about 20,000 and upwards as well as for wet-on-wet printing. Multicolour machines can be assembled from individual printing units according to the building-block principle. Modern rotary letterpresses reach working speeds of 8000—10,000 sheets per hour. In order to achieve sufficiently smooth and correct feed, the machines are generally equipped with pile feeders. Operations not directly concerned with the printing process proper should be carried out so as not to interrupt it. Therefore, large pile feeding units are used so as not to cause work interruptions on the machine, this applies also to the delivery end of the machine. Exchangeable cylinders in conjunction with suitable makeready machinery can reduce standing time in (sheet-fed) rotary letterpresses very considerably. By using highly pigmented inks fed to the printing forme over a system of highly developed inking units with rapid and intensive " ink distribution " as well as by means of accurate sheet guidance over transfer drums it is possible nowadays to achieve high qualities in multicolour wet-on-wet printing. Longest transfer zones, in some cases with suitable drying systems—especially on perfector machines—assist in speeding up ink drying between individual printing units.

In certain drying systems (e.g. gas heating) static electricity is removed from paper and with it corresponding printing difficulties. Longer delivery distance assists in obtaining better piling characteristics of fresh prints. Faultless delivery of printed sheets can further be achieved by using chain controlled delivery grippers and pneumatic sheet slow down. For economical reasons interleaving is, as a rule, no longer practiced to-day, not to mention the fact that it would be very difficult at high working speeds. If necessary, powder spraying may be used. A very thin powder layer enables outside air to penetrate the pile and to reach the printed picture thus assisting in the quick setting (drying) of ink. By such measures the disadvantages of relatively short intervals between printing and delivery piling of the sheets that follow one another can be overcome. Suitable quick setting inks can bring further relief.

Oil proof sealing of drive elements, central lubrication, controls for missed and double sheets increases operating safety and handling of the machine is considerably simplified by push button control, well arranged control elements, easy access to essential parts—especially the forme cylinder—as well as through roller wash-up devices, etc. These factors contribute at the same time to an essential reduction in standing time.

Intensive research was conducted in the field of curved printing plates in an effort to make letterpress rotaries competitive with comparable machines of other printing processes. The printing forme is the decisive element of machine design.

It appears that stereotype plates are too heavy and too costly even if using exchangeable cylinders. The necessary tension and adjusting devices of the forme cylinder are relatively complicated, even if tension locking devices are used. The necessary curved plates in the form of wrap-around plates will, within the foreseeable future, become generally available. Use of one step etching machines in printing plants is increasing rapidly; however, the large plate sizes necessary in practical operations are not yet available. Metal plates as well as synthetic plates (e.g. Nylon, Dycril) are under development. Extensive tests have been conducted with plates of 0·8 to 1·0 mm thickness. The relatively shallow relief of these plates calls for inking units having special performance; it is possible, nevertheless to utilize experiences made with inking units on machines of indirect offset (or dry offset). After thorough training of workers, accurate mounting and registering of large printing formes should not prove too difficult because similar difficulties have already been satisfactorily overcome in other printing processes.

In summarizing it may be said that the sheet fed rotary letterpress due to its continuous working principle (beginning at a certain print order level) can, if compared with flat bed letterpress, contribute considerably to rationalization by reducing unproductive time with the help of special feeder pile change systems and continuous sheet delivery as well as by profiting from short makeready, easy operation and ready maintenance. It also facilitates the transition to multicolour machines.

The spread of the (sheet-fed) rotary letterpress machine is conceivably a matter of print order size and capital investment as well as one of curved plate formes which can guarantee high printing quality. On the basis of present developments it can be expected that this type of machine will soon be in regular production and will be used more and more.

GRAVURE PRINTING

by Hans Sander

Stockholm

THE PRODUCTION of big weekly magazines is dominated by Heatset letterpress printing in U.S.A. In Europe gravure is the dominating printing method but offset also comes into the picture, especially in France and Scandinavia.

Printing speed, printing quality, fidelity and short time from copy to printing element are of the greatest importance when printing weekly magazines. Printing of weekly magazines in Heatset letterpress on machine coated paper has for a long time fulfilled these demands. Web offset Heatset printing is almost at the same point as letterpress. Gravure printing, however, has hitherto not been able to fulfil the above-mentioned demands.

Below is a short discussion of the possibilities for gravure printing today.

CYLINDERMAKING

Today it is a slow and expensive route from the copy to the cylinder. Improvements have, however, been effected through the use of scanning methods, etching machines, Rotofilm, developing machines and half-tone methods.

The competition in time with television and increased volume of four-colour printing have promoted the use of the engraving machines. Here experiments are being made with electro-mechanical and electronic engraving methods.

The drawback of electro-mechanical engraving is low production speed and crude etching. The electronic etching method is better in this respect, but it is much more complicated and expensive.

FIDELITY

Conventional gravure gives the best four-colour picture when everything is perfect.

However, it is very difficult to obtain a standard product by the conventional method. The half-tone methods are much easier to standardize and this is of very great importance, especially for four-colour advertising. Scanning methods and standardization of the process inks also contribute to better fidelity.

PRINTING QUALITY

Missing dots are a dominating flaw in printing quality. In conventional gravure, missing dots are more obtrusive than with the half-tone methods. When printing speed is increased from 10,000–20,000 rev/hr the number of missing dots sometimes will increase, due to the following:

Too fast drying of inks,

Too large a distance from the doctor blade to the impression point; and

Improper inking of the cylinder.

Missing dots are, however, mainly caused by the roughness of the paper. In four-colour printing it is often very difficult to avoid missing dots, caused by the last colour down, the black. One way to control this is by continuously decreasing the amount of extender in the ink and the evaporation speed of the solvent from the first colour down, to the last colour down.

Gloss is another important factor in printing quality. Here the paper is of dominating importance. However, inks with a high content of resin give a better gloss than inks with a low content.

Careful control of viscosity during printing will also contribute to a better printing quality.

PRINTING SPEED

After the war the printing speed in Europe for four-colour printing, was 6,000–10,000 rev/hr. Today the printing speeds are 10,000–20,000 rev/hr and in the U.S.A. 15,000–25,000 rev/hr. Some printing plants in Europe are experimenting with printing speed for a one colour job of about 1400 ft/min that is 30,000 rev/hr with slow solvent and high temperature on the drying system. The following conditions have contributed to this increase in speed in colour printing:

A very fast jet stream of air in the drying equipment (50 m/sec).

Development of a new doctor blade system; and

Fast inks with narrow cut solvents.

PAPER

The progress here is in increased ability to provide good quality print with properties of paper which affect trouble-free passage through a machine at high speed—so called "runability." Controlled moisture in the paper (7·5%) and addition of sulphate pulp has increased the runability. The printing quality on " Magazine paper " has been increased by a better paper, having

a very low Bendtsen No. for the surface,

an increased ash content together with

closer control of porosity, brightness and opacity.

Use of blade-coated paper has made it possible to print gravure on coated stocks without any missing dots. Gravure printing in Europe has achieved good results in four-colour printing by using " Magazine paper ". This paper is normally composed of 70% Mechanical and 30% Chemical pulp. On this relatively cheap paper it has been possible to obtain better four-colour prints than with any other printing method. It is probably very hard to introduce a paper, which is considerably more expensive than the " Magazine paper ". However, to compete in printing quality with offset and letterpress on machine coated paper the development of paper for weekly magazines and gravure printing probably will follow two lines:

(a) Thin blade coated paper (50–60 g/m²) with base paper from Mechanical pulp.

(b) Peroxide bleached " Magazine paper " with very good surface and moderate ash content.

Progress of web Heatset offset printing on newspaper or on S/C News will also have an influence on the final establishment of paper quality for rotogravure printing for weekly magazines.

INK

The development of AC cool inks or Low Therm inks is a development that permits high speed printing without heat in four-colour printing. The performance of these inks depends in solvent with very narrow cuts and resins with a very good solvent release and proper solvent retention.

Water emulsified gravure inks (5% water) are another new development that will be of interest.

To understand what occurs during printing, it is very important to know something about the ink transfer. In letterpress and offset the ink transfer has been studied rather carefully. However, in gravure printing very little is known about the ink transfer. Therefore it is necessary to begin research in this field to achieve a better function of the ink and a better printing quality.

PACKAGING

The use of gravure in this field is increasing, especially on plastic foil. The price of plastic foil today is reaching the same level as that of paper and this will favour gravure printing in packaging.

FUTURE NEWSPAPER PRINTING—OFFSET?

by R. W. PRINCE

ANPA Research Institute, Inc., Easton, Pa., U.S.A.

THERE is a growing interest in the United States among newspapers of all sizes in the possibility of printing by web offset. Several hundred newspapers with circulations under 5000 have shown interest in the possibility of offset as the most satisfactory way of converting from flat-bed to rotary newspaper printing. The small daily newspaper sees in offset an opportunity to compete by producing a product of higher quality and, perhaps, with more economy than can be produced by the conventional newspaper letterpress process. The economy may be derived from the selection of composing method, reduced capital investment, and better utilization of available labor force. Several daily newspapers are now printing by web offset and claiming economies in the operation.

Weekly newspapers are also interested but look for maximum utilization of the press equipment. There are several web-fed offset presses in the United States now printing up to sixty weekly newspapers every week. Such plants are, essentially, only printing plants. In other words, plates or material in a forme from which plates can be made readily are supplied to the printing plant by each individual weekly newspaper.

Some larger newspapers in the metropolitan class are also watching the development of offset closely, because they are interested in the possibility of printing their supplements by the offset process to take advantage of the improvement in color reproduction on newsprint that is possible over conventional R.O.P. newspaper letterpress printing. Many newspapers now buy their supplements from gravure printing establishments; but ,also, many would prefer to prepare and print their own supplement material in their own plant. One possibility, which is intriguing, is to couple a conventional newspaper letterpress with an offset color unit. Such an arrangement would permit the daily printing of high-quality color but would require precise control of " running " register or register along the length of the web. Some of the larger newspapers are giving serious attention to the possibility of using facsimile to transmit composed newspaper material to several satellite printing plants, which would print the daily product by offset.

We have, then, weeklies, small dailies, and metropolitan newspapers all showing interest in the possibility of using web-fed offset. What are the problems they face?

There appears to be no outstanding problem to the use of web-fed offset by weekly newspapers. However, the small daily newspaper must consider its labor problem and platemaking time. Many of the smaller daily newspapers are afternoon papers. They must adhere to their press time. This means that all the composition, photography, and platemaking must be done in time to meet their present press schedule. If it requires additional manpower to meet this deadline, then the offset process is not appealing. Also, many of our smaller newspapers do not have photographic equipment because it has not been necessary to their present operation. Therefore, they are lacking in photographically trained personnel when they convert to offset. There has been some experience to indicate that the preparation of negatives suitable for making offset plates has constituted a bottleneck in the smaller newspaper offset operation.

The major problem the metropolitan newspaper must consider before it converts to offset is the cost of offset ink and the possibility of an increased cost in newsprint suitable for offset production. We have, then, two distinct problems. The smaller daily newspapers must consider production time and manpower and the larger metropolitan daily newspapers must consider the costs of newsprint and news ink, as well as the need to maintain press speeds equivalent to modern newspaper letterpresses.

Most newspapers now utilizing the offset process are setting their composition in hot type and photographing reproduction proofs to obtain a negative from which to make an offset plate. Some newspapers are utilizing " cold-type " composition produced with justifying typewriters. Others utilize Fotosetters or the equivalent to produce photocomposition, but both methods introduce problems in page make-up. Two problems in this area are outstanding. One is the problem of handling make-over material. The other is the problem of handling classified advertising. It is presently easier to adjust a page make-up in hot metal than it is to make the same adjustment in photographic film. The same general problem applies to the classified advertising pages because a variable amount of the advertisements are held over for several days but are subject to immediate cancellation. Therefore, frequent make-over of the classified page is required. Also, most " cold-type " composing machines presently available and suitable for composition of text matter have type faces which are larger than the 5 pt., 6 pt., and 7 pt. commonly used for classified advertisements.

Web-fed offset does offer some interesting possibilities as a new concept in

T

newspaper production. The system appears to offer a substantial improvement in printing quality on newsprint. It offers an ideal way of directly
utilizing photocomposing methods and, therefore, potentially can reduce the
time required to process a newspaper through the composing room to the
press. In addition, for the smaller daily newspapers web-fed offset offers
the opportunity to increase the speed of printing over a flat-bed operation
and, therefore, may meet economically the problem of increased circulation,
which many of the smaller newspapers are experiencing. Plant size and plant
construction are also factors which appear more attractive when considering
offset than when considering rotary letterpress. It has been demonstrated
many times that offset color reproduction on newsprint is, at present, far
superior to what can be hoped for, for some time to come, from conventional
R.O.P. color printed by conventional newspaper letterpress.

There are still unsolved problems, however, which, until solved, will
prevent a sudden swing to this process by newspapers of the metropolitan
class. Many newspapers make extensive use of the wire services. Conversion
of this material to columns of type on film presents a problem which must be
solved without upsetting the potential economy of the system. The larger
daily newspapers require dulpicate plates of each page for a straight run.
If several presses are required to meet the circulation requirement, then
many duplicate plates for each page must be made. The stereotype process
will produce up to four duplicate plates per minute. Metropolitan newspapers
need this same plate production rate to consider the offset process.

Looking into the future, one might ask if we must settle on the offset
process as the ultimate in newspaper production. Not necessarily. At the
ANPA Research Institute we are considering future newspaper production
systems, and this consideration goes beyond the methods presently employed
in any area of the graphic arts. For example, the final printing need not be
done with more or less conventional inks. Electrostatic and ferromagnetic
printing systems are possible and may be more suitable to a completely
new production system. Both systems permit " dry " printing; and, in the
case of a ferromagnetic printing system, no plates would be required as a
supply item. Of course, any consideration of a different newspaper production system must be based on potential savings either in manpower or in
supplies and materials.

The present newspaper production system utilizes many processes which
have no direct bearing on the final printing. Columns of type are set but are
not used for printing. Photoengravings are made, which a commercial
engraver could sell as such; but, in a newspaper, these engravings are not
used except for the preparation of replicas. Even in the offset process it is
necessary to compose each entire page in film form; but, usually, one cannot
print from the film but must use the film for the preparation of a printing plate.

A future newspaper production system should be designed to minimize the number of operations which are not in themselves useful in printing the final product. It would seem to follow that, if these supplementary production operations can be minimized, total operational costs can be reduced.

WEB OFFSET IN FRANCE

MME BENEDITE (Comment): The reasons for great interest in web offset in France are as follows:

(1) Newspaper editors, although they feel the need for colour, do not believe that in France, the quality of R.O.P. colour is sufficient to meet the requirements, especially of advertisers. This opinion explains their hesitation to invest in R.O.P.

(2) Many trials of gravure preprinted web insertions have been made, and are still occasionally used, but though successful regarding quality, is prohibitive in cost for the following reasons:

    (a) the process requires a better grade of paper and of greater substance

    (b) preprinting gravure is costly

    (c) the high wastage figures (a rather large quantity of preprinted paper is wasted)

(3) It is believed that web offset can be the answer to their needs, both for quality and price:

    Ordinary newsprint runs very well on high-speed rotary presses.

    There is no necessity for drying the ink.

    The standard basis weight is sufficient.

    The fluffing is rather low, as compared to some better grade papers, and does not necessarily require surface treatment of the sheet.

    The most important improvement that should be made is in the brightness of the sheet. A mild bleaching of the ground wood is a possible answer.

T*

RECENT DEVELOPMENTS IN PAPERMAKING— A SHORT SURVEY FROM THE PRINTER'S VIEWPOINT

by G. E. CARLSSON

The Swedish Graphic Arts Laboratory, Stockholm

PAPER is without any doubt the most important material used by the printing industry and the printers have accordingly every reason to pay great attention to what is going on in paper technology. Paper as well as printing technology is in constant development, and like all other technical development is taking place at a much greater rate of progress than earlier.

The improvement of printing processes is quite dependent upon the possibility of producing paper which can meet the special demands raised by the printing process. The increased printing speed has already created problems in this respect. It is primarily the increase (with speed) of the work to split the ink film between forme and paper which has to be taken into consideration. Another matter of importance at increased printing speed is the capability of the paper surface to be properly wet by the ink during extremely short moments of contact.

RAW MATERIALS

When discussing the development of papermaking the question of raw materials will certainly first of all attract interest. Will our natural and traditionally exploited wood resources suffice in the future for the strongly increasing demand for paper, which will be accelerated by the rise of material as well as cultural standard in the underdeveloped countries?

Many new raw materials for paper have been examined and quite a number of them have definitely come into practical use; others will surely soon assume importance.

Pulps from hardwood such as birch, beech and chestnut have in recent years been produced in an ever increasing quantity with good results and economy. And this has happened in spite of the quite interesting fact that in Sweden only about 10 years ago we considered rooting out the birch in our northern forests and replacing with coniferous trees. The Scandinavian countries export now considerable quantities of birch sulphite pulp, and this has decreased the demand for esparto pulp.

Bamboo is a raw material for pulp, which in many countries, for instance India, is of increasing importance. Bamboo is easily cooked, produces a paper with good formation and is specially useful for the production of strong paper.

Bagasse is another raw material, which has now acquired a real importance for paper production. The supply is plenteous and the price low. Thus it is estimated that Egypt alone gets enough bagasse for a yearly production of 750,000 tons pulp. The price is at present about 12 dollars a dry ton for bagasse, from which the pith has been removed. Techniques for the production of newsprint with pulps from bagasse and eucalyptus are fully developed.

Straw has also got a markedly increased usage for pulp production specially in Central Europe and great quantities of paper are now produced with a high content of straw pulp. The problem of fluffing has been eliminated through surface sizing of the paper.

But even if we can depend upon a heavily increased production of pulp from the raw material sources just mentioned, it seems quite certain that the expected great increase in future paper consumption will nevertheless be provided mainly through planting of fast-growing Pinus and Eucalyptus in regions with suitable climatic conditions.

Papers from synthetic fibre is another line of development which perhaps has especially been given publicity. The high cost of production of synthetic fibres with a degree of fineness required for papermaking makes it unrealistic to reckon upon this possibility except for special purposes. Paper made of synthetic fibres may thus be used only for products, which demand very high strength and wearability and where the price is of secondary importance, for instance maps.

PULPING

Regarding pulp manufacture, some newer production methods can be mentioned. Mechanical pulp can thus be produced from hardwood through pretreatment of the wood with chemicals. This type of mechanical pulp, called semi-groundwood, is unlikely to be used to any extent in the manufacture of printing papers. Various methods of producing high-yield sulphite pulp through continuous cooking processes are other innovations in pulping. Pulp produced in this way has been used in newsprint.

Peroxide-bleaching of mechanical pulp is another new process which is widely used in some countries. It may be assumed that such pulp will become important for the production of low-grade printing papers such as magazine paper.

Neither the new raw materials for pulp, nor the newer methods of pulping discussed here have caused or are likely to lead to any substantial change in the qualities of traditional printing paper. The increased use of hardwood pulp has, however, from the printer's viewpoint certain advantages, for it makes a paper which is softer and more opaque than one made from softwood pulp alone.

PAPERMAKING

No substantial changes in the design of the paper machines has occurred and is not to be expected in the near future. The trend towards higher machine speeds, bigger machines and increased automation is common.

The paper industry has now accepted papermaking as a process industry and has consequently made use of experiences of automation in other process industries. The intense development of regulation technology, the installation of automatic instruments for measuring the substance and moisture content of the running web and many other control improvements have resulted in a product which with respect to quality is more uniform than could be made by earlier manual regulation of the paper machine.

The use of dispersion agents in the stock allows a better formation on the wire and has also facilitated the drainage, which has made higher machine speeds possible without enlargement of the drying section.

Through quite new types of retention agents, primarily acrylic acid compounds, a considerably improved retention of fillers and fine-fibres can be attained. It is stated that paper with 25–30% fillers homogeneously distributed in the paper can be produced even at high machine speeds with the aid of such retention agents.

Paper machines with double wires, especially the Inverform-machine have attracted much attention but will most likely become important, in the first instance, for boardmaking, as their use in papermaking is not economic.

Some innovations within the papermaking machinery which may be of special interest to the printers on account of the possibilities of producing increased smoothness of the paper, is a new type of press called a burnishing press and some improvements in the calendering. In a burnishing press the press cylinder has a chrome, polished surface, which effects a better finish of the paper surface. The difficulty of getting an even pressure over the whole width of the cylinders in wide machines and super-calenders has meant that other ways than the traditional crowning and manually directed local-cooling have been sought. One such project is based upon cylinders with very long shafts in double bearings with regulation of the pressure distribution through change of the relative position of the bearings. Another scheme uses cylinders filled with oil and regulation of their crown through variation of the oil pressure.

The production of machine-coated paper has increased very much during the last 15 years and such papers have an ever growing use in all the three principal printing processes. At the same time the coating technique has developed considerably and the papermaker has now many different coating methods from which to choose. The most recent trend seems to be a departure from coating in the paper machine and instead to use separate coating machines, which are considerably less complicated than brush-coating machines. In such cases it is not adequate to speak about machine-coated paper and the usual term is offmachine-coated. The experience from the production of machine-coated paper seems to be that coating in the paper machine is often not economic on account of the complication of the machine operation. The efficiency of a paper machine is the product of the efficiency of the single parts, and an individual section with low efficiency can thus spoil the output of the machine. But even if the coating is done separately it may be assumed that a light precoating very often will be carried out in the paper machine. This has a good effect with regard to the quality of the end product and may not give rise to disturbance of the running of the paper machine.

In this connection the pigmented papers can be mentioned, which are a rather new type of paper. They have got a very thin layer of pigment mainly intended to fill out the cavities of the paper surface with the aid of an ordinary size-press. They are not coated papers in the strict sense.

Many different methods of applying the coating are now in use but a trend to more uncomplicated machinery is quite clear. The combination of coating with one single cylinder and levelling the coating layer with an air knife is a method of some interest. The latest development in the U.S.A. suggests that the trailing-blade method, provides a very even coating in a very simple manner.

The traditional binders for the coating, casein and starch have, to a certain extent but never completely, been superseded by synthetic plastic emulsions, such as Accronal and Latex.

THE PRINTER'S VIEWPOINT

What effect has the development of papermaking had upon the quality of printing paper and have the results produced by the paper industry satisfied the demands, which the development of printing technique has made upon the paper in various respects?

It is not possible to give a general answer to this question with regard to the very different demands upon the paper in letterpress, lithographic and gravure printing. The paper for each printing process must accordingly be discussed separately.

The letterpress printers have good reason to complain about the two-sidedness of the paper with great difference between the content of fillers and surface bonding strength of the two sides. The felt side of the paper has usually a very low surface bonding strength, which often prevents the full use of the high speed in modern printing machines with maintained quality of the print. Many examples can be given of cases when the wire side of the paper has been printed with a speed of 3000 copies per hour, but the low surface strength of the felt side has necessitated a reduction of the speed to 1000 and sometimes even down to 600 copies per hour. The increased speed of the paper machines has without any doubt increased this serious disadvantage, which can completely detract from the economic result of a printing run. The especially high demands upon softness and compressibility of letterpress printing paper have prevented the increase of the surface strength through harder beating of the stock or surface sizing of the paper.

It is possible that machine-coated papers particularly with regard to these circumstances may acquire a dominating position in letterpress printing. Machine-coated paper does not have this two-sidedness but it must, however, meet the printers' demands for sufficient surface strength, softness and absorptive properties. The machine-coated papers are on account of their smooth surface very good for halftone printing but have up to now very often caused trouble for the printer. Uneven distribution of the coating layer over the sheet as well as from sheet to sheet has thus been a drawback, showing up now and then. Pin-holes and blisters in the surface of the coating, so small that they cannot be observed by visual inspection, can turn up as white spots on the printed surface and thus spoil the printing result. Variations of the oil absorbency have further caused troubles with drying and smudging of the ink. Problems sometimes arise owing to the hardening of the coating surface by volatile products originated during the drying process of the ink and can cause disturbing gloss effects in the print. This hardening can also be associated with a discolouring of the unprinted paper surface.

It remains, however, to see if the problems mentioned can be looked upon as the growing pains of a relatively new production and will disappear when more experience has been accumulated.

The previously mentioned new retention agents in combination with improved methods of calendering may, however, lead the development in another direction. A coated paper will surely, with respect to the cost of material as well of the manufacture, always be more expensive than an uncoated paper, especially as the earlier expectation of the possibility of getting good printing papers through machine-coating of low substance raw papers with high mechanical pulp content was not realised.

Newspaper printing is mainly done by the letterpress process and a quantitatively so important paper as newsprint must not be omitted in this connection. In no other section of the paper industry has the development of bigger and especially fast-running machines been so pronounced as in newsprint manufacture. The speed of the newsprint machines has more than doubled during the last twenty years and this progress has been followed by the newspaper printers with certain apprehension. They have feared that the higher speed would deteriorate the quality. Their fears were yet ungrounded, as the modern newsprint machines have, in spite of their high speed, through various mechanical improvements produced a paper, which as a rule is of better and more uniform quality than can be produced in older machines. The increased machine speeds have, however, caused certain problems because of the necessity to increase the content of chemical pulp in order to get sufficiently high strength of the web to run without breaks in the paper machine. This circumstance has resulted in a lower opacity of the newsprint, which is a disadvantage for the printer.

The generally practised surface sizing of paper and board intended for lithographic printing has substantially decreased the earlier very frequent problems with fluffing and fibre deposition on the blanket in this printing process. Machine-coated papers have a considerable use, also, for lithographic printing and their water resistance has generally been adequate. Problems with scumming and tinting appear, however, from time to time. The demands upon good dimensional stability have, through the common use of four colour presses, been less pronounced.

In gravure printing the paper now presents great problems. This is due to the fact that very little research has been done in the matter until recently. An investigation of the extensive literature on the printability of paper, shows how little research has been devoted to paper problems in gravure printing. A gravure paper must have a very high content of fillers, but at the present high speed of the paper machines the fillers will be so unhomogeneously distributed in the paper that the printing result shows up quite differently on the two sides of the paper.

During recent years many attempts have been made to use machine-coated papers in gravure printing, but the results have as a rule not been very successful. The reasons for this have not been fully elucidated and it is not yet definitely established whether the inadequate quality of the print is caused by the hardness of the paper or insufficient absorbency. The report, which has been presented by the Graphic Arts Research Laboratory at this conference has shown that machine-coated paper is very poorly wet by news ink at high printing speed and it is probable that the same conditions exist with regard to gravure ink.

The reason for the desire to use machine-coated paper in gravure printing seems primarily to be the better brightness of this paper in comparison with ordinary magazine paper. A higher brightness can, however, be obtained in other ways and it seems likely that papers with peroxide-bleached mechanical pulp and a high content of fillers more homogeneously distributed with the aid of retention agents will provide a better solution of the problem.

STANDARDIZATION

A matter which is now being discussed by printers is the possibility of standardizing paper qualities with the values of the most important properties fixed within reasonably narrow tolerance limits. The exhaustive work which is now going on practically all over the world on the standardization of paper-testing methods can provide a basis for such a standardization, but much remains still to be done, especially with regard to printability testing methods. Some papers which are now manufactured by mass production such as newsprint, can already be considered as standardized, although no exact quality specifications are stated in the contracts.

Standardization in the future will surely depend mainly on the printing industry itself. The prevailing custom of ordering special qualities of paper even in very small quantities for all kinds of printed matter, caused by what is said to be artistic considerations or by advertising people's permanent quest for originality will surely be an obstacle to the development of standardization. This state of affairs must be regretted, for standardization of paper qualities would lead to lower production costs as well as to con-siderably less difficulties in the printing and converting of paper in the Graphic Arts industry.

INDEX